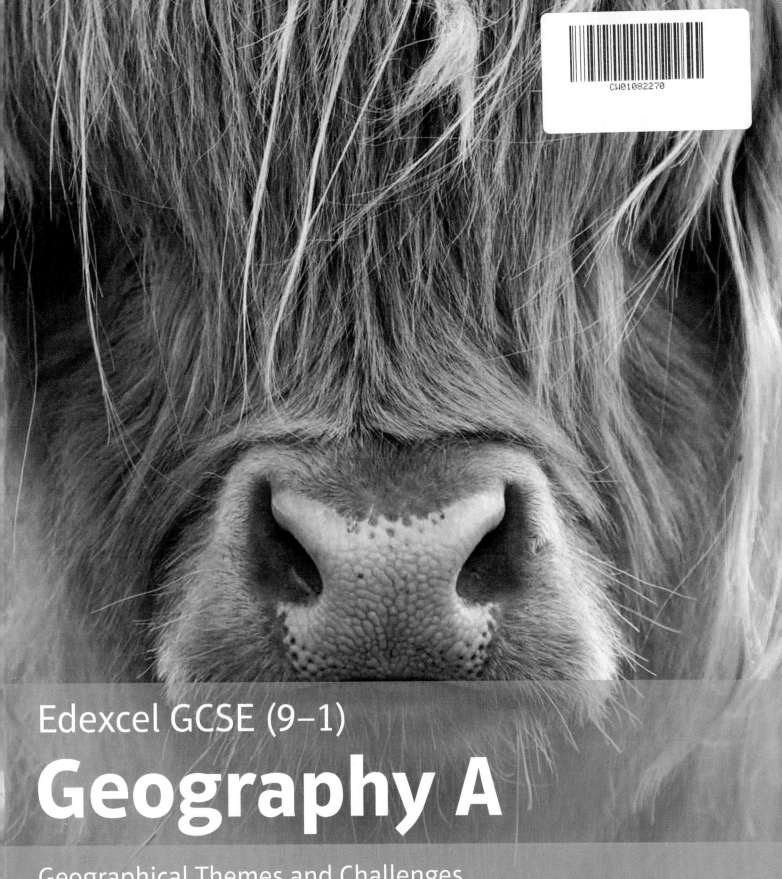

Edexcel GCSE (9–1)

Geography A

Geographical Themes and Challenges

Series Editor: John Hopkin

Authors: Rob Bircher   Michael Chiles   Rob Clemens   Phillip Crossley   David Flint   Paul Guinness

PEARSON

Published by Pearson Education Limited, 80 Strand, London, WC2R 0RL.

www.pearsonschoolsandfecolleges.co.uk

Copies of official specifications for all Edexcel qualifications may be found on the website:
www.edexcel.com

Text © Pearson Education Limited 2016
Designed by Colin Tilley Loughrey for Pearson
Typeset, illustrated and produced by Phoenix Photosetting, Chatham, Kent
Original illustrations © Pearson Education Limited 2016
Cover design by Malena Wilson-Max for Pearson
Picture research by Susie Prescott
Cover photo/illustration © Getty Images: Cultura/Echo

The rights of Rob Bircher, Michael Chiles, Rob Clemens, Phillip Crossley, David Flint and Paul Guiness
to be identified as authors of this work have been asserted by them in accordance with the Copyright,
Designs and Patents Act 1988.

First published 2016

19 18 17 16
10 9 8 7 6 5 4 3 2

British Library Cataloguing in Publication Data
A catalogue record for this book is available from the British Library

ISBN 978 1 446 92775 5

Printed in Italy by Lego S.p.A.

Websites
Pearson Education Limited is not responsible for the content of any external internet sites. It is essential
for tutors to preview each website before using it in class so as to ensure that the URL is still accurate,
relevant and appropriate. We suggest that tutors bookmark useful websites and consider enabling
students to access them through the school/college intranet.

A note from the publisher

In order to ensure that this resource offers high-quality support for the associated Pearson
qualification, it has been through a review process by the awarding body. This process confirms
that this resource fully covers the teaching and learning content of the specification or part
of a specification at which it is aimed. It also confirms that it demonstrates an appropriate
balance between the development of subject skills, knowledge and understanding, in addition to
preparation for assessment.

Endorsement does not cover any guidance on assessment activities or processes (e.g. practice
questions or advice on how to answer assessment questions), included in the resource nor does it
prescribe any particular approach to the teaching or delivery of a related course.

While the publishers have made every attempt to ensure that advice on the qualification and its
assessment is accurate, the official specification and associated assessment guidance materials
are the only authoritative source of information and should always be referred to for definitive
guidance.

Pearson examiners have not contributed to any sections in this resource relevant to examination
papers for which they have responsibility.

Examiners will not use endorsed resources as a source of material for any assessment set by
Pearson.

Endorsement of a resource does not mean that the resource is required to achieve this Pearson
qualification, nor does it mean that it is the only suitable material available to support the
qualification, and any resource lists produced by the awarding body shall include this and other
appropriate resources.

Contents

About this book 4

How to use this book 5

Thinking Geographically 6

Where in the world will Edexcel Geography take you? 8

Component 1 The Physical Environment 10

Topic 1 The Changing Landscapes of the UK 11

Overview 12

1A Coastal Landscapes and Processes 18

Fieldwork: Investigating Coastal Landscapes 36

1B River Landscapes and Processes 44

Fieldwork: Investigating River Landscapes 62

1C Glaciated Upland Landscapes and Processes 70

Writing Geographically 90

Thinking Geographically 92

Topic 2 Weather Hazards and Climate Change 95

Thinking Geographically 124

Topic 3 Ecosystems, Biodiversity and Management 127

Writing Geographically 150

Component 2 The Human Environment 152

Topic 4 Changing Cities 153

Fieldwork: Investigating Changing Urban Environments 180

Fieldwork: Investigating Changing Rural Environments 186

Thinking Geographically 194

Topic 5 Global Development 197

Writing Geographically 224

Thinking Geographically 226

Topic 6 Resource Management 229

Overview 230

6A Energy Resource Management 236

6B Water Resource Management 254

Component 3 Geographical Investigations: Fieldwork and UK Challenges 272

Topic 7 Geographical Investigations – Fieldwork 273

Topic 8 Geographical Investigations – UK Challenges 275

Writing Geographically 294

Glossary 296

Index 30

Acknowledgements

About this book

Welcome to the Edexcel GCSE Geography Specification A course. This book has been written specially to help you learn about the world you live in. By the end of the course you will know far more about our fascinating and dynamic planet Earth and how it works, as well as developing the understanding and skills that will help to you think like a geographer, now and in the future.

What will I learn?

There are three parts to the course, called components, each with its own exam paper.

Component 1 The Physical Environment

Have you ever wondered:

- Why landscapes in some places are different from others?
- Why flooding is becoming more common, and what we can do to respond to it?
- How climate change affected the UK in the past, and why it is becoming such a hazard today?
- Why tropical rainforests are rich in plants and wildlife, and how we can manage the world's forests for the future?

In this component you will learn about the physical processes which create and change landscapes, and how people and environments interact.

Component 2 The Human Environment

Have you ever wondered:

- Why most people around the world have settled in cities, and how they can be made better places to live?
- Why some places are developing much faster than others?
- Why food, energy and water are in such demand, and how we can manage them for the future?

In this component you will learn about human geography and issues about people and the environment.

Component 3 Geographical Investigations

In this component you will investigate physical and human environments through fieldwork:

- One fieldwork investigation focuses on the processes in a river or coastal landscape
- One fieldwork investigation focuses on changes in a city centre, or in a rural settlement.

You will also use your geographical knowledge and understanding from Components 1 and 2 to explore some big challenges like sustainability, population and climate change in the UK today.

How to use this book

This book is practical and easy to use. The diagram below shows how some of the book's features will support your learning.

Learning objectives provide a clear overview of what you will learn in each section. The objectives increase in difficulty.

Maps at different scales help you locate geographical examples and case studies.

Clear **diagrams** help you understand key ideas and develop your skills.

Checkpoints help you review your learning, with activities to strengthen and challenge your knowledge and understanding.

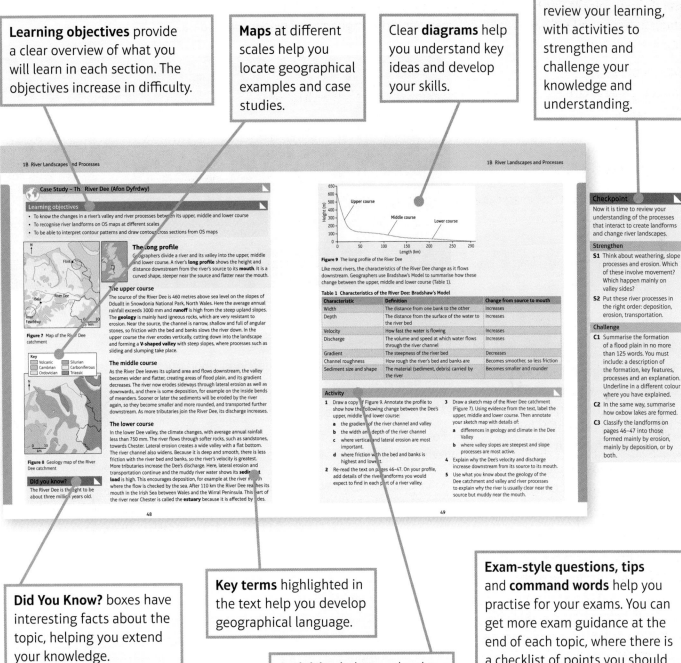

Did You Know? boxes have interesting facts about the topic, helping you extend your knowledge.

Key terms highlighted in the text help you develop geographical language.

Activities help you develop understanding and broaden your knowledge and skills.

Exam-style questions, tips and **command words** help you practise for your exams. You can get more exam guidance at the end of each topic, where there is a checklist of points you should know, plus sample answers and comments on these.

Engaging **photos** bring geography to life.

Exam-style question

Explain why different processes interact to form waterfalls.

(4 marks)

Exam tip

When answering a formation question, you must include an explanation of how the processes lead to the landform. An **annotated** sketch is a useful way of explaining a complete sequence of processes.

Command word

When asked to **describe** a physical process you should give the main characteristics.

Thinking Geographically

You have already done quite a lot of geographical thinking in Key Stage 3. Through your Edexcel GCSE Geography course you will think more widely and more deeply about the world. Thinking geographically is about asking geographical questions, learning about places, patterns and processes, using geographical language and working with data.

Figure 1 The Earth at night

Activity

1   Think geographically about the satellite image in Figure 1: write out the W questions, aiming to think of at least one question for each 'W'.
2   Use an atlas to help you try to find answers to your questions.

Exam tip

In the exam, including real examples and places in your answers helps show you really know the subject.

Enquiry

Geographers constantly ask questions: good questions help us think geographically about the world. Some useful ones are:

The W questions: What, Who, When, and especially Where, HoW and Why.

For deeper thinking, try adding 'might', 'could' or 'ought': for example, 'Where might …'.

* **In this book** you will find plenty of these questions in the activities and you will also use them to help structure your fieldwork investigations.

Places

Geographers need to build up good knowledge and understanding of places so they can think geographically – from the corner of a street to whole cities, regions, countries, continents and oceans. We are interested in where places are, what they are like, why they are different and changing, and how they are connected. Investigating places helps build our understanding of the world and develops important skills, including using maps, atlases, photographs and satellite images.

* **In this book** you will study three in-depth case studies of places, as well as located examples from different countries 🌍 . Both these are highlighted by green vertical bands alongside the text and you can see where to find these on pages 8–9.
* You will also find mini-case studies throughout the book, showing geography in action in real places.

Patterns and processes

Geographers investigate how and why our world changes – we call these processes. Processes create patterns in the landscape, for example the shape of a river valley or desert, the track of a storm or how land is used in different parts of a city.

- **In this book,** in Topics 1–3, you will learn about physical processes and how they change landscapes.
- Topics 4–6 focus on human processes at city, country and global scales.
- Throughout the book you will learn about how people and environments interact to change places. That will help you understand geographical connections, especially when you study the UK as a whole in Topic 8.

Finding out about processes, patterns and connections helps you understand the world – and think like a geographer.

Exam tip

In the exam, including diagrams or sketch maps can really help show your understanding of patterns and processes. In any of the three papers you may be asked about how people and the environment affect each other.

Language and literacy

Geographers use language to think geographically. We use many key geographical words like 'cyclone' and 'urbanisation' to help us describe the world and understand how it works.

- **In this book** key words you will need to learn are highlighted in the text and defined in the Glossary at the end of the book.

When, as geographers, you talk or write geographically, using well-structured sentences and texts helps show your understanding clearly.

- **In this book** there are extra pages with support for using language and activities to help you improve your writing and grammar. They will help you to write good answers, especially longer written answers which really test your thinking.

Exam tip

In the exam, using geographical language helps show you really understand the subject. There are four extra marks on each paper for good use of language.

Numeracy and statistics

Geographers use numbers to think geographically. Data helps us to find out more about the world, and to show accurately what we have discovered from different types of maps, graphs and images. We also collect, present and analyse our own data from fieldwork investigations.

- **In this book** each topic includes data presented in different forms, with activities to help you learn the skills you will need.
- There are also extra pages with support and activities to help you improve your understanding of using maths and statistics. These will help where you need to work with data.

Exam tip

In the exam you will be asked to use your number skills in all three papers – you can use a calculator.

Progression

On the 'Preparing for your exams' pages, alongside the sample answers is a symbol containing a number. This symbol indicates that the sample answer has been graded with a numbered step on the Pearson Progression Scale. Our Geography progression scale and map can help teachers and students to assess progress, and can be downloaded free from the Pearson website.

Where in the world will Edexcel Geography take you?

In this book you will use case studies and located examples, both labelled like this 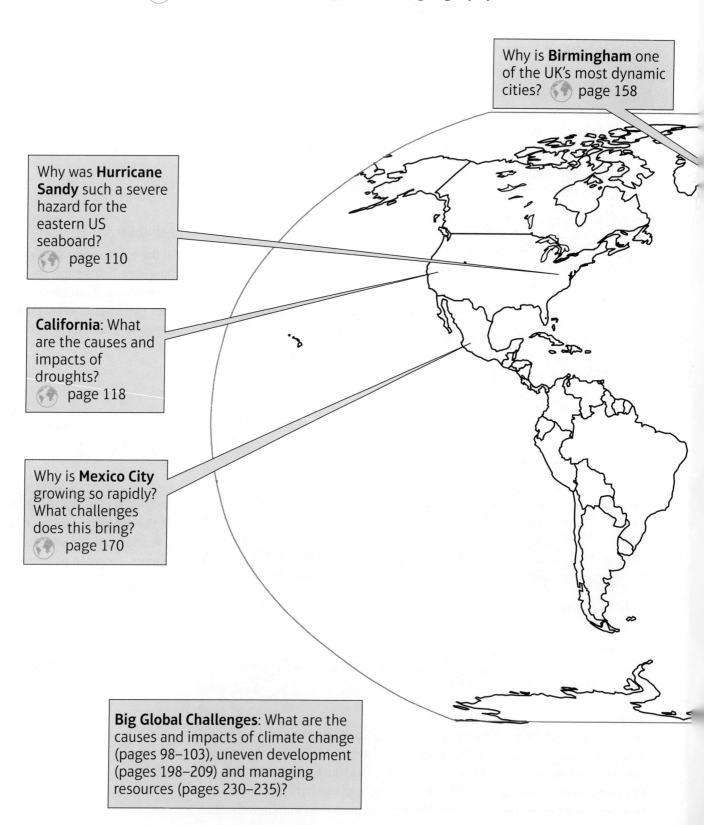, to help you get the **big picture of geography**.

Why is **Birmingham** one of the UK's most dynamic cities? page 158

Why was **Hurricane Sandy** such a severe hazard for the eastern US seaboard? page 110

California: What are the causes and impacts of droughts? page 118

Why is **Mexico City** growing so rapidly? What challenges does this bring? page 170

Big Global Challenges: What are the causes and impacts of climate change (pages 98–103), uneven development (pages 198–209) and managing resources (pages 230–235)?

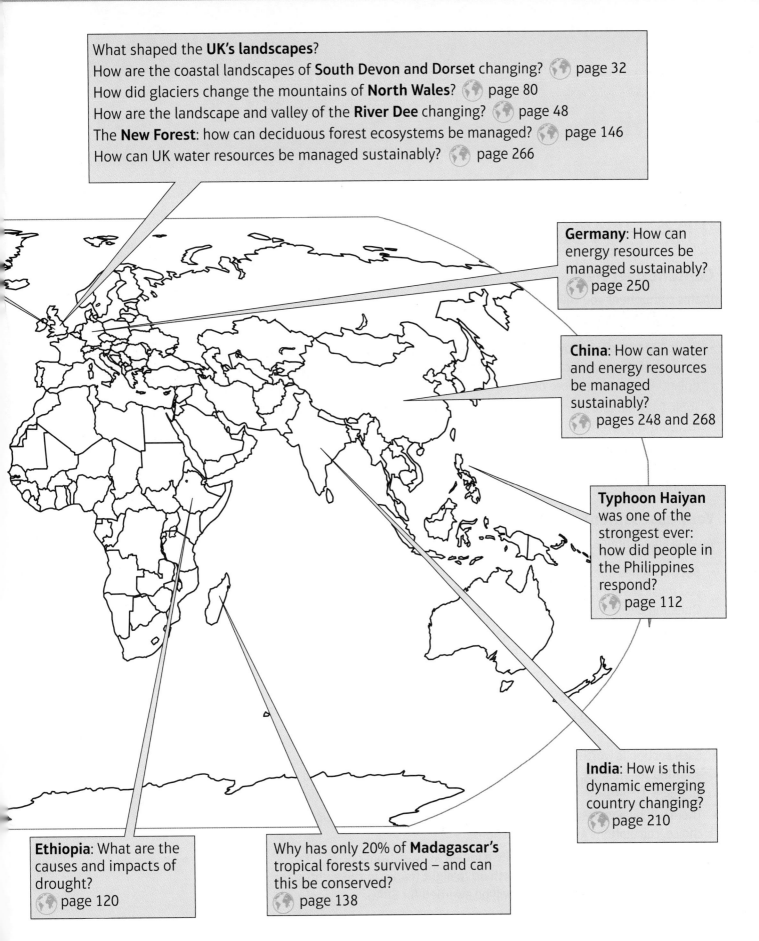

What shaped the **UK's landscapes**?
How are the coastal landscapes of **South Devon and Dorset** changing? page 32
How did glaciers change the mountains of **North Wales**? page 80
How are the landscape and valley of the **River Dee** changing? page 48
The **New Forest**: how can deciduous forest ecosystems be managed? page 146
How can UK water resources be managed sustainably? page 266

Germany: How can energy resources be managed sustainably? page 250

China: How can water and energy resources be managed sustainably? pages 248 and 268

Typhoon Haiyan was one of the strongest ever: how did people in the Philippines respond? page 112

India: How is this dynamic emerging country changing? page 210

Ethiopia: What are the causes and impacts of drought? page 120

Why has only 20% of **Madagascar's** tropical forests survived – and can this be conserved? page 138

Component 1
The Physical Environment

Content overview

In this component you will learn about the physical processes which create and change landscapes, and how people and environments interact.

- Topic 1 starts with an overview of landscapes in the UK, before you choose two out of three landscapes and processes – coastal, river or glaciated upland – to study in more depth.

- Topic 2 investigates global climates and climate change, and then you will focus on two weather hazards: tropical cyclones and drought.

- Topic 3 starts with an overview of global ecosystems, before you focus on the biodiversity and the management of tropical rainforests and deciduous woodlands.

Your assessment

You will sit a 1 hour and 30 minute exam, with three sections.

- **Section A** has questions about the changing landscapes of the UK: you must answer Question 1 (UK overview), and then choose **two** from Question 2 (coasts), Question 3 (rivers) **or** Question 4 (glaciated uplands).

- **Section B** has questions about weather hazards and climate change: you must answer **all** the questions in this section.

- **Section C** has questions about ecosystems, biodiversity and management: you must answer **all** the questions in this section.

- You may be assessed on geographical skills in any section, and can use a calculator.

- Each section is worth 30 marks; in addition, up to four marks will be awarded for spelling, punctuation, grammar and use of geographical language (SPAG).

- There will be a variety of different question types, including multiple-choice, calculations and open questions.

- Open questions are where you write a longer answer, from one or two sentences to extended writing worth up to eight marks. In the eight-mark questions, four additional marks will be awarded for SPAG.

1 | The Changing Landscapes of the UK

The physical geography of the UK varies greatly due to its complex and diverse geology, a result of it being subject to a variety of plate tectonic processes over an extended period of time. The combination of these past processes, and subsequent continual physical processes, means that the UK has a rich variety of distinctive landscapes.

Your learning

In this section you will investigate key learning points:

- the characteristics and distribution of the UK's main rock types
- the role of geology and past plate tectonic processes in forming distinctive UK landscapes
- how human activity changes landscapes over time
- the role of physical processes on coastal, river and glacial landscapes
- how the UK's weather and climate affects the rate of change on coastal, river and glacial landscapes
- the significance of the location of named coastal, river and glacial landscapes in the UK, and the factors that have resulted in change.

Overview

Types of rocks

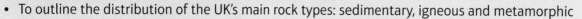

Learning objectives

- To outline the distribution of the UK's main rock types: sedimentary, igneous and metamorphic
- To know the characteristics of the UK's main rock types: sedimentary, igneous and metamorphic
- To understand the role of geology and past tectonic processes in upland/lowland landscape development

There are three main rock types that make up the Earth's crust. The different rock types are characterised by the different processes that formed them.

- **Sedimentary rocks** are formed of small particles that have been eroded, transported, and deposited in layers, such as sandstone; or from the remains of plants and animals, for example limestone and chalk.
- **Igneous rocks** are created by volcanic activity when magma or lava cools, forming rocks made of crystals that are usually hard. Examples are granite and basalt.
- **Metamorphic rocks** are formed from other rocks changed by extreme pressure or heat. They are usually formed from layers or bands of crystals and are very hard. Examples of metamorphic rock include shale that is compressed into slate, or limestone that is transformed into marble.

The role of geology and plate tectonic processes

Millions of years ago, Britain was much closer to plate boundaries than today. There were many active volcanoes, and plate movements caused massive folds and **faults** in the rocks. These **tectonic processes** helped shape the **geology** and landscapes of today.

UK upland landscapes are formed of harder, resistant rocks which have eroded at a much slower rate. These include the igneous and metamorphic rocks found in Scotland, North Wales, the Lake District and parts of south-west England (Figure 1). Around 300 million years ago tectonic processes caused molten **magma**, under intense pressure, to rise through the Earth's crust. Some magma reached the surface as lava – whilst some magma cooled and solidified underground. Today these are areas of high relief, for example the Cairngorms in Scotland and Dartmoor in Devon.

Many lowland UK landscapes are formed from softer, younger sedimentary rocks, which are less resistant to erosion. Examples are the North and South Downs in south-east England. These hills are formed of chalk, with even softer clay in the valleys between them.

Some upland areas are also formed of harder sedimentary rocks. An example is **carboniferous limestone**, formed 250–350 million years ago when Britain was surrounded by warm tropical seas rich in plant and animal life. When the plants and sea creatures died, the calcium in their shells and skeletons built up in layers on the seabed, forming limestone made of calcium carbonate.

Exam-style question

State **one** characteristic of a sedimentary rock.   **(1 mark)**

Exam tip

When asked to give one characteristic it is important you only provide one answer. If you do make a mistake, put a neat line through your incorrect answer.

Command word

In **identify**, **state** or **name** questions you need to recall or select information such as a characteristic of a landform.

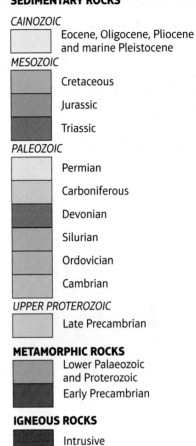

Key
SEDIMENTARY ROCKS

CAINOZOIC
Eocene, Oligocene, Pliocene and marine Pleistocene

MESOZOIC
Cretaceous
Jurassic
Triassic

PALEOZOIC
Permian
Carboniferous
Devonian
Silurian
Ordovician
Cambrian

UPPER PROTEROZOIC
Late Precambrian

METAMORPHIC ROCKS
Lower Palaeozoic and Proterozoic
Early Precambrian

IGNEOUS ROCKS
Intrusive
Volcanic

BGS Copyright Permit IPR/123-16CT

Figure 1 Geological map of the UK and Ireland

Activity

Look at Figure 1.

1 Describe the distribution of the UK's main rock types. You could use the UK countries to help get you started, or use directions, e.g. 'The rocks in the north of the UK…'.

Tip When describing a distribution, remember to use the PQE (general Pattern, Qualifications, Exceptions) technique.

2 Copy and complete the table below.

	Sedimentary	Igneous	Metamorphic
Rock characteristics			
Rock formation			
UK locations			

UK upland and lowland landscapes

Learning objectives

- To know the location of distinctive UK upland and lowland landscapes
- To recognise the key features of distinctive upland and lowland landscapes
- To understand how distinctive upland and lowland landscapes result from the interaction of physical processes

Figure 2 Bowerman's Nose

Activity

1 **a** Draw a sketch of the photograph of Bowerman's Nose.

   b Annotate this with details from the text to show how it was formed, and evidence that it is still being weathered by present day climatic conditions.

2 What is the difference between grykes and clints?

3 Draw a flow diagram to show how Malham Cove formed, starting with 'earth movements'.

Dartmoor is an example of an upland landscape formed when a massive dome of magma developed underground 290 million years ago. As it cooled and contracted to form granite, cracks known as **joints** developed. The presence of the weaker joints made the rock vulnerable to **freeze thaw weathering**, where the repeated freezing, expanding and thawing of water causes fragments of rocks to become detached. Over time, as the granite became exposed on the surface, erosion and mass movement processes like slumping removed the broken-up granite. Blocks of rock with fewer joints are left behind, and the largest blocks are left standing. These landforms are Dartmoor's famous **tors**, like Bowerman's Nose (Figure 2), surrounded by **clitter slopes** covered in smaller rocks. The tors continue to change from the influence of freeze thaw and chemical weathering.

The landscape near Malham in the Yorkshire Dales shows how the carboniferous limestone rocks and physical processes interact to create cliffs, deep gorges, impressive valleys, beautiful waterfalls and unusual limestone pavements. One distinctive landform is Malham Cove, a high limestone cliff shaped like an amphitheatre. Over millions of years, earth movements caused the large Middle Craven Fault to form with the softer rock slipping, creating a line of limestone cliffs. About 15,000 years ago at the end of the last ice age, melting water from glaciers created a massive waterfall which eroded the cliff backwards to its current position. The combination of the water flowing over the cove, as well as erosion, weathering and mass movement processes, created the rounded face seen today.

Along the top of Malham Cove the unique structure of the carboniferous limestone has created **limestone pavements**. The rock is made of blocks with horizontal lines (planes) and vertical cracks (joints). As rainwater passes through the lines of weaknesses in the rock, it causes a chemical reaction which enlarges the joints and bedding planes. The widening and deepening of the cracks on the surface form **grykes**, exposing blocks of limestone called **clints**, and creating the pavement.

The North and South Downs

Around 75 million years ago, during the **Cretaceous Period**, Britain was covered by warm, tropical seas; this resulted in the marine deposits that created the chalk foundations for the North and South Downs. Thirty million years ago, large earth movements caused the compacted layers of sediment to be forced upwards, creating a giant, chalk-covered dome. Over many years, water eroded the chalk, revealing the older sandstones and clays beneath, which form the High and Low Weald. The North and South Downs formed from the remaining chalk at the edges of the dome. The dome (called the Weald-Artois Anticline) experienced erosion, which removed the softer rocks at the centre of the dome and left the two escarpments of the North and South Downs. The South Downs escarpment consists of the steep **scarp slope** and the **dip slope** where the slope is gentler. At the top of the escarpment there are gently rolling hills. During the last ice age the processes of weathering and erosion created the V-shaped dry valleys, distinct hilltops and ridges that form the landscape today.

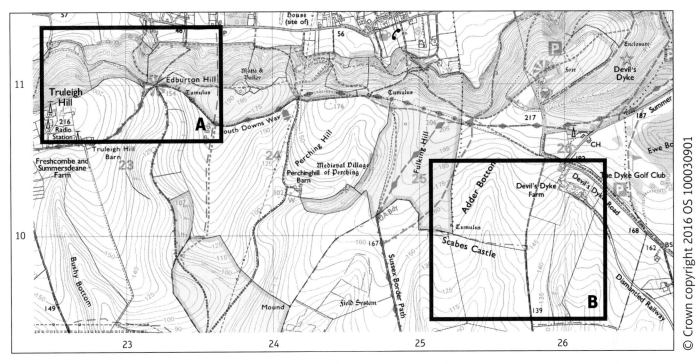

Figure 3 1:25,000 OS map extract of Devil's Dyke in the South Downs

Activity

Study Figure 3.

1 Describe the routes of the minor roads.

2 Identify and describe the possible recreation land use shown on the map.

3 Locate the chalk escarpment.

4 Look at the contour pattern for boxes A and B. This represents the scarp slope and dip slope of the chalk escarpment.

   a Decide which box represents the scarp slope and which box represents the dip slope. Justify your decision.

   b Describe the contour patterns for the scarp slope and the dip slope.

Tip Remember, when looking at contour patterns, the closer the lines are together then the steeper the slope.

Human activity on UK distinctive landscapes

Learning objectives

- To know how the landscape of the South Downs provides resources for agriculture, forestry and settlement
- To understand how human activities shape the landscape of the South Downs over time

Did you know?

The South Downs National Park is covered by about 5600 hectares (ha) of chalk downland. One reason for this could be that only 45% of chalk grassland in the National Park is designated as a Site of Special Scientific Interest (SSSI).

Exam-style question

Assess the importance of human activities in creating distinctive UK landscapes.

(8 marks + 4 SPAG)

Exam tip

For this style of question it is important to provide a well-developed argument that looks at a number of human activities on UK landscapes. The answer should be focused on specific examples through the use of relevant case study points.

Command word

Assess questions ask you to focus on how significant something is. You need to look at all the different factors and identify which are most important.

Agriculture

The South Downs **National Park** is an example of how distinctive landscapes result from human activity over time. Around 85% of the National Park is farmed, with approximately 1100 farm businesses operating. Chalk grassland is ideal for the grazing of sheep and training racehorses because the grass is short and rich in nutrients, whereas clay grassland is more suitable for dairy cows due to the longer grass length. On the south-facing lower slopes of the South Downs, the deeper soils are more suitable for **arable** farming like wheat, barley and vine **cultivation**. Farming on the South Downs brings advantages and disadvantages, some of which are given in Table 1.

Table 1 Advantages and disadvantages of farming on the South Downs

Advantages	Disadvantages
The income generated from farming supports the local economy; agricultural businesses account for approximately 6% of employment in the park.	The decline in arable farming and changes in farming practices have reduced the presence of arable plants, which has damaged wildlife habitats.
Arable farming has contributed towards supporting rare bird species on the Downs, which include the corn bunting, grey partridge, skylark and stone curlew.	There has been a significant decline in chalk grassland from the use of chemicals in farming.
The formation of hedgerows and field margins has led to **wildlife corridors** for bats.	The decline of traditional practices, such as extensive sheep grazing, has led to **scrub encroachment** on the remaining chalk grassland.

Figure 4 Farming in the South Downs National Park

Forestry

The South Downs National Park has a widespread mix of deciduous and coniferous woodland covering a total of 23.8% of the park (38,420 ha) and is a key feature of the western half of the National Park. The distribution of woodland across the National Park is uneven, with the west being significantly more wooded than the east. Human activity on woodland areas of the UK has increased, resulting in large areas being cleared. Human intervention in woodland landscapes has advantages and disadvantages (see Table 2).

Table 2 Advantages and disadvantages of forestry on the South Downs

Advantages	Disadvantages
A large percentage of the woodland that makes up the South Downs National Park is made up of ancient trees, which provide habitats for a diverse range of wildlife.	The removal of woodland for new developments is threatening some of the ancient large-leaved lime woodland. This may be very like the 'wildwood' that covered the South Downs after the last ice age.
The timber harvested from the National Park woodland is a valuable sustainable product, with growing markets in construction and fuel for heating.	Many of the hazel and chestnut **coppices** are under threat, because people no longer manage them in the traditional way. As they become overgrown, so the quality of the woodland and **biodiversity** declines.

Settlements

The chalk escarpments that make up the ridge and valley scenery of the North and South Downs were suitable for the development of **spring-line settlements**. The settlements were built on the south slopes with shelter from the naturally formed slope.

120,000 people live in the South Downs National Park, making it the most populated in the UK. With 74 people per km² it also has the highest population density. It is mainly rural, but surrounded by a number of major towns and cities. The South Downs has the largest market towns of any UK National Park – Lewes, Petersfield and Midhurst. The character of these and many other settlements throughout the National Park originates from the use of local building materials.

In recent years, many of the settlements in the North and South Downs have experienced new developments, which have not always reflected local character in terms of traditional design and materials. This has resulted in some loss of local distinctiveness. Along with the change in the local character of the buildings, many historic features, like the traditional wooden signage, have been replaced with standard metal signage; there has also been a decline in community facilities such as the post office, general store, pub or school.

Activity

1 State one advantage and one disadvantage of forestry in the South Downs.

2 What has been the impact of population pressure on settlements in the National Park?

Checkpoint

Now it is time to review your understanding of how upland and lowland landscapes result from the interaction of geology, physical processes and human activity over time.

Strengthen

S1 Use Figure 1 to shade the main areas of igneous and sedimentary rocks on an outline map of the UK. Use an atlas to locate Dartmoor, the Yorkshire Dales and the South Downs, then label them on your map.

S2 Add to your map details of the geology of the three landscapes and whether they are upland or lowland. What is the link between tectonic processes, geology and where upland and lowland landscapes are in the UK?

Challenge

C1 Draw an outline sketch of Figure 4. Add annotations to show how geology and processes like weathering and erosion have created the South Downs landscape.

C2 Add more annotations in a different colour showing how human activities have changed this landscape over time.

The coastal zone and coastal processes

The coastline is where the land meets the sea. The coastline of the UK is diverse in terms of its landscapes, ranging from dramatic cliffs to fine sandy beaches, and is constantly changing due to the interaction of different physical processes and the impact of human activities.

The impact of marine processes at the coast

Coastal **erosion** involves the action of waves wearing away the rocks along the coastline and removing the coastal **sediments**. There are four main processes of coastal erosion.

1 **Hydraulic action** – when waves crash against the cliff, the impact, force and weight of the water against the rocks wears away the rocks. It also compresses air in joints and faults in the rock, causing pressure to build and loose rocks to be dislodged. As the waves retreat, the compressed air is released, often explosively, causing the rock to weaken further.

2 **Abrasion** – this happens when fragments of rock, pebbles and sand are picked up by the waves and thrown against the cliff face, causing pieces of rock to break off.

3 **Solution** – this is the chemical action on rocks by seawater. It is most effective on limestone rocks, in which the calcium is dissolved and carried away in solution.

4 **Attrition** – rock fragments and pebbles carried by the waves are reduced in size as they collide against each other and the cliff face. They are eventually broken down into sand-sized particles, which are more easily transported by waves.

The impact of land processes at the coast

Different processes act on the land after waves have undercut the bottom of the cliff, weakening what lies above.

Weathering is the breakdown of rocks at or near to the surface of the ground. The three key weathering processes that can affect rocks exposed at the coast are as follows.

1 **Mechanical (freeze thaw)** – this is caused by the repeated freezing and thawing of water in a crack or hole in the rock. When water freezes, it expands by about 10%, causing stresses within the rock. When the ice melts, water seeps deeper into the rock along the deepened crack. After repeated cycles of freezing and thawing, fragments of rock may break off.

Figure 1 Destructive waves smash against the coastline at Dawlish in Devon, March 2014

2 **Chemical (acid rain)** – rainwater is slightly acidic. When rain falls on rocks such as limestone and chalk a weak chemical reaction takes place, causing the rock to weaken and break down.

3 **Biological** – the roots of growing plants can widen cracks in rocks. Burrowing animals and nesting birds on cliff faces can also cause the rock to weaken and decay.

Mass movement is the downslope movement of rocks and soil from the cliff top under the influence of gravity.

1 **Rock falls** – these happen suddenly when pieces of rock from a weathered cliff fall. This often occurs as the rock at the base of the cliff has been undercut by the action of the waves, leaving the rock above unsupported and causing it to collapse.

2 **Slumping** – this often occurs after long periods of rainfall. The rain seeps through **permeable** rocks such as sandstone. At the junction where the permeable rock meets an **impermeable** rock such as clay, the **saturated** soil and weaker rock slumps and slides in a rotational manner along a curved surface.

3 **Sliding** – this is similar to slumping but the movement of material occurs along a flat surface, usually a **bedding plane**. Large amounts of soil and rock move downslope rapidly and can cause a lot of damage.

Transportation

The eroded material will be **transported** along the coastline by different processes depending on the size of the material and the amount of energy in the waves. The methods of transport are the same as those in the river channel (see Figure 2 on page 45): large boulders are rolled along the seabed by waves (**traction**), smaller boulders are bounced (**saltation**), sand grains are carried in suspension, and lime from limestone and chalk rocks dissolves and is carried in solution. The transport of sand and pebbles along the coast by waves is called **longshore drift** (see page 24).

Deposition

Deposition occurs when there is not enough energy to carry the eroded material any further. This material is deposited or laid down, for example as sand in a bay to form a beach.

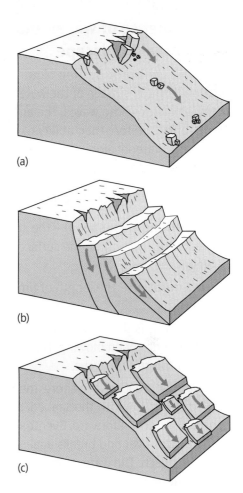

(a)

(b)

(c)

Figure 2 (a) Rock fall (b) Slumping (c) Sliding

Exam-style question

Describe **one** type of weathering that might have an impact on coastal landscapes.   **(2 marks)**

Exam tip

A good answer will give the details of the process, explaining how it works.

Activity

Create a mind map to represent the physical processes that cause changes to coastal landscapes. On your mind map, include:

a   the definition of each physical process with a suitable drawing

b   an explanation for how each physical process will cause a coastal landscape to change.

Tip When creating your mind map, use a colour code to represent erosion, weathering and mass movement processes.

The influence of waves and geology on the coastal landscape

Waves are generated by wind blowing over the sea. Friction with the surface of the water causes ripples to form, which grow into waves. The amount of energy in waves, and therefore their ability to erode, transport or deposit material along the coast, depends on their height.

The height and energy of waves are determined by:

- **wind strength (or speed)** – the stronger the wind, the greater the friction on the surface of the sea, and the bigger the wave
- **wind duration** – the length of time the wind has been blowing
- **fetch** – this is the distance of open water over which the wind has been blowing: the longer the fetch, the more powerful the wave.

As a wave approaches the shore, the base of the wave is slowed by friction with the seabed, but the upper part continues to travel forward. Eventually the top of the wave topples over and breaks against the cliff face or onto the beach. The water that surges up the beach until it runs out of energy is called the **swash**. The water that then runs back down the beach under gravity is called the **backwash**.

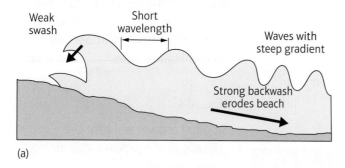

(a)

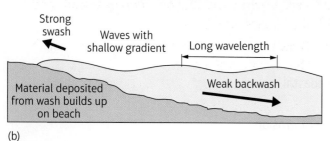

(b)

Figure 3 (a) Destructive and (b) constructive waves

Types of wave

There are two types of wave that move towards the coast: destructive waves and constructive waves. Each of these waves can change the shape of the coastline but in different ways.

Destructive waves are formed by strong winds that have blown over large fetch areas. The waves are powerful and lead to coastal erosion. Destructive waves are tall and steep, they are closely spaced and break frequently – typically, between 11 and 15 waves break per minute. The backwash is much stronger than the swash, so rocks, pebbles and sand are carried back out to sea. If beaches form, they tend to be narrow and steep and offer cliffs little in the way of protection as they cannot absorb much of the wave energy.

Constructive waves are associated with light winds. The waves have less energy and encourage deposition. They are low in height and widely spaced, breaking gently – typically, between six and nine waves break per minute. The swash is stronger than the backwash, so more material is carried up the beach than is removed. The resulting beaches tend to be wide and shallow, and they help to protect the cliffs from erosion as the wave energy is absorbed by the beach.

Activity

1 Create a table to compare the characteristics of destructive and constructive waves. Include formation, energy, shape, breaking characteristics and coastal impact.

2 Explain why constructive waves are more likely to deposit sediments than destructive waves.

Geological structure: concordant and discordant coasts

The UK's coastline includes distinctive landforms that are a result of wave action and physical processes interacting with the local geological structure and rock type.

The coastline around the Isle of Purbeck, part of the Dorset Coast in southern England, has different geological structures (Figure 4). The coastline from Studland to Durlston Head is an example of a **discordant coast** because bands of resistant and less

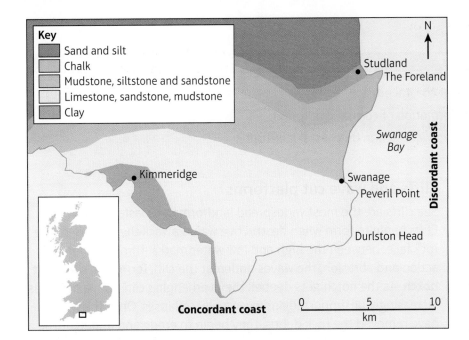

Figure 4 Map to show the geological structure of the Isle of Purbeck, Dorset

> ### Did you know?
>
> Dorset and East Devon are part of the Jurassic Coast World Heritage Site, famous for its important fossil sites and varied geology. The varied geology explains Dorset's magnificent scenery, for example where erosion has attacked joints and faults in the rock to form inlets and bays.

resistant rocks run at right angles to the coastline. The southern coastline, from Durlston Head to Kimmeridge, is a **concordant coast** where bands of resistant and less resistant rocks run parallel to the coastline.

Headlands and bays

Hydraulic action and abrasion erode sea cliffs. On a discordant coast they erode at varying rates as rocks of different hardness and resistance meet the sea. The stronger or harder rocks, such as the chalk at Studland and limestone south of Swanage, are able to resist wave attacks and erosion for longer. These sections of cliff stand out as prominent rocky **headlands** – for example, The Foreland to the north (chalk) and Peveril Point to

the south (limestone). The softer or weaker rocks, such as the mudstones and siltstones found at Swanage, are eroded back more quickly to form **bays** – Swanage Bay, for example.

Fewer bays and headlands are formed along concordant coastlines where the rock type is the same along its length, and so the rate of erosion is similar. If the outer rock is a more resistant rock, such as limestone, the cliffs are likely to be high and steep. The harder rock acts as a barrier, but if breached, the sea is able to erode the softer rock behind. This creates a **cove** – a circular area of water with a narrow entrance from the sea (Figure 5).

> ### Activity
>
> 1 Draw a sketch of the geology of the Isle of Purbeck, Figure 4. Using evidence from the text:
>   a label bands of more resistant and less resistant rock
>   b add labels for 'headland', 'bay' and 'cliff'.
> 2 Explain why chalk outcrops form headlands and mudstones form bays.
> 3 Draw an annotated sketch of Figure 5 to explain the formation of a cove.
> 4 Suggest reasons why even resistant rocks such as limestone are eroded by the sea.

Figure 5 Lulworth Cove on the Dorset Coast, west of the Isle of Purbeck

Landforms of coastal erosion

Learning objectives

- To know the characteristics of landforms of coastal erosion
- To understand the role of erosion in the formation of coastal landforms
- To understand the influence of geology and wave action on coastal landforms

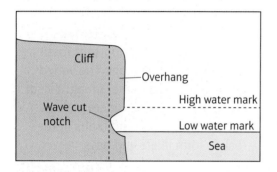

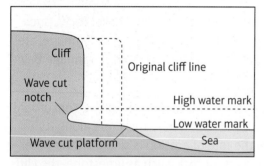

Figure 6 Formation of a wave cut notch and a wave cut platform

Cliffs and wave cut platforms

Sea cliffs are the most widespread landforms of coastal erosion. Cliffs begin to form when destructive waves attack the bottom of the rock face, between the high and low water marks. Through hydraulic action and abrasion, the waves undercut the cliff, forming a **wave cut notch**. As the notch gets deeper, the overhanging cliff above becomes increasingly unsupported and eventually collapses. Once the waves have removed the rock debris, they begin to erode and undercut the new cliff face. Through a continual sequence of wave erosion and cliff collapse, the cliff face and coastline gradually retreat inland.

A gently sloping rocky area is left at the bottom of the retreating cliff. This is called a **wave cut platform**. The platform is covered at high tide but exposed at low tide. Its surface is not smooth because differences in rock structure are picked out by abrasion to create many grooves, rock pools and ridges within the bare rock.

Caves, arches and stacks

Caves, arches and stacks form at headlands, where the rocks are relatively hard or resistant. As destructive waves break against the headland, any lines of weakness in the rock such as joints or faults are attacked. Through hydraulic action and abrasion, the waves erode the rock along the joint or fault which will increase in size and may eventually form a **cave**.

Waves continue to erode the cave, in particular through hydraulic action. When a wave breaks, it blocks off the entrance to the cave and traps air within it. The trapped air is compressed, increasing the pressure on the sides, roof and back wall of the cave. If the cave forms part of a narrow headland, the pressure from the waves may result in the back of the cave being pushed through to the other side. The cave then becomes a natural **arch**, as it is open on both sides.

Continued erosion by the sea widens the arch. As the sea undercuts the base of the arch, more pressure is placed on the top of the arch. Eventually the weakened roof of the arch collapses, leaving a **stack**, a pinnacle of rock, separated from the mainland.

Further erosion and weathering over time may cause the stack to collapse to leave a small, flat **stump**, which is often covered by the sea at high tide.

Exam-style question

Explain two physical processes that lead to the formation of wave cut platforms. **(4 marks)**

Exam tip

When answering formation questions, always name processes and explain how they operate to create the landform. Using a sketch may help, provided that it is annotated for formation.

Figure 7 Old Harry Rocks, Handfast Point, Dorset

Checkpoint

Now it is time to review your understanding of the processes that change the coastal landscape, and the influence of geology.

Strengthen

S1 Think about erosion, weathering and mass movement processes. How do waves influence these processes?

S2 Put these landforms of erosion in order of formation: stack, cave, headland, arch.

S3 Why are resistant rocks also eroded?

Challenge

C1 What conditions are needed for a large and powerful wave to form?

C2 Describe a headland and explain its formation in no more than 125 words. You must include: a description of its key features and explain the processes and influences in its formation. Underline in a different colour where you have explained.

C3 Explain why fewer headlands and bays are formed along concordant than discordant coastlines.

Did you know?

One of the best known stacks in the UK is Old Harry near Studland in Dorset (Figure 7). Old Harry and his wife (a stump) were at one time part of a chalk band that stretched from Dorset to the Isle of Wight.

Activity

1   Draw a sketch of the landforms shown in Figure 7 and annotate it to:
    a   describe the landforms
    b   explain their formation.

2   Why do caves not form in soft or less resistant rock?

Landforms of coastal deposition

Learning objectives

- To know the characteristics of landforms of coastal deposition
- To understand the role of transportation and deposition in the formation of coastal landforms
- To understand the influence of geology and wave action on coastal landforms

Transportation – longshore drift

Waves approaching the coast carry sand and pebbles. Longshore drift is the process of **transportation** which moves sand and pebbles along the coast. Waves often approach the coast at an angle. The swash carries the sand and pebbles up the beach at the same angle as the wave. The backwash then draws the sediment back down the beach at right angles to the coastline, as this is the steepest gradient. The process is repeated, resulting in a zigzag movement of sediment along the coast (Figure 8). The general direction of longshore drift around the coasts of the UK is controlled by the direction of the **prevailing wind**. Along the Dorset Coast in southern England, prevailing south-westerly winds cause longshore drift movements from west to east.

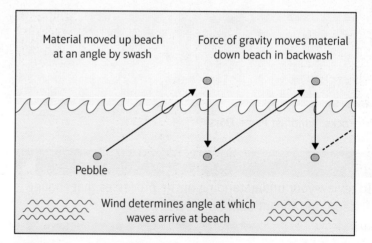

Figure 8 The process of longshore drift

Beaches

Beaches are formed when eroded material is transported by longshore drift and deposited by constructive waves along the coastline. Sandy beaches are often found in sheltered bays (known as bay head beaches). They are usually wider than pebble beaches and slope gently down to the sea. Pebble beaches are often found in areas where cliffs are being eroded and where there are high-energy waves. They have steep gradients.

The **profile** (cross section) of beaches is rarely smooth. At the top end, they may include a **storm beach** made up of boulders and shingle deposited by the largest waves during storm conditions. Below this, a ridge of shingle and sand, called a **berm**, marks the normal high tide. A series of berms can be left by a retreating tide. The smallest material (sand) is deposited near the sea.

Spits

A **spit** is a long and narrow ridge of sand or shingle, one end of which is attached to the land while the other end projects out to sea (Figure 9). If the spit is formed of sand, sand dunes are usually found at the back of it. The area behind the spit is sheltered, leading to the deposition of silt and mud and the creation of a **saltmarsh**.

The formation of a spit begins in the same way as that of a beach. Material is transported along the coast by longshore drift and is deposited where there is a bend in the coastline or a river mouth occurs. Gradually, more and more sediment is deposited, forming a ridge that extends into the sea. Fresh water and seawater are trapped behind this ridge as it forms. As the ridge extends into deeper and more open water, the tip is affected by the wind and waves approaching from different directions. These cause the end of the spit to curve.

Figure 9 An aerial photograph of Dawlish Warren sand spit and the estuary of the River Exe, Devon

Figure 10 The bar and lagoon at Slapton Sands, near Dartmouth, Devon

Bars

A **bar** is a ridge of sand or shingle across the entrance to a bay or river mouth. Fresh water is trapped behind it to form a **lagoon**, such as Slapton Sands, near Dartmouth, Devon (Figure 10). The formation of a bar begins in the same way as a spit. Material is transported along the coast by longshore drift and deposited where there is a bend in the coastline. Deposition then continues in a line across the entrance to the bay or river mouth, trapping fresh water behind.

Activity

1   State one similarity and one difference between spits and bars.

2   Draw a sketch of the landforms shown in Figure 10 and annotate it to:

    a   describe the landforms

    b   explain their formation.

How geographers investigate coastal landscapes using OS maps

Grid references

All OS maps include a numbered grid.

- **Eastings** are the vertical lines with numbers that run eastwards across the top or bottom of the map.

- **Northings** are the horizontal lines with numbers that run northwards up the side of the map.

Grid references are used to locate places on maps. Four-figure grid references are used to give a general location by referring to the square in which a feature is located. Six-figure grid references are used to give a precise location. Always work first from west to east, before working from south to north ('along the corridor and up the stairs').

For example, in Figure 11, the four-figure grid reference for Ballard Point is 0481. The six-figure grid reference for the same feature is 048813 – it is 8/10s going east and 3/10s going north in the square.

Scale and distance

Maps come in many different **scales**. Here, Figure 11 is at a scale of 1:50,000. This means that the map represents things 50,000 times smaller than they really are.

If a map's scale is 1:50,000, then 1 cm on the map represents 500 metres in reality, and 2 cm represents 1 km. Whatever the scale of the OS map, a grid square is always 1 km × 1 km.

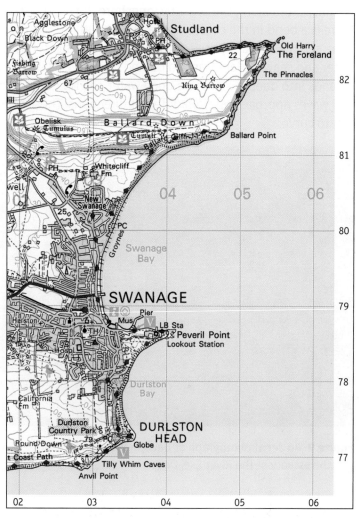

Figure 11 Extract from 1:50,000 OS map of Swanage, Dorset

© Crown copyright 2016 OS 100030901

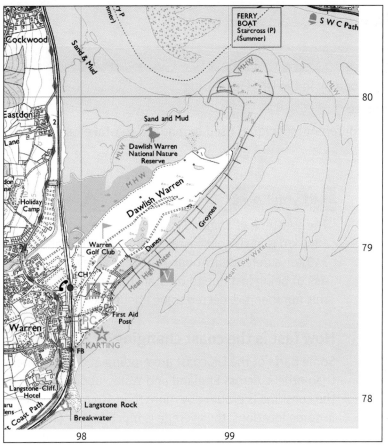

Figure 12 Extract from 1:25,000 OS map of Dawlish Warren, Devon

© Crown copyright 2016 OS 100030901

Coastal OS map symbols

On OS maps of coastal areas, the same symbol can be used for different landforms. For example, the flat rock symbol for cliffs and wave cut platforms, and the sand symbol for beaches and sand dunes. To identify a coastal landform on an OS map follow these steps.

1   Find the high water mark: this is shown by a black line on 1:50,000 maps and a blue line (labelled 'Mean High Water Springs' in places) on 1:25,000 maps.

2   On which side of the high water mark is the symbol? Cliffs and sand dunes will be on the landward side; wave cut platforms and beaches will be on the seaward side.

Some landforms such as cliffs are shown using two different symbols. In Figure 11:

• a rock symbol is used to represent the vertical cliffs between The Foreland and Ballard Point

• a steep slope symbol is used to represent Ballard Cliff. This indicates that the cliff is not completely vertical – some slumping may have occurred.

Activity

1   Study Figure 12. How long is the spit? Give the distance between the railway station in square 9778 and the end of the spit in square 9980.

2   Draw a sketch map of the spit in Figure 12 and annotate it to:

    a   describe the key features

    b   explain how different processes interact to produce these key features.

Tip Draw a grid of 4 cm squares then copy the spit accurately and draw the mean high water line. Add a north point, scale and title to your sketch.

Exam-style question

Study Figure 12. Identify the landform at 980780.   **(1 mark)**

Exam tip

First check where the symbol is in relation to the high water mark – is it on the landward or seaward side?

Checkpoint

Now it is time to review your understanding of the processes of coastal transport and deposition and how we use OS maps to study the coastline.

Strengthen

S1 Describe the process of longshore drift.

S2 Put these landforms of deposition in order of formation: lagoon, spit, bar, saltmarsh.

S3 How do you tell the difference between a beach and an area of sand dunes on an OS map?

Challenge

C1 What conditions are needed for coastal deposition to occur?

C2 Compare the characteristics and profiles of a sandy beach and a pebbly beach.

C3 Study Figures 11 and 12. Identify as many coastal landforms as you can. Note down a four- or six-figure grid reference for each. Categorise them into landforms of erosion and of deposition.

The causes and effects of coastal erosion

Learning objectives

- To know why coastal erosion and the risk of coastal flooding in the UK is increasing
- To know how coastal erosion and flood risk is managed
- To understand the advantages and disadvantages of different techniques used to manage coastal erosion and flood risk

Coastal areas provide economic, environmental and recreational opportunities, which is why many people in the UK choose to live within the coastal zone. For some of these people, coastal erosion and the threat of flooding are real concerns. Coastal erosion is the removal of material from the coast by wave action, causing the coastline to retreat inland. This results in loss of land and damage to buildings, roads and railways. It can increase the risk of coastal flooding. Figure 13 shows places at greatest risk from flooding in England and Wales.

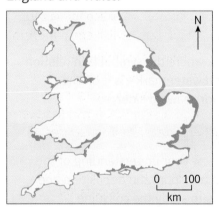

Figure 13 Places in England and Wales most at risk from coastal erosion and flooding

Figure 14 Coastal erosion with active landslips at Aldbrough, Holderness, Yorkshire

Did you know?

The coastline of England is 4500 km long: about 1800 km is at risk of coastal erosion, of which about 340 km is defended. About 200 homes are currently at risk of being lost due to coastal erosion, but by 2029 this number is expected to be about 2000.

How fast is the coast changing?

Some parts of the UK coast are eroding at a faster rate than others. Across England and Wales, about 28% of the coastline is eroding by more than 10 cm each year; in some locations, the average is much higher (Table 1). Coastal erosion is not always gradual; many metres of land may be lost in a sudden landslip or after a great storm, which may occur just once in five or ten years.

Table 1 Mean rates of coastal erosion

Site	Retreat in a 10-year period (metres)	Cause
Happisburgh, Norfolk (cliffs 7–10 metres high)	90	Failure of coastal defences
Sidestrand, Norfolk (cliffs 60 metres high)	20	Large but not frequent landslides
Aldbrough, Holderness, Yorkshire (cliffs 17 metres high)	26	Smaller but frequent landslides; significant wave and storm damage

Rates of erosion are expected to increase by 2080 because of rising sea levels and increasing storms, brought about by **climate change**.

Rising sea level

Sea level along the English Channel has risen by about 12 cm in the past 100 years. Levels are expected to rise by another 11–16 cm by 2030 due to **global warming**. A warmer **climate** causes seawater to expand and also causes the ice sheets and glaciers to melt, leading to increased sea levels as a result. The likely effects are as follows.

- Cliffs that are currently being undercut and collapsing will continue to retreat; the position of the wave cut notch and the level of the wave cut platform may change.
- Areas of 'soft' coastline (clays and gravel) may experience more erosion and retreat due to more frequent and stronger storms.

Storms and storm surges

A **storm surge** is a large-scale increase in sea level (up to 3 metres around the UK) as gale-force winds drive water towards the coastline. Surges can last from hours to days, span hundreds of kilometres and cause significant damage and loss of life.

The North Sea storm surge of 1953 was one of the worst natural disasters to hit the UK. The storm lasted two days, flood defences were breached and coastal towns in Lincolnshire, East Anglia and Kent were devastated as seawater rushed into the streets. In England, 307 people were killed and 24,000 properties and 65,000 hectares were damaged.

In December 2013, a storm generated another major North Sea storm surge which coincided with one of the highest tides of the year. Due to coastal defences and early warnings, flood-related deaths and major damage were avoided. In January and February 2014, a sequence of very deep depressions driven by the **jet stream** towards the UK coincided with very high winds. The resulting storm surges caused widespread damage and flooding along the south coast.

Human causes of coastal erosion and impacts

The coast works as a naturally interconnected and balanced system. Erosion in one place leads to the transport and deposition of sediments in another. Human activities such as farming, urban and industrial development affect coastal landscapes, and can also affect coastal processes.

- Structures like groynes are built to trap sand, for example to protect a tourist beach. However, removing sediment from the system results in increased erosion further along the coast.
- Dredging also removes sand and gravel from the system. In 1897, over 600,000 tonnes of gravel were dredged from the sea bed to build Plymouth Docks in Devon. Soon afterwards, wave action eroded the 5 metre high beach protecting nearby Hallsands village, which was then destroyed by storms in 1917.
- Erosion from sea cliffs is an important source of sediment for nearby beaches. If cliffs are protected from erosion, for example to protect houses, the supply of sediment into the coastal system stops, resulting in beach erosion somewhere else.

Erosion affects a variety of coastal land uses.

- **Settlements** – over 20 million people in the UK live on the coast. At Holderness, for example, over 29 villages have been lost due to erosion in the past 1000 years.
- **Tourism** – plays a major part in local economies: for example, about 13% of jobs at Dawlish are in tourism.
- **Infrastructure** – roads, railways, oil refineries and ferry and shipping ports are located along the coast. For example, the Esso oil refinery at Fawley, near Southampton, is the largest in the UK. It handles over 2000 ships a year, transporting 22 million tonnes of crude oil.
- **Agriculture** – sea level rise and increased coastal erosion is already leading to the loss of farmland.

Activity

1   Study Figure 13 and an atlas.
    a   Describe the distribution of places with the greatest risk of coastal erosion and flooding.
    b   Explain why the risk is higher in these places than in other coastal areas.
2   Study Table 1.
    a   Calculate the mean rate of erosion per year for each location.
    b   Suggest reasons for the high amount of coastal erosion at each location.
3   Explain why the risk of coastal erosion and flooding in the UK is likely to increase this century.

Managing coastal erosion and flood risk

The Department for Environment, Food and Rural Affairs (Defra) is responsible for the protection of the coastline from flooding and erosion in England and Wales. It does this by deciding which parts of the coastline should be protected and how.

Shoreline Management Plans

To make these decisions manageable, the coastline has been divided into short sections. The Environment Agency and local authorities are then responsible for deciding how coastal erosion and flood risk should be managed in each one. Together, they develop a **Shoreline Management Plan (SMP)** in order to:

- reduce the threat of flooding and erosion to people and the environment

- benefit the environment, society and economy, in line with the government's **sustainable** development principles.

Possible plan policies

1 **No intervention** – no planned investment in defending against flooding or erosion.

2 **Hold the line** – maintain the existing shoreline by building defences.

3 **Managed realignment** – allow the shoreline to change naturally, but manage and direct the process.

4 **Advance the line** – build new defences on the seaward side.

In most cases, a decision is made to 'hold the line'. By taking this approach, authorities have the option of using soft- or hard-engineering techniques.

Soft engineering takes a more natural approach, allowing the processes to work and the land to change in a more environmentally sustainable way.

Table 2 Advantages and disadvantages of soft-engineering techniques

Advantages	Disadvantages
Beach nourishment (recharge) – sand or shingle is added to a beach to make it higher or wider	
The beach can absorb more wave energy and protect the coastline. Sediment is obtained locally so it blends in. Easy and cheap to maintain. Encourages tourism.	Needs constant maintenance, which can become expensive. The work is often undertaken in the summer, which can cause disruption to beach users.
Sand dune regeneration – grasses, bushes and trees are planted to stabilise dunes	
Helps the dunes to develop and maintains a natural coastal environment. Popular with people and wildlife. Relatively cheap.	Areas of the beach have to be fenced off, prohibiting access. It takes time for the dune vegetation to become established.

Figure 15 Sea wall, rock armour and beach nourishment (recharge) at Torcross, Slapton Sands, Devon

Exam-style question

Describe how a beach nourishment (recharge) management strategy might affect the coastline.

(3 marks)

Exam tip

When you are asked to explain something, show you can use geographical terms correctly. In this case, start by defining beach nourishment and how it works, then link this with different impacts on the coastline.

Hard engineering involves building artificial defences, usually out of concrete, to interrupt natural processes or to dissipate the energy of the waves to lower their impact on the coastline.

Table 3 Advantages and disadvantages of hard-engineering techniques

Advantages	Disadvantages
Sea walls – *concrete walls, about 3–5 metres high, built at the foot of cliffs or the top of a beach; sometimes curved to reflect the waves back out to sea*	
They are effective at stopping the sea. They often include a walkway or promenade.	They can be obtrusive and unnatural to look at and can restrict access to the beach. They are very expensive to build and to maintain. They can increase erosion of the beach.
Groynes – *wooden or rock structures built along the beach at right angles*	
They are quick to construct. They trap sediment and broaden the beach. The beach then absorbs the wave energy. A bigger beach can attract more tourists.	Interrupting the movement of sediment can have an impact further along the coast. Rock groynes can be unsightly.
Rip rap *(rock armour) – large boulders piled at the foot of the cliff or the top of the beach*	
The boulders force the waves to break, dissipating their energy and protecting the cliffs. They can be quickly put in place. They are relatively cheap and easy to maintain.	Boulders are usually from other regions or from abroad, so transport costs can be high. They do not fit in with the local geology. They can impede access to the beach.

Figure 16 Sea wall and rip rap (rock armour) at Dawlish Warren, Devon

Activity

1 Summarise the main costs and benefits of soft and hard engineering, adding examples of different techniques.

2 With the help of a diagram based on Figure 16, describe what is meant by rip rap and explain how it works.

Checkpoint

Now it is time to review your understanding of the causes of coastal erosion and flooding and how they can be managed.

Strengthen

S1 Give two reasons why people in the UK will be at greater risk of coastal flooding in future.

S2 How are storms contributing to the increasing threat of coastal erosion and flooding in the UK?

S3 Is a 'no intervention' management plan appropriate or should all areas at risk of coastal flooding have some protection? Explain your answer.

Challenge

C1 Explain how the UK's weather and climate make it difficult to predict the likelihood of future coastal flood events.

C2 Explain how human activity may be increasing coastal erosion and the impact of coastal flooding on people and the environment.

C3 Explain why beach nourishment (recharge) and sand dune regeneration may be a useful way of managing coastal flooding in the long term.

Case Study – Changes to the Dawlish Warren sand spit

Learning objectives

- To know how people and the environment interact at Dawlish Warren
- To know how human and physical factors cause change to Dawlish Warren sand spit
- To understand how coastal management techniques can lead to change in coastal landscapes

The sand spit at Dawlish Warren, a seaside resort on the south coast of Devon, is a classic coastal landform (see Figure 9). The spit extends for about 2 km north-eastwards, protecting the Exe Estuary from the open sea (see Figure 12). Natural processes are constantly changing the spit and, like many areas of the UK coast, it has also been used and changed by people for centuries. Today, the Dawlish Warren sand spit is an important resource for people and the environment.

- The spit was designated a Local Nature Reserve in 1978 and a National Nature Reserve in 2000. It provides a unique habitat for a range of coastal species – birds and flowering plants – and is internationally important for wading birds and wildfowl.

- The fishing industry is a historically and culturally important aspect of the Exe, providing locally caught fresh seafood. Mussels are harvested in the calm waters behind the spit. There is also the potential to source oysters from these waters.

- The spit is a popular tourist destination. The tourist resort on the Warren attracts about 480,000 visitors each year, mostly during the summer months when visitor numbers can reach 20,000 each day.

- The area is served by a wide range of public transport, including trains, buses and ferries. There is a car park at the west end of the spit, but no surfaced roads; footpaths and tracks allow easy access to the beach. In summer, visitors can arrive by hovercraft at the eastern end of the spit.

- The spit is home to a few residential properties and a number of small businesses that provide goods for tourists and jobs for local people (about 13% of local employment is through seaside tourism).

- The Exe Estuary is popular for water-based recreational activities, including sailing, windsurfing, kitesurfing, water-skiing, jet-skiing and kayaking. Locals and visitors also use the spit for walking and playing golf.

With a growing tourist industry and an important fishing industry, pressure on the Dawlish Warren sand spit is likely to increase. A major problem is the increasing risk of erosion and flooding.

Physical factors changing the spit

When Dawlish Warren was originally formed 7000 years ago, it was two sand spits – the Outer Warren and the Inner Warren – separated by Greenland Lake. By the 1930s, erosion had caused the two Warrens to join, enclosing the lake and creating a single spit.

The spit has continued to change due to erosion and deposition. Figure 17 shows the outline of the spit from 1938 to 1962. High spring tides accompanied by strong winds (storm surges) have driven waves across the ridge that forms the spit's southern and eastern extents.

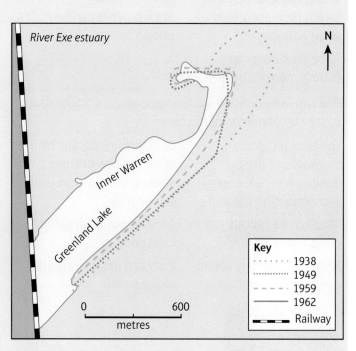

Figure 17 Erosion and loss of land at Dawlish Warren sand spit, Devon

Erosion of the beach and dunes has caused the spit to retreat. As a result of the 2013–14 storms, for example, about 5 metres of sand was lost from the southern face of the sand dunes. At the same time, sands transported from the south and south-west have helped to rebuild some areas and extend the spit to the east.

Human factors changing the spit

Housing development, construction of flood defences and transport links have all played their part in shaping the coastline around Dawlish Warren. In the 1930s, there were bungalows on the eastern end of the spit. By the end of the 1940s, these had been washed away by a series of storms and high tides, and the 'hook' visible today had disappeared beneath the sea.

The first sea defence was built on the western end of Dawlish Warren in 1917. Granite boulders were used as rock armour (rip rap) to protect the railway line. After the storms in the 1940s, British Rail positioned railway sleeper barriers at the foot of the dunes and planted trees to help stabilise them, but the dunes continued to retreat inland. The first wooden groynes were installed on the beach in 1959.

Storms throughout the 1960s continued to erode the dunes, threatening the spit's habitat, tourism industry and function as a breakwater for the Exe Estuary. New coastal defences were installed in the early 1970s, including:

- a 300 metre long concrete sea wall next to the existing rock armour **revetment**, with a promenade on top
- a 300 metre 'backbone' of rock-filled wire baskets (gabions) beneath the sand dunes to hold them in place
- 18 groynes to try to stabilise beach levels.

Following storms in 1989 and 1990, the western end of the spit was repaired with 35,000 tonnes of granite imported from Norway and deposited at the foot of the sea wall.

Activity

1   Study the information about the resources of the Dawlish Warren sand spit.

   a   Make **three** lists of resources: economic, environmental and social (some may be in more than one category).

   b   Describe the impact a growing tourist industry may have on the resources on and around the spit.

2   Draw a sketch of Figure 18.

   a   Label the coastal management strategies and annotate them to explain how they will protect the sand spit from erosion.

   b   What impact might these coastal defences have on the coastline further east?

Figure 18 Coastal management strategies at Dawlish Warren, Devon

Protecting the Dawlish Warren sand spit in the future

As sea levels continue to rise and storms are becoming more powerful, protecting Dawlish Warren, its people and their properties is becoming more difficult. The impacts of the storms in recent years have been substantial: coastal defences breached, people's homes damaged and flooded, businesses closed, roads and railways destroyed or disrupted (Figure 19), farmland flooded and the psychological trauma of dealing with flooding.

Figure 19 A large section of the sea wall under the railway line at Dawlish collapsed in the storms of February 2014

The Dawlish Warren Beach Management Scheme

Following the storms of 2013 and 2014, the Environment Agency and Teignbridge District Council have proposed a range of works that are needed at Dawlish Warren to allow the sand spit to continue to protect the Exe Estuary from storm waves. They have settled on a 'hold the line' scheme to include:

- recharging the beach at Dawlish Warren by adding extra sand
- maintaining the sea wall and rock armour at the western end of the spit, near to the tourist facilities and village
- repairing, replacing and possibly extending the wooden groynes along the beach
- building a new flood defence near the visitor centre to reduce the risk of tidal flooding to Dawlish Warren village
- removing the rock-filled wire baskets (gabions) to allow the sand dunes to follow a more natural alignment.

The £14 million scheme will help to reduce the risk of flooding to nearly 2900 properties and shelter the main railway line from storms. Despite this, there are still some concerns about the scheme and its impact on local residents and the Exe Estuary (Figure 20).

The scheme is putting birds before people…
There is a legal requirement to replace lost habitats. New ones will be found so that people, properties and businesses can still be protected.

The scheme costs a lot of money…
The cost of not investing in coastal defences is very much higher.

Farmers will have to give up land for these new habitats…
Areas of new habitat will only be created where landowners agree and they will receive financial recompense for any lands lost.

What about the effect on our beach…
Recharging the beach will improve it and protect it from sea level rise. Sand will be sourced locally so it matches the current beach.

Protecting parts of the Exe Estuary will cause other parts to flood…
Some areas are already at risk of flooding. The scheme will not increase the risk of flooding to roads, buildings or other infrastructure.

Figure 20 Some concerns about coastal defences and responses to these

The environmental impact of coastal defences

While coastal defences help to reduce coastal erosion and the risk of tidal flooding, they also prevent the coastline from evolving in response to natural processes. With the building of the railway, sea wall and groynes around Dawlish, for example, sand is no longer being transported by longshore drift to the spit. This can cause **coastal squeeze** where coastal habitats such as saltmarshes are prevented from moving inland in response to storms or rising sea level, and so become smaller over time.

As the Dawlish Warren sand spit forms a nationally, as well as an internationally, renowned habitat, its environmental features need to be protected. If any habitats are lost due to 'squeeze', new ones will have to be provided. These are called **compensatory habitats**, and some have already been created on the rivers Axe and Avon in Devon.

Adaptation and resilience

A word of warning – coastal defences are only ever able to defend against events that we are able to predict with reasonable accuracy (from monitoring, measuring and modelling); they are not able to adapt to changing conditions (unexpectedly powerful storm surges). Instead, we need to adapt to cope with the risk of flooding by adapting our homes, for example:

- installing electrical sockets higher on the walls
- having solid floors to make cleaning up easier

- being prepared and knowing what to do when a flood warning is issued.

If a flood does occur, then resilience is required to deal with the social, economic and environmental impacts. Community resilience in areas at risk of coastal flooding or erosion is about:

- how people prepare for disasters
- what they do when they strike
- how they pull together to rebuild the community afterwards.

Activity

1 Examine why the Dorset and East Devon coast is prone to coastal erosion and flooding.

2 Do you think coastal defences should be built to protect the coastline at Dawlish Warren? Explain and justify your view.

Exam-style question

Examine the impact of coastal erosion on the Dorset and East Devon coast and how it can be managed.

(8 marks)

Exam tip

You need to break down this 'examine' question into its different parts: the different erosion processes and management strategies on this coast and how they are linked.

Checkpoint

Now it is time to review your understanding of how physical and human processes interact to change coastal landscapes.

Strengthen

S1 Produce a timeline of coastal landscape change for Dawlish Warren. Highlight changes due to nature and those due to human intervention.

S2 Why is it necessary to protect Dawlish Warren sand spit?

S3 Summarise the ways in which people can prepare for and recover from the impact of coastal flooding at Dawlish Warren.

Challenge

C1 What are the likely outcomes of not protecting Dawlish Warren spit? Think about economic, environmental and social impacts, and the costs and benefits of each.

C2 Explain how protecting the coast in one area may create problems further along the coastline.

Investigating Coastal Landscapes

Learning objectives

- To understand how to conduct a geographical investigation of coastal processes through landscape evidence
- To know how to choose enquiry questions, fieldwork methods and data sources for an investigation into coastal landscapes
- To know how to present, analyse and evaluate data collected from a coastal investigation

Figure 21 The beach at Dawlish Warren, Devon

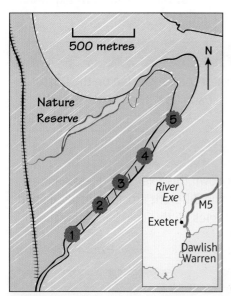

Figure 22 A sketch map of Dawlish Warren in Devon showing the sample sites

Activity

1. Read the text about Dawlish Warren and study Figure 21. Create another key question that would help answer the main task question.

2. Using Figure 22 and an atlas, write an overview of the location of Dawlish Warren and the fieldwork investigation.

(F) The enquiry question

When conducting a geographical enquiry, it is important to have a purpose. One way to do this is to ask a task question.

For this enquiry on coasts, the task question is:

How and why does the beach at Dawlish Warren change along its length?

A sand spit has formed at Dawlish Warren in Devon, extending about 2 km north-eastwards from the mainland. Prevailing wind conditions along the south coast of England mean that sediment is transported by longshore drift from the west to the east end of the spit. However, groynes have been built at regular intervals to help stabilise the beach. The aim of this enquiry is to discover if the beach changes from west to east, and if this is linked to natural processes or the management of the beach.

To help answer the task question, geographers next devise some key questions. These help to provide a focus for the enquiry.

For this task, a key question could be:

Does the sediment change in size and shape further along the beach?

You might expect sediment size to decrease and roundness to increase from west to east on Dawlish Warren beach as it is transported by longshore drift. However, groynes act as sediment traps, interrupting the natural movement of material, so their presence may also influence beach sediment characteristics.

(F) Locating the study

It is important to show the study location. Use maps at different scales, as in Figure 22. The main map shows study sites, while the inset map gives the regional location. This helps to set the scene.

As well as describing your study location, you need to explain your choice of study sites. This may depend on the data collection method(s) you choose. At Dawlish Warren, for example, study sites were chosen at regular intervals at every third groyne along the beach (Figure 22). These five sites were approximately 300 metres apart at the high tide mark. Each one was measured 5 metres to the east of the end of the groyne. This gave a representative sample along the beach and a chance to collect the samples before high tide.

F Methodology

Once you have decided on some suitable key questions and located your investigation, the next stage is to choose the methods you will use to collect your data. Geographers use both **primary data** (data that is collected first hand) and **secondary data** (data that has already been published). In your investigation, you need a mixture of **quantitative** methods (using numbers), such as measuring the size and shape of beach sediment, and **qualitative** (descriptive) methods, such as a field sketch.

For each method, it is important that you decide where and how you will collect the data and why the data collected will help to answer the overall task question. You cannot collect data from every part of the coastal area or measure every pebble on the beach, so you need to sample.

- **Random sampling** – data is collected by chance. An example might be picking up stones from the beach with your eyes closed.
- **Systematic sampling** – the locations of the sites are found at equal intervals from each other. An example might be to measure the dimensions of a pebble every 20 metres along the beach.
- **Stratified sampling** – is used when the study area has significantly different parts. An example might be measuring pebble characteristics at either end of the beach (Figure 23).

An example of how to present your methodology is shown in Table 4.

Exam tip

You need to investigate two secondary sources:

- a geology map, such as the BGS online Geology of Britain viewer
- one other secondary source.

Table 4 Measuring the size and shape of sediment along a beach

Method	Outline of method	Purpose of method	Recording
Measuring the size and shape of beach sediment. Sample measurements collected at Sites 1–5. Each site is located 5 metres to the east of the end of the groyne (at the high tide mark).	At each site, we placed the quadrat down and randomly selected (eyes closed) 10 particles of sediment. Using the ruler, we measured the longest axis of each piece of sediment. We then decided what shape each piece was by comparing it to the Power's scale of roundness.	We measured sediment size and shape at five points along the beach so we could see if there was a difference between them. We used random sampling to allow an equal chance of each size of particle being selected.	We had drawn up a table in class and entered the data at the beach. We also sketched some of the sediment particles to show the different shapes.

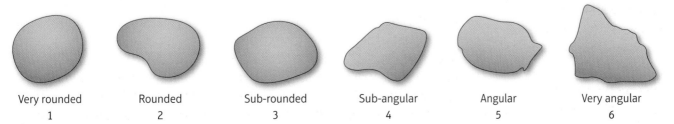

Very rounded	Rounded	Sub-rounded	Sub-angular	Angular	Very angular
1	2	3	4	5	6

Figure 23 Sediment shape using the Power's scale of roundness

Activity

Find Dawlish Warren on the BGS online Geology of Britain viewer. Using the geology key, draw a sketch map to show the solid geology (bedrock) and superficial deposits.

Exam-style question

Study Table 6. Calculate the mean sediment size at Sites 1–5.

(1 mark)

Exam tip

Calculate the mean by adding the numbers in each column (for size) and dividing by the number of sediment samples (four).

If you are investigating different key questions, you will have to use different methods for collecting your data. These may include:

- drawing beach profiles using distance and angle measurements
- taking measurements either side of the groynes to compare sediment build up
- using field sketches and maps to record the details of coastal landforms
- conducting a questionnaire to survey the thoughts of local people about the impact of coastal processes or the effectiveness of coastal management techniques.

Risk assessment

Now that you have decided on the methods you will use to collect your data, you need to produce a risk assessment with your teacher's guidance before you collect and record your data. In your risk assessment, you should consider: the potential risks, the severity of each risk – on a scale of 0 (low) to 10 (high) – and how the risk can be managed (Table 5).

Table 5 Risk assessment

Risk	Severity rating	Management
Being swept away by waves	6/10	Only conduct fieldwork at low tide and in fair weather. Work with a partner and stay 5 metres from the sea.

Recording data

Make sure you record the same information for each site – in this case, the site number, and the size and shape of each sediment sample. An extract of a data sheet is shown in Table 6.

Command word

When asked to **calculate** you work with numbers to solve a problem. Show your working and include the unit (for example, millimetres).

Table 6 An extract of sediment data collected by a geography student at Dawlish Warren

Sediment	Site 1		Site 2		Site 3		Site 4		Site 5	
	Size (mm)	Shape	Size (mm)	Shape	Size (mm)	Shape	Size (mm)	Shape	Size (mm)	Shape
1	46	3	47	2	98	3	52	1	88	4
2	24	2	55	2	56	3	96	1	77	4
3	36	2	53	1	87	4	67	3	94	3
4	63	1	68	3	82	2	106	4	90	3
Mean		2		2		3		2		3.5

F Data presentation

Once you have collected your data, you then need to decide how to present it. Geographers use a range of graphical techniques to present their findings. For your investigation, you should aim to produce a number of simple and sophisticated techniques. A sophisticated technique is one that uses at least two variables to represent the data, for example using a scattergraph to investigate if there is a correlation between sediment size and roundness.

Techniques that could be used to present information for the coastline at Dawlish Warren include:

- annotated photographs/field sketches – for example, to show coastal management techniques
- line graphs to represent continuous data – for example, beach profiles showing a cross section of the beach from the shoreline to the top of the beach
- bar graphs to represent group values – for example, to show the number of pebbles of different sizes along a beach
- pie charts, also to represent group values – for example, to show frequency of roundness of sediment
- GIS maps to present spatial data; these can be used with located photographs and data for different sites – for example, to show coastal erosion and flood risk.

Presenting data on sediment characteristics

The students measured sediment size at five sites, then calculated the mean value for each site (see Table 6). Figure 24 shows an example of how the students presented their data for sediment size in a scattergraph.

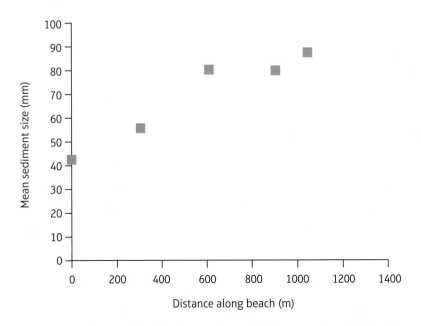

Figure 24 Scattergraph of sediment size with distance along the beach

F Analysis and conclusions

The next stage of the enquiry is to analyse the data collected to begin answering your key questions. When analysing your data, it is important to:

- **describe** the general trends from your data – for example, 'The mean sediment size is greatest at Site 5'
- **make comparisons** using data – for example, 'Site 1 has a mean sediment size of 42.25 mm whereas at Site 5 the mean sediment size is 87.25 mm'
- **explain** the patterns of your data with links to geographical theory – for example, 'The sediment has increased in size along the beach and become more angular, which we did not expect as the direction of longshore drift is from west (Site 1) to east (Site 5). We would need to carry out another investigation to see if the groynes are affecting the results'.

Read the extract below from an analysis a student wrote about data collected at Dawlish Warren. The student gave a structured response with:

- reference to the figure and data (red)
- use of geographical terminology and theory (green)
- an explanation of their data and links to geographical theory (yellow).

> The sediment size on Dawlish Warren spit increases from Site 1 to Site 5. The scattergraph shows that this is a positive correlation. The values calculated from Table 6 show that the mean sediment size at Site 1 was 42.3 mm and increased to 87.3 mm at Site 5. This shows an overall increase in mean sediment size of 45.0 mm. This was not what we were expecting as longshore drift would usually result in smaller, rounder sediment being deposited along the beach.

Activity

1 Discuss the two paragraphs showing the student's analysis and conclusion. For **each** paragraph decide: what is good about it, how it might be improved or developed, anything that you think should be added. Justify your decisions.

2 Rewrite the **second** student paragraph with your suggested improvements.

Next you need to write a conclusion for each key question as well as the overall task question. When writing your conclusion, it is important to:

- focus on your task question and key questions: what did your investigation find out?
- summarise your findings from the data you collected and presented and link each finding to the evidence
- point out any anomalies in your data – these are results that are very different from what you expected: you might try to explain them
- refer back to any theory that related to your investigation; for coasts, you should refer to longshore drift and wave types.

You then need to write your overall conclusion to the task question, in this case: 'How and why does the beach at Dawlish Warren change along its length?' Read the extract below from a conclusion written by a student.

> The purpose of my investigation was to find out if the characteristics of the sediment on Dawlish Warren beach change along its length, and why. I can conclude that with distance along the beach, from west to east, the sediment becomes larger and more angular. This was not the conclusion that I was expecting. It is possible that the groynes are interrupting the process of longshore drift.

ⓕ Evaluation

The final part of the enquiry is to evaluate your investigation. Here you think about how well you answered the task question or theory, and how you could improve or develop the process. The key questions below will help you review your data collection methods, results and conclusions.

- How successful and useful were your methods for sampling and collecting data? Could they be improved?
- How accurate were your results? Did your data collection methods affect the results?
- Did missing or inaccurate data make the investigation unreliable or affect your conclusions?

Activity

1 Read the students' reflections in Figure 25. Discuss which ones are about:

   a strengths and weaknesses in the investigation

   b the accuracy of the data

   c missing data or the size of the sample.

2 Suggest how the data collection methods could be improved if other students repeated the study.

When I was measuring the size of the sediment, I wasn't always sure which was the longest axis. Maybe we should have measured three axes and taken a mean.

I found it difficult to decide where the sediment fitted on the roundness scale.

We used 30 cm rulers – they weren't that good for measuring smaller pebbles.

We worked on five sites on the beach. I think we should have taken samples at more sites between the groynes.

The results weren't what I was expecting. We can't really explain the results unless we do another investigation.

Figure 25 Students' reflections on their geographical investigation of Dawlish Warren

Checkpoint

Now it is time to review your understanding of how to plan and conduct an investigation into coastal landscapes and processes.

Strengthen

S1 With a partner, note down two things you can remember about each of the following: the enquiry question, locating the study, presenting data and evaluation.

S2 Classify the following into simple and sophisticated presentation techniques: scattergraph, pie chart, bar graph, located photo, located bar graph. Explain why in each case.

S3 Explain why it is important that a student's conclusion is linked to their task question.

Challenge

C1 For random, systematic and stratified sampling, note examples of how each could be used in a coastal investigation.

C2 Write out example(s) of the methods below, deciding if they are qualitative or quantitative, primary or secondary, and the strengths and limitations of information gained from each of them:

   a method(s) to measure longshore drift

   b method(s) to investigate the impact of coastal processes on local people

   c method(s) to investigate coastal landforms

   d method(s) to evaluate the effectiveness of coastal defences.

Coastal Landscapes and Processes

The coastline is constantly changing due to the processes that act upon it. Processes of coastal erosion and deposition create distinctive and dramatic landforms. Human activities can lead to changes in coastal landscapes which affect people and the environment. Efforts to protect the coast from erosion and flooding are challenging, and are not always effective or sustainable.

Checklist

You should know:

- [ ] the physical processes at work on the coast – weathering, mass movement, erosion, transportation and deposition
- [ ] how the physical processes interact to shape coastal landscapes
- [ ] the influence of geological structure and rock type on coastal landforms
- [ ] how constructive and destructive waves shape coastal landforms
- [ ] how the UK's weather and climate affect rates of coastal erosion and retreat, and impact on landforms and landscapes
- [ ] the role of erosional processes on the development of headlands and bays, caves, arches, cliffs, stacks and wave cut platforms
- [ ] the role of depositional processes in the development of bars, beaches and spits
- [ ] how human activities have affected coastal landscapes
- [ ] the effects of coastal erosion and flooding on people and the environment
- [ ] the advantages and disadvantages of different coastal defences used on the coastline of the UK
- [ ] how hard- and soft-engineering techniques can lead to change in coastal landscapes
- [ ] how one area of coastline has been influenced by different processes to create its distinctive landscape.

Which key terms match the following definitions?

a The breakdown and decay of rock by natural processes acting on rocks, on cliffs and valley sides.

b The type of coast where the rock type runs parallel to the coastline.

c Direction in which the wind blows most frequently.

d A ridge of sand or shingle deposited by the sea. It is attached to the land at one end but ends in a bay or river mouth.

e The distance a wave has travelled towards the coastline over open water, the longer the fetch the more powerful the wave.

f A flat area of rock at the bottom of cliffs seen at low tide.

g The movement of material along a beach transported by wave action.

h An isolated column of rock, standing just off the coast that was once attached to the land.

i Strategies using artificial structures (e.g. concrete) to prevent river or coastal flooding.

j A gently breaking wave with a strong swash and weak backwash.

k A wooden barrier built at right angles to the coast, used to break waves and reduce the movement of sediment along the coast.

To check your answers, look at the Glossary on pages 296–301.

Coastal Landscapes and Processes

Question 1   Explain why rip rap is a useful way to protect some coastlines.   (4 marks)

Student answer

Rip rap are large boulders which are used to protect the base of cliffs from the erosional force of the waves. The rocks act as a barrier between the cliffs and the sea. The spaces between the rocks help to dissipate the wave energy so that the waves hit the cliff with less force, preventing the cliffs from being eroded quickly.

Verdict

This answer provides a clear and precise explanation of what rip rap is, and how it reduces erosion at the base of the coastal cliff, and would be awarded full marks.

Exam tip

When you are asked to explain something, make sure that you use the correct geographical terms and check that your explanation links the process (rip rap) back to the feature (coastline). Be concise but accurate, and make sure you answer only what the question is asking.

Question 2   Examine how coastal processes have influenced the formation of a spit.   (8 marks + 4 SPAG)

Student answer

The spit at Dawlish Warren has been formed due to the process of longshore drift. The prevailing wind is from the south-west, which means that the waves hit the south-facing coast at an angle. This pushes the sediment up the beach in the swash. The material then comes back down the beach at right angles in the backwash. This is due to gravity. This zigzag movement of material along the beach will create a spit which has a curved end with a saltmarsh behind it.

Verdict

The student has referred to the prevailing wind and the process (longshore drift), used correct geographical terms and a named example. However, they have focused on longshore drift and have not linked the process to the formation of the spit, which is what the question asks for.

Exam tip

When writing about processes relating to the formation of a feature, link each process back to the feature. To answer this question fully, you need to write about the bend in the coastline. In the example of Dawlish Warren, this is due to the River Exe estuary. You need to write about deposition at the point where the coastline changes direction, and how longshore drift continues along the previous direction of the coast, building up deposited materials away from the coast into the open sea. You then need to explain why the spit has a curved end and has not progressed all the way across the estuary. Finally, you could explain why there is a saltmarsh behind.

1B | River Landscapes and Processes

Drainage basins and river processes

Learning objectives

- To know the different processes that change river landscapes
- To understand the main processes operating in river channels
- To understand how geology and erosion, transport and deposition interact to form distinctive river landforms

Watershed
The boundary of a drainage basin separates one drainage basin from another and is usually high land, such as hills and ridges.

Tributary
A stream or small river that joins a larger stream or river

Source
The starting point of a stream or river, often a spring or lake

Confluence
A point where two streams or rivers meet

Mouth
The point where a river leaves its drainage basin and flows into the sea

Figure 1 The drainage basin

A **drainage basin** is the area of land drained by a river and its **tributaries**. When it rains, much of the water usually finds its way into rivers eventually, either by moving across the surface or by going underground and moving through the soil or the rock beneath.

Figure 1 shows the location and definition of the key features of a drainage basin.

The impact of processes on river landscapes

Different processes in the drainage basin act to change the river landscape.

Weathering is the breakdown and decay of rock by natural processes, usually acting on the river valley sides. The following are three key weathering processes that can affect river valleys.

1. **Mechanical (freeze thaw)** – this happens when rainwater enters cracks or gaps in the rock and then freezes if temperatures drop below zero. The water expands as it turns into ice and then exerts pressure on the rock, causing it to break into smaller pieces.

2. **Chemical (acid rain)** – all rain is slightly acidic. If the air is polluted by factories and vehicles, it can become more acidic. When rain falls on rocks, the acid in it can react with weak minerals, causing them to dissolve and the rock to decay.

3. **Biological weathering** – the roots of plants, especially trees, can grow into cracks in a rock and split the rock apart.

Exam-style question

Describe **one** way chemical (acid rain) weathering might have an impact on river landscapes.
(2 marks)

Exam tip

A good answer will link together two descriptive points that give the details of the process.

Command word

When asked to **describe** a physical process you should give the main characteristics.

Mass movement is the movement of rocks and soil downslope due to gravity, helped by weaker rocks, steep slopes and heavy rainfall. Mass movements can be very slow – only a few millimetres a year – or sudden and rapid. Types of mass movement that affect river valleys include the following.

1   **Soil creep** – where individual particles of soil move slowly down a slope.
2   **Sliding** – where material moves rapidly downslope in one go, for example in a landslide. In a **slump**, the material often rotates as it moves.
3   **Flows** – where masses of soil or rock, usually mixed with water, flow like liquid downhill.

The material moves down valley sides and collects at the bottom, where a river may then erode it. This makes the slope steeper, causing more mass movement.

River **erosion** involves the action of water wearing away the rocks and soils on the valley bottom and sides. Rivers have most energy for eroding and transporting **sediment** when there is a large amount of water and a steep gradient. Four key erosion processes can affect river valleys.

1   **Hydraulic action** – this results from the sheer force of the water hitting the river bed and banks and wearing them away. This action is particularly important during high-**velocity** flows.
2   **Abrasion** – this is caused by material carried in the river rubbing against the bed and banks of the channel, so wearing them away. Overall, abrasion causes most erosion.
3   **Solution** – river water is slightly acidic, so it can dissolve some rocks and minerals in contact with the river. Limestone and chalk are most affected.
4   **Attrition** – sediment particles carried in the river collide with each other, causing the edges to be knocked off. The continued collision of particles in the river causes them to become rounder and smaller downstream.

Activity

Create a mind map to represent the physical processes that cause changes to river landscapes. On your mind map, include:

a   the definition of each physical process with a suitable drawing
b   an explanation for how each physical process will cause a river landscape to change.

Tip When creating your mind map, use a colour code to represent erosion, weathering and mass movement processes.

Transportation of load in a river

A river picks up and carries material as it flows downstream. The four types of **transportation** processes are shown in Figure 2.

Deposition

When a river no longer has enough energy to carry its load, **deposition** occurs. As the river's **discharge** and velocity reduce, the heaviest material is deposited first, for example after flooding.

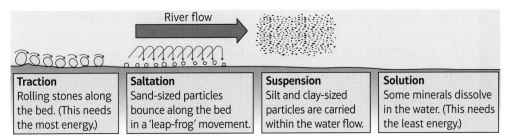

Traction	Saltation	Suspension	Solution
Rolling stones along the bed. (This needs the most energy.)	Sand-sized particles bounce along the bed in a 'leap-frog' movement.	Silt and clay-sized particles are carried within the water flow.	Some minerals dissolve in the water. (This needs the least energy.)

Figure 2 River transportation processes

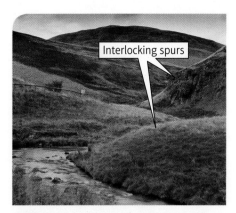

Figure 3 Interlocking spurs in the upper course of a river

How do river processes form distinctive landforms?

Interlocking spurs

Near their **source**, rivers are small and do not have a lot of power. They tend to flow around valley side slopes, called spurs, rather than being able to erode them. The spurs are left interlocking, with those from one side of the valley overlapping with the spurs from the other side. You can see these **interlocking spurs** labelled in Figure 3.

Exam-style question

Explain why different processes interact to form waterfalls.
(4 marks)

Exam tip

When answering a formation question, you must include an explanation of how the processes lead to the landform. An **annotated** sketch is a useful way of explaining a complete sequence of processes.

Waterfalls and gorges

A waterfall is formed along a river when a band of hard, more resistant rock lies over a band of soft, less resistant rock. The river erodes the less resistant rock at a faster rate, gradually undercutting the more resistant rock. The continued erosion of the soft rock by abrasion and hydraulic action causes an overhang of the hard rock. Eventually, the hard rock cannot support its own weight and collapses under the force of gravity. The force of the falling water and abrasion by large, angular boulders leads to erosion of the river bed and the formation of a **plunge pool**. As the soft rock continues to be eroded and the hard rock collapses, a steep-sided **gorge** is formed as the waterfall retreats upstream. Gorges form in hard rocks, where **vertical erosion** by rivers is dominant.

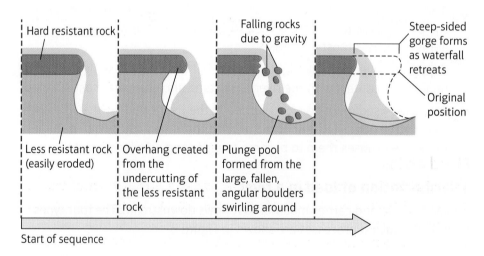

Figure 4 The stages in the formation of a waterfall

Figure 5 A meander bend on the River Dee in Cheshire

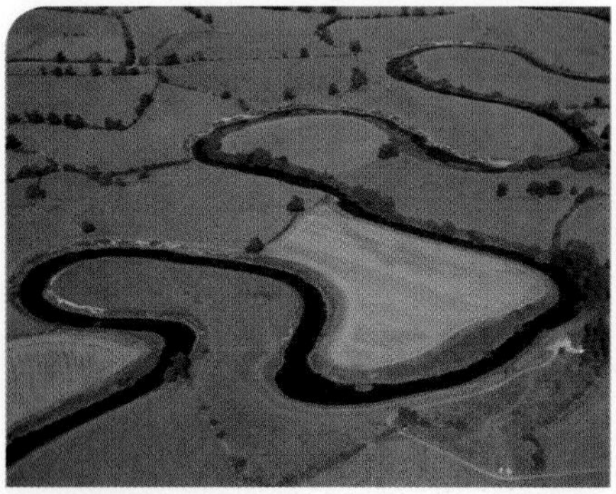

Meanders

Meanders are bends in a river's course, commonly found on a river's flood plain. The flow of the water swings from side to side, directing the line of maximum velocity and the force of the water towards the outside of the bend. This results in **lateral erosion** by undercutting and an outer, steep bank is formed. This is called a **river cliff**. On the inside of the bend

the velocity and force of the water is less, leading to deposition and the formation of a gently sloping bank, known as a **slip-off slope**. The material deposited is called a **point bar** and is characteristically curved in shape. Due to erosion and deposition, the **cross section** of a meander is asymmetrical – steep on the outside of the bend, gentle on the inside.

Oxbow lakes

As a meander bends and develops, its **neck** becomes narrower. Eventually the river may erode right through the neck, especially during a flood. Water then flows through the new, straight channel and the old bend is abandoned by the river. Deposition at the neck seals off the bend, which gradually begins to dry up, leaving behind a horseshoe-shaped lake (Figure 6).

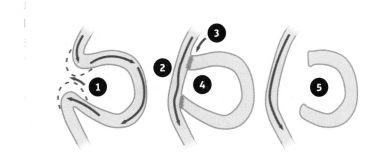

1 Narrow neck of the meander is gradually being eroded.

2 Water now takes the quickest route.

3 Deposition takes place, sealing off the old meander.

4 The meander neck has been cut through completely.

5 Oxbow lake – left behind when meander completely cut off.

Figure 6 Formation of an oxbow lake

Flood plains

A **flood plain** is the flat area of land either side of a river in its lower course. It is formed by erosion and deposition. Lateral erosion on the outside bends of meanders means they **migrate** across the valley floor and can erode the valley sides, so the valley floor becomes wide and flat. During floods, the flood waters spread out across the valley floor. As they slow down, with less energy for transport, the river deposits fine sediments called **alluvium**.

Levees

Levees are natural embankments of sediment formed along the banks of rivers that carry a large load and occasionally flood. In times of flood, water and sediment come out of the channel as the river overflows its banks. As it overflows, the river immediately loses velocity and energy and deposits the larger and heavier sediment first, on its banks. Repeated flooding causes these banks to get higher, forming levees.

Activity

Study Figure 5.

1 Draw a sketch of the meander bend shown in Figure 5. On your sketch label the key geographical features, for example river cliff.

2 Annotate your sketch to:

   a describe the key features

   b explain how different processes interact to produce these key features.

Checkpoint

Now it is time to review your understanding of the processes that interact to create landforms and change river landscapes.

Strengthen

S1 Think about weathering, slope processes and erosion. Which of these involve movement? Which happen mainly on valley sides?

S2 Put these river processes in the right order: deposition, erosion, transportation.

Challenge

C1 Summarise the formation of a flood plain in no more than 125 words. You must include: a description of the formation, key features, processes and an explanation. Underline in a different colour where you have explained.

C2 In the same way, summarise how oxbow lakes are formed.

C3 Classify the landforms on pages 46–47 into those formed mainly by erosion, mainly by deposition, or by both.

Case Study – The River Dee (Afon Dyfrdwy)

Learning objectives

- To know the changes in a river's valley and river processes between its upper, middle and lower course
- To recognise river landforms on OS maps at different scales
- To be able to interpret contour patterns and draw contour cross sections from OS maps

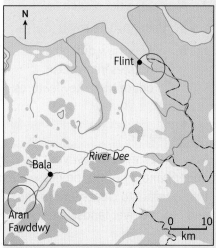

Figure 7 Map of the River Dee catchment

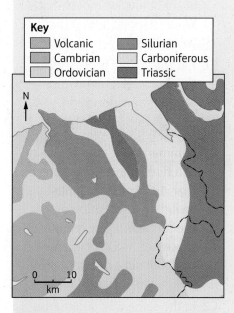

Figure 8 Geology map of the River Dee catchment

Did you know?

The River Dee is thought to be about three million years old.

The long profile

Geographers divide a river and its valley into the upper, middle and lower course. A river's **long profile** shows the height and distance downstream from the river's source to its **mouth**. It is a curved shape, steeper near the source and flatter near the mouth.

The upper course

The source of the River Dee is 460 metres above sea level on the slopes of Dduallt in Snowdonia National Park, North Wales. Here the average annual rainfall exceeds 3000 mm and **runoff** is high from the steep upland slopes. The **geology** is mainly hard igneous rocks, which are very resistant to erosion. Near the source, the channel is narrow, shallow and full of angular stones, so friction with the bed and banks slows the river down. In the upper course the river erodes vertically, cutting down into the landscape and forming a **V-shaped valley** with steep slopes, where processes such as sliding and slumping take place.

The middle course

As the River Dee leaves its upland area and flows downstream, the valley becomes wider and flatter, creating areas of flood plain, and its gradient decreases. The river now erodes sideways through lateral erosion as well as downwards, and there is some deposition, for example on the inside bends of meanders. Sooner or later the sediments will be eroded by the river again, so they become smaller and more rounded, and transported further downstream. As more tributaries join the River Dee, its discharge increases.

The lower course

In the lower Dee valley, the climate changes, with average annual rainfall less than 750 mm. The river flows through softer rocks, such as sandstones, towards Chester. Lateral erosion creates a wide valley with a flat bottom. The river channel also widens. Because it is deep and smooth, there is less friction with the river bed and banks, so the river's velocity is greatest. More tributaries increase the Dee's discharge. Here, lateral erosion and transportation continue and the muddy river water shows its **sediment load** is high. This encourages deposition, for example at the river mouth where the flow is checked by the sea. After 110 km the River Dee reaches its mouth in the Irish Sea between Wales and the Wirral Peninsula. This part of the river near Chester is called the **estuary** because it is affected by tides.

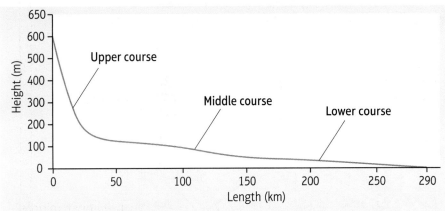

Figure 9 The long profile of the River Dee

Like most rivers, the characteristics of the River Dee change as it flows downstream. Geographers use Bradshaw's Model to summarise how these change between the upper, middle and lower course (Table 1).

Table 1 Characteristics of the River Dee: Bradshaw's Model

Characteristic	Definition	Change from source to mouth
Width	The distance from one bank to the other	Increases
Depth	The distance from the surface of the water to the river bed	Increases
Velocity	How fast the water is flowing	Increases
Discharge	The volume and speed at which water flows through the river channel	Increases
Gradient	The steepness of the river bed	Decreases
Channel roughness	How rough the river's bed and banks are	Becomes smoother, so less friction
Sediment size and shape	The material (sediment, debris) carried by the river	Becomes smaller and rounder

Activity

1   Draw a copy of Figure 9. Annotate the profile to show how the following change between the Dee's upper, middle and lower course:

   a the gradient of the river channel and valley

   b the width and depth of the river channel

   c where vertical and lateral erosion are most important

   d where friction with the bed and banks is highest and lowest.

2   Re-read the text on pages 46–47. On your profile, add details of the river landforms you would expect to find in each part of a river valley.

3   Draw a sketch map of the River Dee catchment (Figure 7). Using evidence from the text, label the upper, middle and lower course. Then annotate your sketch map with details of:

   a differences in geology and climate in the Dee Valley

   b where valley slopes are steepest and slope processes are most active.

4   Explain why the Dee's velocity and discharge increase downstream from its source to its mouth.

5   Use what you know about the geology of the Dee catchment and valley and river processes to explain why the river is usually clear near the source but muddy near the mouth.

Exam-style question

Study Figures 10 and 11. Which of the following is the best description of the River Dee on **each** map?

☐ A   A mountain stream near its source

☐ B   A river meandering across its flood plain

☐ C   A river flowing through a steep-sided valley

☐ D   A lowland river close to its mouth   **(2 marks)**

Exam tip

If you check the map carefully, this type of question is usually straightforward. But watch out for choices which are nearly correct, but not quite right.

Investigating river landscapes using OS maps

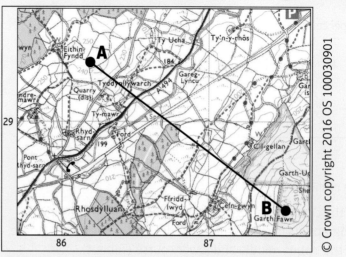

Figure 10 Extract from 1:25,000 OS map of the River Dee south west of Lake Bala

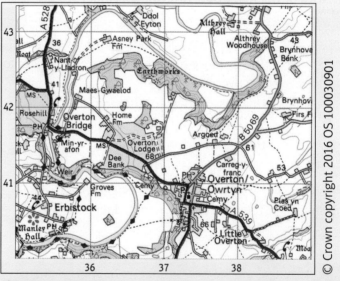

Figure 11 Extract from 1:50,000 OS map of the River Dee near Erbistock, Wrexham

Activity

1   Study Figures 10 and 11.

2   Choose one grid square from **each** map that includes the river. Draw two squares with sides 50 mm in your notes, then sketch the course of the channel across each.

   a   Decide whether the maps are of the upper, middle or lower course. Write a title for each sketch map including this information and its location.

   b   Annotate details about the river channel, for example its width and shape as it flows through the river valley.

   c   Look back to pages 46–47, then use map evidence to identify landforms in each part of the Dee Valley. Label them on your sketch maps, or list them with grid references.

How to draw a contour cross section

Contours are lines joining places of equal height above sea level. They also tell us how much the land slopes.

- Contours that are close together on the map show where the land slopes steeply.
- Contours further apart on the map show gentle slopes.
- Areas with few contours, or none at all, are flat: there is little or no gradient.

Drawing a cross section through the contour lines shows what the landscape looks like (Figure 12).

1 Choose where you are going to make your cross section. Place a strip of paper across the contour lines on the map.

2 Mark on the strip of paper each place where a contour line crosses it. Label the heights of the contours on your paper.

3 Make the horizontal axis the same length as your strip of paper.

4 The vertical axis is the height of the land from the lowest point to the highest point on the cross section.

5 Use the information on your strip of paper to plot the heights on the graph paper.

6 Join the dots and label some of the landscape features.

Activity

1 Read the information about contours and then look again at Figures 10 and 11.

   a Find areas of flat land, gentle slopes and steep slopes on the two maps.

   b Describe the steepness of the valley sides and floor in each part of the River Dee.

2 Re-read 'How to draw a contour cross section' above.

   a Draw a contour cross section between points A and B on Figure 10. Annotate details of the valley height and slopes, and the river channel.

   b Choose and draw a cross section of a contrasting part of the river valley from Figure 11, and add similar details.

   c Write a paragraph comparing the two contour cross sections, and what they show about different parts of the Dee Valley.

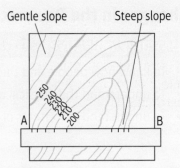

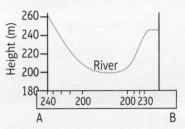

Figure 12 How to draw a contour cross section

Checkpoint

Now it is time to review your understanding of landscapes and processes in different places along the long profile of the river.

Strengthen

S1 Describe the shape of a typical long profile of a river.

S2 Describe the differences in contour patterns you would expect to see on an OS map of the upper and middle course of a river.

Challenge

C1 Match these river landforms with the section(s) of a river's course where they are most likely to appear: levee, flood plain, interlocking spurs, meander, oxbow lake.

C2 Summarise the reasons for changes in the shape of a river's valley as it flows from source to mouth.

Changes in the Dee catchment

Learning objectives

- To know how people and the environment interact, causing change in the Dee Valley
- To understand the physical and human causes of flooding
- To understand the effects of flooding on people and the environment, and why the risk of flood is increasing

Figure 13 Flood embankments on the channelised section of the River Dee at Chester

Activity

1 Re-read pages 48–49 about the resources of the Dee Valley.

   a Make three lists: economic, environmental and social resources (some may be in more than one category).

   b Describe the impact a growing population may have on the resources of the Dee Valley.

2 Give examples of human activities which may reduce, and may increase the River Dee's discharge.

As you have found out, natural processes are constantly changing the River Dee and its valley. Like most UK rivers, they have also been used and changed by people for centuries. Today the River Dee and its valley are important resources for people and the environment.

- Ninety-four per cent of the catchment is rural, including forestry, sheep farming and pasture in the upper valley, and dairy farming and arable farming in the lower valley.
- The river is an important source of water for approximately three million people in Wales and north-west England.
- The river supports large areas of important habitats, including rare plant and wildlife species such as those for the otter and water vole.
- The River Dee and its estuary are famous for commercial and recreational fishing.
- Parts of the catchment, such as the Snowdonia National Park, contain beautiful landscapes which are popular for recreation and tourism.
- Key communication routes run alongside the River Dee, including the Chester to Holyhead railway line, as well as the A55 and the A483 primary roads.

With a growing population, particularly in urban parts of the catchment, pressure on the Dee Valley is likely to increase. A major problem is the increasing flood risk.

Human factors changing the river

In the summer the Dee's natural flow does not provide enough water to meet the demand from people and industry. Growing demand in the 1960s led to a number of **reservoirs** being built to store water during the winter months. One of the reservoirs, Llyn Celyn, can collect 327,000 cubic metres of water a day. A second reservoir, Llyn Brenig, collects 800,000 cubic metres of water a day and can hold 60 million cubic metres in total. These reservoirs help control the river's flow, and can reduce its discharge.

Near Bangor-on-Dee in the middle course of the river, earth embankments are used to protect farmland and properties from flooding. A land drainage pumping system at Worthernbury Meadows helps to remove excess flood waters.

Between 1972 and 1976, 8 km of the River Dee underwent **channelisation** between Chester Weir and its estuary to improve navigation (Figure 13). This change to the river's course resulted in increases to its velocity and discharge.

Physical factors changing the river

The UK's climate is naturally variable from year to year. In particular, the amount and intensity of rainfall has a direct effect on river flows. In periods of **drought**, river flows are low; by contrast, heavy rainfall and high surface runoff cause high river flows, when most erosion and transportation occur.

In future, climate change could lead to more variable weather, including an increased flood risk across the whole Dee catchment. In the Dee Estuary, rises in sea level will add to the flood risk.

Predicting the risk of flooding in the Dee catchment

The Environment Agency is responsible for managing the risk of flooding in England, as well as protecting the environment and water quality. It has produced a River Dee Catchment Flood Management Plan. By 2100, the plan predicts an increased risk of flooding caused by:

- increasing population – more people will be in areas at risk
- urban development and changes in land use, causing increased runoff
- climate change, including 20% increase in river flows, and a one metre sea level rise.

Together, these factors will increase the number of properties in the catchment at risk from a 1% flood event from 4200 to 6400, with most impact on Chester.

Did you know?

You can download flood maps from the Environment Agency website. The Environment Agency uses probability to talk about how likely it is that a flood of a particular size will happen. A **1% flood event** has a 1 in 100 chance or greater of happening each year, or a probability of 0.01.

Activity

Study Figure 14 and an atlas.

1 Describe where the places with the biggest increase in flood risk are and explain this pattern.

2 Draw a sketch map of Figure 14.

   a Label one or more areas of flood plain.

   b Identify and label one area where development on the flood plain puts property at risk, and one type of land use suitable for the flood plain.

   c Label where there are flood embankments and where the River Dee has been channelised.

3 You have learned about physical short- and long-term changes in the Dee catchment.

   a Storms and droughts are short-term events: describe how they affect river processes.

   b Climate change is a long-term change: summarise its likely effects in the Dee catchment.

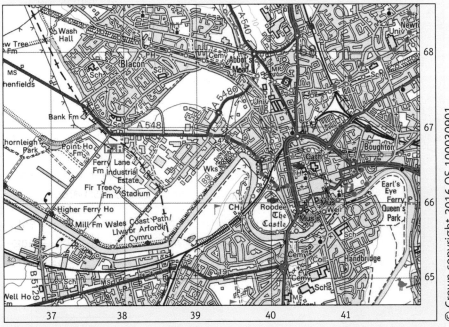

© Crown copyright 2016 OS 100030901

Figure 14 Extract from 1:50,000 OS map of the River Dee at Chester

Figure 15 Flooding in Bangor on the River Dee, 2011

Activity

Study Figure 16.

1 Use the scale to estimate the size of the flooded area in Figure 16.

2 Identify **three** ways the river flooding might affect people living in the areas shown in Figure 16.

3 The South Downs is an upland area. Explain how the relief and different rock types affect the pattern of flooding.

Did you know?

A total of 4.6 million people in the UK are at risk from river or coastal flooding. Building on flood plains has put 2.3 million properties at risk of flooding.

Activity

Study Figure 17.

1 Classify the different effects of flooding in the UK into social, environmental and economic effects.

2 Which of the four flood events do you think is the odd one out? Explain carefully why you think it is different from the other three. Then find a different odd one out, or a different reason.

The causes and effects of flooding in the UK

River flooding is a natural hazard that has affected people and the environment in the UK for centuries. It can be made worse by human activities. Since 1998, significant flooding has occurred somewhere in the UK every year, and sometimes twice in a year. The average annual cost of damage from flooding is between £500 million and £1 billion.

Physical causes of flooding

A river floods when it overflows its banks causing water to spread out onto nearby land. A number of physical factors can lead to rivers flooding.

1 **Intense rainfall** – during periods of heavy rainfall, the soil and rocks can quickly become saturated. As **infiltration** is reduced, water flows over the surface and into the river at a faster rate.

2 **Duration of rainfall** – long periods of rainfall cause the soil to become saturated and prevent further infiltration of rainwater, leading to increased surface runoff.

3 **Snow melt** – in some places a lot of snow falls during the winter months. When temperatures rise above zero in the spring, all the snow that has built up melts, releasing large volumes of **meltwater**.

4 **Rocks** – different rock types in the catchment can affect flooding. **Permeable** rocks such as chalk allow water to soak in, so reducing surface runoff. **Impermeable** rocks such as clay do not allow water to pass through them, so rainwater will run off the surface and straight into the river channel (Figure 16).

5 **Relief** – water reaches the river channel much faster where slopes are steeper.

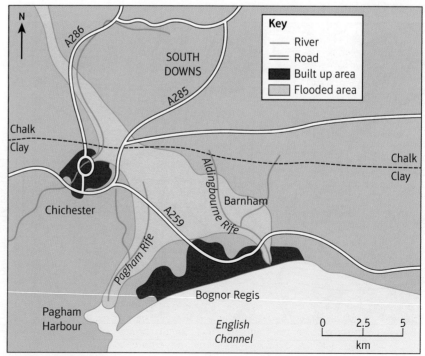

Figure 16 A map showing the areas affected by the flooding near Chichester

54

Human causes of flooding

1 **Deforestation** – vegetation collects, stores and uses water from rainfall: this is called **interception**. Plant roots also encourage water to pass into soil and rock, so vegetation reduces runoff: if it is removed, more water can reach the river channel more quickly.

2 **Urbanisation** – in towns and cities, rainwater will not infiltrate the hard, impermeable surfaces of concrete and tarmac. This causes the water to run off immediately into drains and river channels.

Climate change

Although any single flood event cannot be linked to climate change, most scientists think that a warmer climate is making extreme weather more likely. Warmer air can hold more water. One factor in a number of recent events is a change in the behaviour of the **jet stream**, which has brought more intense storms across the UK. In turn, this change in the jet stream may be linked to rising Arctic temperatures. Scientists believe these intense storm events, which would have previously occurred once in 100 years, are now more likely to happen once every 80 years in southern England.

The effects of flooding on people and the environment

Floods can have wide-ranging environmental, economic and social effects. Figure 17 shows some recent flooding events and the effects these had.

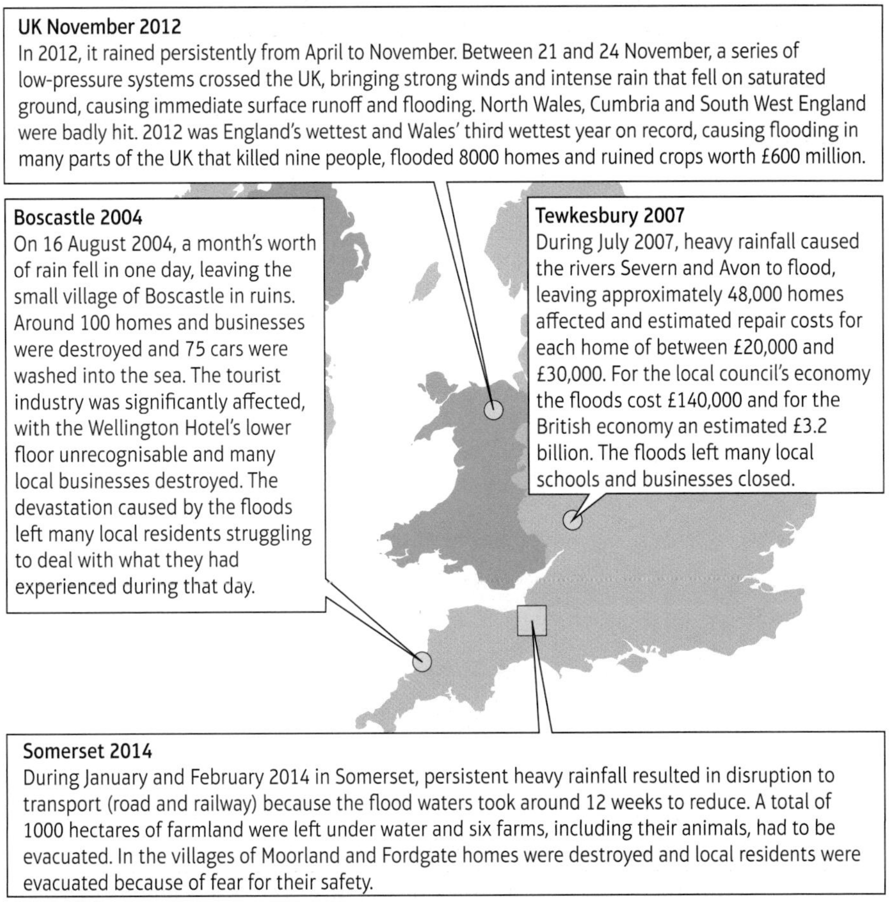

> **UK November 2012**
> In 2012, it rained persistently from April to November. Between 21 and 24 November, a series of low-pressure systems crossed the UK, bringing strong winds and intense rain that fell on saturated ground, causing immediate surface runoff and flooding. North Wales, Cumbria and South West England were badly hit. 2012 was England's wettest and Wales' third wettest year on record, causing flooding in many parts of the UK that killed nine people, flooded 8000 homes and ruined crops worth £600 million.

> **Boscastle 2004**
> On 16 August 2004, a month's worth of rain fell in one day, leaving the small village of Boscastle in ruins. Around 100 homes and businesses were destroyed and 75 cars were washed into the sea. The tourist industry was significantly affected, with the Wellington Hotel's lower floor unrecognisable and many local businesses destroyed. The devastation caused by the floods left many local residents struggling to deal with what they had experienced during that day.

> **Tewkesbury 2007**
> During July 2007, heavy rainfall caused the rivers Severn and Avon to flood, leaving approximately 48,000 homes affected and estimated repair costs for each home of between £20,000 and £30,000. For the local council's economy the floods cost £140,000 and for the British economy an estimated £3.2 billion. The floods left many local schools and businesses closed.

> **Somerset 2014**
> During January and February 2014 in Somerset, persistent heavy rainfall resulted in disruption to transport (road and railway) because the flood waters took around 12 weeks to reduce. A total of 1000 hectares of farmland were left under water and six farms, including their animals, had to be evacuated. In the villages of Moorland and Fordgate homes were destroyed and local residents were evacuated because of fear for their safety.

Figure 17 Flood events in England and Wales

Checkpoint

Now it is time to review your understanding of the causes of flooding and the effects on people and the environment.

Strengthen

S1 Draw a concept map of the physical and human causes of flooding. Then add details of the causes, the links between them and any examples of relevant flood events from these pages.

S2 What is the difference between short- and long-term effects of flooding? Provide one or more examples of each.

S3 Give examples of suitable and unsuitable uses of land in flood plains.

Challenge

C1 Describe how human activities can increase and reduce the flood risk in a catchment like the River Dee.

C2 Turn a 1 in 100 flood into a percentage. Which is more likely to flood: land with a 1 in 100 or 1 in 1000 chance of flooding?

C3 Explain why climate change makes flooding more likely over time, but cannot be blamed for a single flooding event, for example, the Somerset floods in 2014.

The UK's increasing flood risk

Learning objectives

- To know why the risk of flooding in the UK is increasing
- To understand and be able to interpret the features of storm hydrographs
- To be able to construct a hydrograph and calculate the lag time

The flood risk in the UK is likely to increase in future. The main reasons are changes to land use, an increasing population and changes to weather patterns, particularly linked to climate change. For example, in December 2013 and January 2014, the UK experienced the wettest two-month period of rainfall since 1910. This led to the ground becoming saturated, causing high runoff and increased river discharge. The River Thames recorded its highest discharge for over 60 years. Figure 18 illustrates the difference between the previous and the most recent highest recorded rainfall.

Activity

Study Figure 18.

1 Which year experienced the lowest January rainfall?

2 What is the difference between rainfall levels for 1988 and 2014?

3 Other than 1988 and 2014, which other year had a similar high level of rainfall?

4 Study Figure 19.

a Work out the length of the Thames between Oxford and Reading.

b Describe the distribution of flood warning and flood alert areas along the River Thames, using geographical language.

5 Some scientists think the weather is becoming more extreme, perhaps linked to climate change. What evidence from the text and Figure 18 supports/does not support this idea?

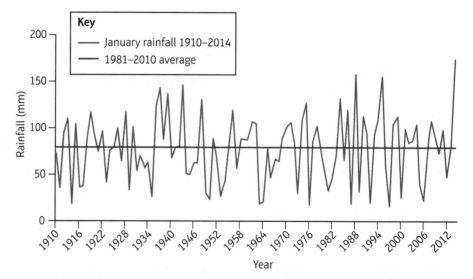

Figure 18 Rainfall in south-east and central southern England, 1910–2014

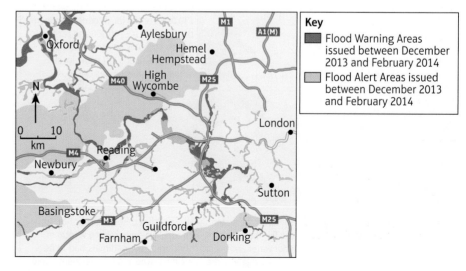

Figure 19 Flood warning and alert areas along the River Thames, January 2014

Storm hydrographs

A **hydrograph** shows how a river responds to a storm event. Figure 20 shows the relationship between rainfall (as a histogram) and the river discharge (as a line graph) for the River Severn in the record-breaking floods of July 2007. The discharge of a river is measured in cubic metres per second (cumecs).

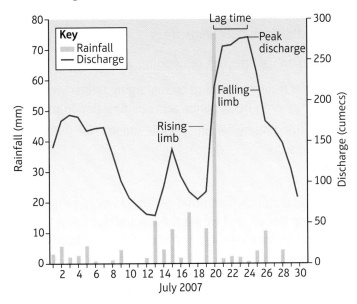

Figure 20 Flood hydrograph of the River Severn at Bewdley, July 2007

A hydrograph has a number of key features including:

- the **rising limb**, which represents the rapid rise in water after a period of heavy rainfall
- the **lag time**, which is the difference between the time of the heaviest rainfall and the point at which the river contains the largest amount of water
- the **falling limb**, which shows the reduction in the amount of rainfall reaching the channel.

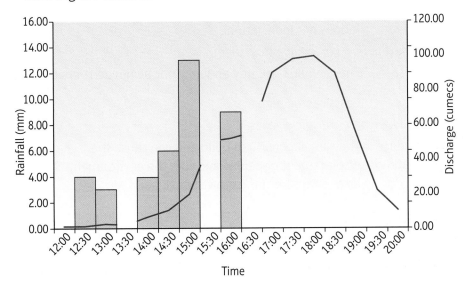

Figure 21 Flood hydrograph of the River Valency at Boscastle, 2004

Activity

Study Figure 21.

1 Copy and complete the flood hydrograph using the data below.

Time	13.30	15.30	16.30
Rainfall (mm)	10	15	3
Discharge (cumecs)	2	50	55

2 Label the rising limb, the lag time and the falling limb.

3 Calculate the lag time.

4 Compare the hydrographs for the River Severn and Boscastle. What are the similarities and differences between the two floods?

Managing flood risk

Learning objectives

- To know how the Environment Agency manages flood risk
- To understand the advantages and disadvantages of different techniques used to manage rivers and reduce flood risk
- To understand how river management techniques can lead to change in river landscapes

The Environment Agency manages the risk of flooding in England by:

- reducing the chances of a flood happening by managing rivers and land use, controlling development in flood plains and building flood defences
- reducing the impact of flooding by helping people prepare for flooding and giving flood warnings.

Flood defences

The Environment Agency works out where flood defences would be most effective in preventing floods, and where they would not cause environmental damage. In the past, people controlled floods by **hard-engineering** methods, often building defences out of concrete. However, these methods are expensive and do not reduce the risk of flooding in other parts of the catchment, and some may even increase it.

Table 2 Advantages and disadvantages of hard-engineering techniques

Advantages	Disadvantages
Embankments (levees) – high banks built on or near riverbanks	
They stop water from spreading into areas where it could cause problems, such as housing.	Flood water may go over the top, and then get trapped behind them.
They can be earth and grass banks, which blend in with the environment.	They can burst under pressure, possibly causing even greater damage.
Channelisation – this involves deepening and/or straightening the river	
This allows more water to run through the channel more quickly, taking it away from places at risk.	Water taken downstream may put other places at risk. It does not look natural.
Flood relief channels – extra channels can be built next to rivers or leading from them	
The relief channels can accommodate high flows so that a river will not overflow its banks.	They can be unsightly and may not be needed very often. Costs can be high.
Dams and reservoirs – barriers constructed to hold back water in artificial lakes	
They are long-lasting and can also be used to produce hydro-electric power (HEP) and provide a local water supply. They can be used for water sports.	They are expensive to build and can cause the displacement of people and ruin the environment. Some lakes suffer from the growth of algae.

Longer term, **soft engineering** may be the answer, using a more natural approach to managing floodwater. This approach aims to create space for floodwater in the landscape, which also reduces the risk of flooding in other areas. Soft defences are usually cheaper, need little maintenance and often provide habitats for wildlife.

Table 3 Advantages and disadvantages of soft-engineering techniques

Advantages	Disadvantages
Washlands – areas on the flood plain that are allowed to flood	
These give a safe place for floodwater to go and help slow floodwaters down. This also improves a river's natural sedimentation processes – the soil structure in the flood plain is restored, making it more efficient at storing water.	Allowing land to flood may limit the use of the land, for recreation for example, or mean a change of land use, for example a change in farmland.
River restoration – restoring the river's original course	
Restoring rivers to a more natural course by taking away embankments aims to slow them down, for example by restoring meanders. Natural rivers are more attractive and create natural habitats for wildlife.	Some flood banks are often still needed, and like flood-plain retention, changes in land use may bring some disadvantages.
Flood-plain zoning – governments allocate areas of land to different uses, according to their level of flood risk	
Flood risk management aims to prevent building homes and businesses in high risk zones. Here, uses such as open space for leisure and recreation are allowed because flooding would be less costly.	These may not be the best places for the different activities in terms of public accessibility. Flood plains are attractive places to build.

Land-use management

The way land is used and managed in a river's catchment has a significant impact on the risk of flooding. Changes in land use such as deforestation and urbanisation increase the amount and speed of surface runoff and river discharge. By contrast, improving land use aims to help rainwater infiltrate into the soil and slow runoff, for example:

- **afforestation** helps reduce the flood risk because woodland intercepts rainfall, and tree roots encourage infiltration of water
- managing farmland can reduce runoff, for example by avoiding overgrazing by animals, and ploughing across slopes rather than downhill
- managing drainage in urban areas more sustainably helps reduce flash flooding, for example by increasing green areas and building ponds to store runoff.

Exam-style question

Describe the differences between soft and hard engineering.   **(4 marks)**

Exam tip

It is important when you are asked to describe the differences that you use connective words such as 'whereas' to form descriptive sentences.

Activity

1 Summarise the main costs and benefits of hard and soft engineering, adding examples of different techniques.

2 Using three shades, colour-code your notes to show which costs and benefits are economic, environmental and social.

3 Explain why zoning and land-use management may be a useful way of managing flood risk in the long term.

4 Look again at the different techniques for hard and soft engineering and land-use management. Thinking about the Dee Valley, can you put them into a rank order?

Reducing the impact of flooding

Figure 22 Flooding around the village of Moorland on the Somerset Levels, 2014

Sometimes flooding is inevitable, as in 2012, 2013 and 2014. Then the Environment Agency tries to reduce the impact on people, land and property. Through its website and the news, the Environment Agency provides an up-to-date overview of potential areas at risk, using flood warning feeds, a live flood warning map and a three-day flood risk forecast. There are three warning levels: flood alert; flood warning and severe flood warning (Figure 23).

Figure 23 The Environment Agency flood warnings

The Environment Agency and local government and agencies work together to educate people about the hazards of living in flood risk areas. They use television, the internet, leaflets, helplines and training exercises to make people aware of what they should do before, during and after a flood. Advice for homeowners includes the following:

- lay tiles on the ground floor and use rugs instead of fitted carpets
- raise the height of electrical sockets to 1.5 metres above ground floor level

- fit stainless steel or plastic kitchens instead of chipboard ones
- position any main parts of a heating or ventilation system, such as a boiler, upstairs
- fit removable door barriers and non-return valves to all drains and water inlet pipes
- replace wooden window frames and doors with synthetic ones.

Local government will only give planning permission to build properties near a river if a full flood risk assessment has been completed. The new laws set out by the government in 2010 state that all new properties built near rivers need to be flood resistant.

Activity

Look back at your learning in this topic. Examine why the River Dee Valley is prone to flooding. Give an example of its impact and a way in which it can be managed.

what to do in an emergency

Listen to and act on the advice of the emergency services. Follow these simple steps to stay safe.

1 Gather essential items together either upstairs or in a high place.

2 Fill jugs and saucepans with clean water.

3 Move your family and pets upstairs, or to a high place with a means of escape.

4 Turn off gas, electricity and water supplies when flood water is about to enter your home if safe to do so. DO NOT touch sources of electricity when standing in flood water.

5 Keep listening to local radio for updates or call Floodline 0845 988 1188.

6 Flood water can rise quickly, stay calm and reassure those around you. Call 999 if you are in danger.

Important! Flood water is dangerous

- Avoid walking or driving through it.
- Keep children and vulnerable people away from it.
- Wash your hands thoroughly if you touch it.

Figure 24 Advice on what to do if flooding occurs

Command word

Examine questions ask you to break something down into its different parts. Here you could explain how different physical and human processes contribute to the flood risk on the Dee, then link these to their impact and ways to manage the floods.

Checkpoint

Now it is time to review your understanding of how flood risk management can reduce the chances of flooding, and its impact.

Strengthen

S1 Give **two** reasons why people in the UK will be at greater risk of flooding in future.

S2 Summarise the advice for homeowners living in a flood risk area.

S3 Explain why planners have strict rules about new development in flood plains.

Challenge

C1 Describe the environmental benefits of soft engineering techniques.

C2 Summarise how the Environment Agency tries to reduce the impact of flooding. Categorise the activities into short, medium and long term.

C3 Compare engineering techniques and land-use management. Which do you think are most likely to reduce the flood risk in places like the Dee Valley in future?

Investigating River Landscapes

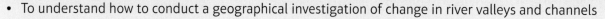

Learning objectives

- To understand how to conduct a geographical investigation of change in river valleys and channels
- To know how to choose enquiry questions, fieldwork methods and data sources for a river investigation
- To know how to present, analyse and evaluate data collected from a river investigation

Activity

1 Using your knowledge of the changes in the long profile of the River Dee, create another two key questions that would help you to answer the main task question.

2 Using your wider geographical knowledge, suggest the results you would expect for your chosen key questions based on a typical river profile. Refer to Bradshaw's Model.

(F) The enquiry question

When conducting a geographical enquiry, it is important to have a purpose. One way to do this is to ask a task question.

For this enquiry on rivers, the task question is:

How do the river valley and channel characteristics vary along the River Dee?

To help answer the task question, geographers next devise some key questions. These help to provide a focus for the enquiry.

For this task, one of the key questions is:

Does the width and depth of the river channel increase as the river flows downstream?

(F) Locating the study

It is important to provide maps showing where the investigation is located. You should include maps at a local and a national scale, plus detailed maps showing your survey or data collection sites. You can then use your location and survey site maps to give a detailed overview of the place in which your investigation will take place. This part of your enquiry helps set the scene.

Figure 25 River Dee at Llanuwchllyn, near Site 4

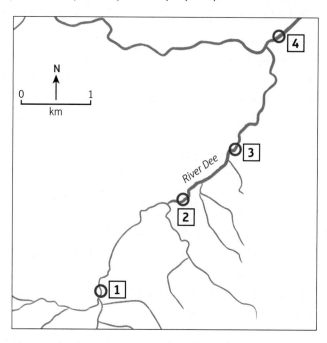

Figure 26 A student's sketch map of survey sites on the upper River Dee

F Methodology

Once you have decided on some suitable key questions and located your investigation, the next stage is to choose the methods you will use to collect your data. Geographers use both **primary data** (data that is collected first hand) and **secondary data** (data that has already been published). In your investigation, you should choose at least three **quantitative** (using numbers) methods, for example measuring the width of a river, and one **qualitative** (descriptive) method, for example a field sketch.

For each method, it is important that you decide where and how you will collect the data and why the data collected will help to answer the overall task question. You cannot collect data from every part of the river or measure every pebble in its bed, so you need to sample.

- **Random sampling** – data is collected by chance. An example might be picking up stones from the river bed at random with your eyes closed.
- **Systematic sampling** – the locations of the sites are found at equal intervals from each other. An example might be to measure the depth of the river every 0.25 metres across its width.
- **Stratified sampling** – is used when the study area has significantly different parts. An example might be measuring the discharge just below every confluence.

An example of how to present your methodology is shown in Table 4.

Did you know?

You can use interactive geology maps from the British Geological Survey (BGS) to support your fieldwork. Use the Geology of Britain viewer on the BGS website to find a map for anywhere in the UK.

Exam tip

You need to investigate two secondary sources:

- a geology map, such as the BGS online Geology of Britain viewer
- one other secondary source.

Table 4 Measuring the width and depth of a river (quantitative method)

Method	Outline of method	Purpose of method	Recording
Measuring the width and depth of the river. Sample measurements collected at Sites 1–4. Each site is located where a tributary joins the River Dee.	We found a suitable representative point at each site. We measured the width from one bank to the other with a tape measure. To measure the depth, at 0.25 metres intervals I placed a metre ruler into the water until it reached the river bed.	We chose this method to investigate how the width and depth of the river changes as it flows downstream – so we are trying to prove Bradshaw's theory.	On a tablet, we set up a simple spreadsheet for the width and depth at each of the four sites. We entered the data directly in the field.

When you investigate the changing river processes, it is also important to find out how people and rivers interact, for example in an area of beautiful landscapes or at risk of flooding. One method you could try to survey the thoughts of local people is to conduct a questionnaire. When deciding on a questionnaire, you should consider the following.

- What questions will allow you to collect the information that you need for your investigation?
- Will the questions be open (allowing people to offer opinions) or closed (for example, yes or no)?

You need to use the Environment Agency River and Sea Levels flood risk mapping site and one other secondary source.

Exam-style question

State whether a questionnaire about people's opinions is a qualitative or quantitative method. **(1 mark)**

Did you know?

Timing how long an orange takes to float for 5 or 10 metres downstream is an easy way to measure river velocity. However, rivers flow faster near the surface, so the results need to be multiplied by 0.85 to allow for the friction along the river bed and banks.

Exam-style question

Study Table 6. Calculate the cross-sectional area of the River Dee at Sites 1–4. **(2 marks)**

Exam tip

Calculate the cross-sectional area by multiplying channel width by mean depth.

Command word

When asked to **calculate** you work with numbers to answer a problem. You must show your working and do not forget to include the unit (e.g. m^2) in your result.

Activity

1 What do you think are the advantages and disadvantages of recording river channel data directly into a spreadsheet on a tablet?

2 Make a blank copy of Table 4.

a Choose **two** investigations from the following: river landscape, velocity and discharge, gradient and bedload. Discuss what you could find out about them, how you could do so and why they will help with answering the main task question.

b For each investigation, describe the methods and explain how and why you would conduct and record them. Use a highlighter to identify where you have explained how you would carry out the methods.

3 You have been asked the following key question, 'How do river processes affect people living in the catchment?' Create a questionnaire that would enable you to gather the information you need to answer this key question.

Now that you have decided on the methods you will use to collect your data, you need to produce a risk assessment with your teacher's guidance before you collect and record your data. In your risk assessment, you should consider: the potential risks, the severity of each risk – on a scale of 0 (low) to 10 (high) – and how the risk can be managed. An example is shown in Table 5.

Table 5 Risk assessment

Risk	Severity rating	Management
Slipping on rocks	6/10	Take care before entering the river and listen to the teacher

Table 6 River Dee channel data collected by a geography student

Channel variable	Site 1	Site 2	Site 3	Site 4
Width (metres, m)	3.30	4.10	6.20	8.80
Mean depth (m)	0.17	0.19	0.28	0.37
Cross-sectional area (m^2)				
Velocity (m/s)	0.08	0.09	0.10	0.13
Discharge (m^3/s)	0.04	0.06	0.15	0.36

Ⓕ Data presentation

Once you have collected your data, you then need to decide how to present it. Geographers use a range of graphical techniques to present their findings. For your investigation, you should aim to produce a number of simple and sophisticated techniques. A sophisticated technique is one that uses at least two variables to represent the data. An example of this would be located graphs of data for the river at different sites. Techniques that could be used to present information for the River Dee include:

- flow-line maps to show velocity or discharge (see Figure 27)
- annotated photographs/field sketches of the river landforms
- river channel profiles
- located proportional circles of mean sediment size
- a GIS map with located photographs and channel data for different sites.

Presenting data on river velocity and discharge

The students measured river velocity at four sites, then calculated the discharge. Figure 27 shows an example of how the students presented their discharge data for the River Dee in a flow-line map.

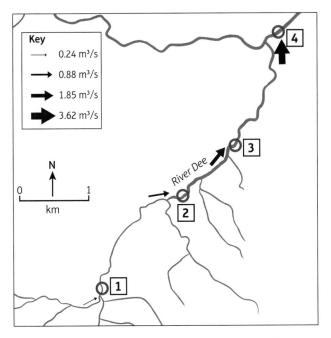

Figure 27 Flow-line map showing discharge on the River Dee

(F) Analysis and conclusions

The next stage of the enquiry is to analyse the data collected to begin answering your key questions. When analysing the data, it is important to:

- **describe** the general trends from your data – for example, 'The width of the river increases travelling downstream'
- **make comparisons** using data – for example, 'The width of the river is greatest at Site 4, measuring 8.80 metres, a difference of 5.5 metres from Site 1'
- **explain** the patterns of your data with links to geographical theory – for example, 'The width of the river has increased because of lateral erosion of the banks due to attrition, hydraulic action and other processes'.

Read the extract below from an analysis a student wrote about data collected along the River Dee. The student gave a structured response with:

- reference to the figure and data (red)
- use of geographical terminology and theory (green)
- an explanation of their data and links to geographical theory (yellow).

> The velocity of the River Dee increases from Site 1 to Site 4 as predicted by Bradshaw's Model. As you can see in Table 5, the mean velocity at Site 1 was 0.08 m/s and increased to 0.13 m/s at Site 4. This shows an overall mean velocity increase of 0.05 m/s. The reason the mean velocity increases is that as the width and depth of the river increases there is less friction against the bank.

Activity

1 Discuss the two paragraphs showing the student's analysis and conclusion. For **each** paragraph decide: what is good about it, how it might be improved or developed, anything that you think should be added. Justify your decisions.

2 Rewrite the **second** student paragraph with your suggested improvements.

Once you have analysed your data using the structure above, you need to write a conclusion for each key question as well as the overall task question. When writing your conclusion, it is important to:

- focus on your task question and key questions: what did your investigation find out?
- summarise your findings from the data you collected and presented and link each finding to the evidence
- point out any anomalies in your data – these are results that are very different from what you expected: you might try to explain them
- refer back to any theory that related to your investigation; for rivers, you should refer to the Bradshaw Model.

You then need to write your overall conclusion to the task question, in this case: 'How do the river valley and channel characteristics vary along the River Dee?'

Read the extract below from a conclusion written by a student.

> The purpose of my investigation was to find out if my chosen valley and channel characteristics vary along the River Dee. I can conclude that as the River Dee flows downstream, the width and depth of the river increases, the bedload alters in size and roundness, and the mean velocity and discharge increase. My data generally supports the Bradshaw Model with only a few anomalies identified.

Ⓕ Evaluation

The final part of the enquiry is to evaluate your investigation. Here you think about how well you answered the task question or theory, and how you could improve or develop the process. The key questions below will help you review your data collection methods, results and conclusions.

- How successful and useful were your methods for sampling and collecting data? Could they be improved?
- How accurate were your results? Did your data collection methods affect the results?
- Did missing or inaccurate data make the study unreliable or affect your conclusions?

Activity

1 Read the students' reflections in Figure 28. Discuss which ones are about:

   a strengths and weaknesses in the study

   b the accuracy of the data

   c missing data or the size of the sample.

2 Suggest how the data collection methods could be improved if other students repeated the study.

Figure 28 Students' reflections on their geographical investigation on the River Dee

Checkpoint

Now it is time to review your understanding of how to plan and conduct an investigation into change in river valleys and channels.

Strengthen

S1 With a partner, note down two things about each of the following: the enquiry question, locating the study, presenting data and evaluation.

S2 Classify the following into simple and sophisticated presentation techniques: flow-line map, bar graph, located pie graph, multiple-line graph, pie graph.

S3 Explain why it is important that a student's conclusion is linked to their task question.

Extend

C1 Think what you know about random, systematic and stratified sampling. Note examples of how each could be used in a river investigation.

C2 Write out example(s) of the methods below, deciding if they are qualitative or quantitative, primary or secondary, and the strengths and limitations of information gained from each of them:

   a method(s) to measure river discharge

   b method(s) to record river landforms and landscapes

   c method(s) to investigate the impact of river processes on local people

   d method(s) to investigate a flood risk in the whole river catchment.

River Landscapes and Processes

Rivers shape the world. The majority of people live on or close to major rivers and we all depend on the food grown on their flood plains. We use rivers for transport, power, water, food and recreation. Rivers are also dangerous; more people are killed by river flooding than by any other natural disaster.

Checklist

You should know:

- [ ] the drainage basin terms – watershed, confluence, tributary, source and mouth
- [ ] the physical processes of erosion, mass movement and weathering
- [ ] the characteristics of a river profile and how these change from the source to the mouth
- [ ] how the UK's weather and climate affect river processes and impact on landforms and landscapes
- [ ] how erosion processes and geology influence the development of river landforms such as interlocking spurs, waterfalls and gorges and river cliffs
- [ ] how depositional processes cause the formation of point bars, flood plains and levees
- [ ] how the interaction of deposition and erosion cause the development of river landforms such as meanders and oxbow lakes
- [ ] why human activities and changes in land use affect river processes and impact on river landscapes
- [ ] the physical and human causes of river flooding
- [ ] how river flooding affects people and the environment
- [ ] the advantages and disadvantages of different defences used on UK rivers
- [ ] how one named distinctive river landscape has been formed and the most influential factors in its change.

Which key terms match the following definitions?

a The area of land drained by a river and its tributaries.

b Fine sediments which are deposited by rivers.

c The movement of material down a slope due to gravity.

d The speed at which a river flows, often measured in metres per second.

e A type of erosion where particles carried by rivers are worn down as they collide with each other, becoming smaller and rounded.

f The flat land in the valley floor each side of a river channel, which is sometimes flooded.

g The deepening and/or straightening of a river to allow it to carry more water.

h A bend formed in a river as it winds across the landscape.

i The starting point of a stream or river, often a spring or a lake.

j A diagram showing the shape of a landscape as if cut through sideways.

To check your answers, look at the Glossary on pages 296–301.

River Landscapes and Processes

Question 1 Explain **one** physical and **one** human cause of flooding.   (4 marks)

Student answer

One cause of flooding is deforestation. This causes flooding because removing the trees reduces interception, causing more rainwater to reach the river channel faster.

A second cause of flooding is urbanisation. This is where humans build near rivers, using hard, impermeable materials. This causes flooding because the rainwater will not infiltrate into the concrete, causing the rainwater to run off into the river channel at a quicker rate.

8th

Verdict

Part 1 is correct – the answer has identified a correct cause, 'deforestation', and explained the reason why this causes flooding – 'reduces interception'.

Part 2 is incorrect. Whilst the human cause is correct, the question asks for **one** physical and **one** human cause of flooding. The student should have explained a physical cause of flooding.

Exam tip

The student has not answered the question being asked. Reading the question through at least a couple of times can help avoid this sort of mistake. Underlining key words can also help you to focus. Finally, if at all possible, leave time to check back on your answers to make sure you really have answered the questions being asked in each case.

Question 2 Explain how different river processes work together in the formation of a meander.   (4 marks)

Student answer

A meander is a bend in a river's course, which is often found in the lower course of a river. The formation of a meander results from a combination of erosion and deposition processes. On the outside of the bend the water is deeper and the current is flowing with greater speed. The force of the water causes undercutting of the bank through abrasion, which is where material carried in the river rubs against the bed and banks of the channel, causing a river cliff to form. On the inside of the bend the water is flowing at a much slower velocity. More friction and therefore less energy means that deposition occurs on the inside of the river bend. Over time sediments are deposited, forming a point bar and slip-off slope and eventually a floodplain.

12th

Verdict

This answer precisely answers the question, by explaining the physical processes that work together to form a meander. It includes key geographical features relating to meanders.

Exam tip

Once again it is important to answer precisely the question being asked – in this case you need to explain the interaction of physical processes to form a meander. You will need to learn the key features of landforms, the physical processes and how these cause the formation. Good answers will also include accurate use of geographical terms.

Glaciers

Learning objectives

- To know what a glacier is, and how and why glaciers formed in the UK
- To understand how past changes in climate led to the development of glacial landscapes in the UK
- To understand why changes in the glacial budget affect glacial growth and movement

Did you know?

This time in Earth's history is known as the **Pleistocene**. It began 2.6 million years ago and ended 11,700 years ago. In the most recent Ice Age, around 18,000 years ago, average global temperature was about 6°C lower than it is today. Ice covered about 30% of the Earth's land area, and sea level was 120 metres lower than today.

The Earth's climate is continuously changing (see Topic 2). Over the past 2.6 million years, long-term rises and falls in temperature have resulted in about 20 cold **glacial periods** interspersed with warmer **interglacials** like today. In the British Isles, these variations in climate resulted in three main glacial periods when ice covered much of the land. Their impact can be seen in the UK's upland landscapes today.

When the climate becomes cold enough, **precipitation** falls as snow. As the depth of the snow increases, its weight compresses the air out of the lower layers, which turn to ice. As the ice becomes thicker, it moves downhill under the force of gravity. When ice moves, it is called a **glacier** (Figure 1).

There are two main types of glacier.

1 **Ice sheet** – this is a moving mass of ice that covers a vast area of the Earth's surface. During the most recent glacial period, ice sheets advanced from Scandinavia to cover the British Isles as far south as the Severn estuary (Figure 2).

2 **Valley glacier** – this is a moving mass of ice that replaces rivers in valleys. During the most recent glacial period, snow and ice accumulated in hollows on the rocky mountainsides of the Cairngorms, Snowdonia and the Lake District. These were the sources of valley glaciers in Britain, which moved down valleys previously eroded by rivers.

The glacial system

A glacier is a system of inputs and outputs (Figure 3). For a glacier to flow, the inputs (snowfall and avalanches) have to exceed the outputs (melting). Snow falls in the **zone of accumulation** (where snow input exceeds snow output), becomes compressed and turns to ice. The weight of the ice and gravity cause the glacier to move downslope. At lower altitudes, parts of the glacier begin to melt (the top, sides and base) and it eventually enters the **zone of ablation**. This is the area where more ice melts than is being supplied. Ablation also occurs along the edges of ice sheets when chunks of ice break off, forming icebergs. This is known as **calving**.

Figure 1 An aerial view of a glacier in Denali National Park, Alaska, USA

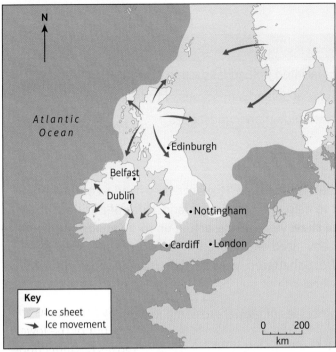

Figure 2 Ice coverage over the British Isles about 18,000 years ago

Activity

1 State **two** ways in which valley glaciers are different from ice sheets.

2 Study Figure 2 and an atlas.

    a Name the **four** upland areas in and around the British Isles from where ice spread.

    b Explain how ice formed and spread to lower ground from these four areas.

3 Explain how the glacial budget affects glacier movement both seasonally and yearly.

The difference between accumulation and ablation is the **glacial budget**. When accumulation exceeds ablation, the glacier grows and advances. When ablation is greater than accumulation, the glacier shrinks and retreats. If accumulation and ablation are equal over a year, the glacier stays the same size and in the same position. Variations in weather and climate cause changes to the glacial budget in the short and long term. In addition, daily (diurnal) changes in weather have an immediate impact on upland landscapes (see pages 72–73).

1 **Seasonally** – in summer, ablation exceeds accumulation because more ice melts in the warmer temperatures. The glacial budget is negative so the glacier retreats. In winter, accumulation exceeds ablation because there is more snowfall and less melting. The glacial budget is positive and the glacier advances.

2 **Many years/centuries** – until about 1850, glaciers had a positive budget and were advancing rapidly in Europe during the 'Little Ice Age' (a period between about 1300 and 1870 during which Europe and North America experienced much colder winters than we do today). Today, the budget is negative due to **global warming**, and glaciers are retreating.

Ice covers about 10% of the Earth's land area today. The majority of this ice is found at extreme latitudes – the Antarctic ice sheet makes up 90% and the Greenland ice sheet 7%. The remaining 3% is in northern Canada and Alaska, and at high altitude, for example in the Himalayas, Andes and the Alps. Much of Britain has been shaped by ice, but the last glaciers retreated around 10,000 years ago to leave a **relict** glacial landscape.

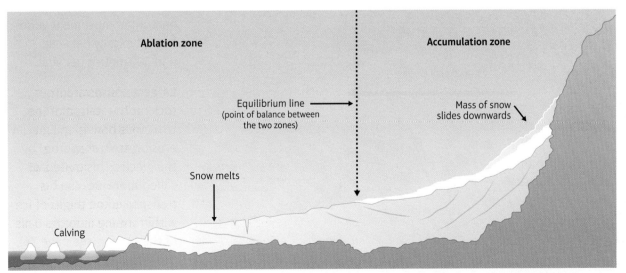

Figure 3 The glacial system

Glacial and post-glacial processes

Learning objectives

- To know the physical processes that once operated in the glaciated upland landscape of the UK
- To know the physical processes that operate on the relict glacial upland landscapes of today
- To understand how physical processes interact to shape glaciated upland landscapes

Glacial erosion

Glaciers are powerful tools of erosion. However, they need a continuous supply of rock debris to help them erode the land. Much of this debris is produced by **freeze thaw weathering** acting on rock outcrops either before the ice sheets advanced and above the surface of valley glaciers. Once produced, the frost-shattered rocks become frozen to the sides and underside of the glaciers.

There are two main processes of glacial erosion (Figure 4).

1 **Abrasion** – the rocks and rock fragments embedded in the sides and bottom of the glacier wear away the rocks over which the glacier moves. The smaller fragments act like sand on a sheet of sandpaper, smoothing and polishing the rock surface, while the angular edges of large rocks make deep grooves, called **striations**.

2 **Plucking** – meltwater beneath a glacier enters joints in the rocks below. When the water freezes, the rocks become bonded to the bottom of the glacier. As the glacier moves, large rocks are torn or 'plucked' from the bedrock, leaving a jagged rocky surface behind.

Exam-style question

Describe **one** way in which valley glaciers move. **(2 marks)**

Exam tip

A good answer will include details of the conditions required for glacial movement.

Glacial movement and transportation

Valley glaciers flow more quickly than ice sheets because of steeper gradients and the presence of more meltwater, which lubricates their flow. This type of movement is called **basal sliding**. In hollows high on the mountainside, movement may be on a curved plane and is referred to as **rotational slip**. The amount of movement varies but is typically between 3 and 300 metres per year.

Large amounts of loose rock produced from freeze thaw weathering and glacial erosion are transported by the glacier. This material, called **moraine**, can be transported on the ice, within the ice or in the base of the glacier (see page 76).

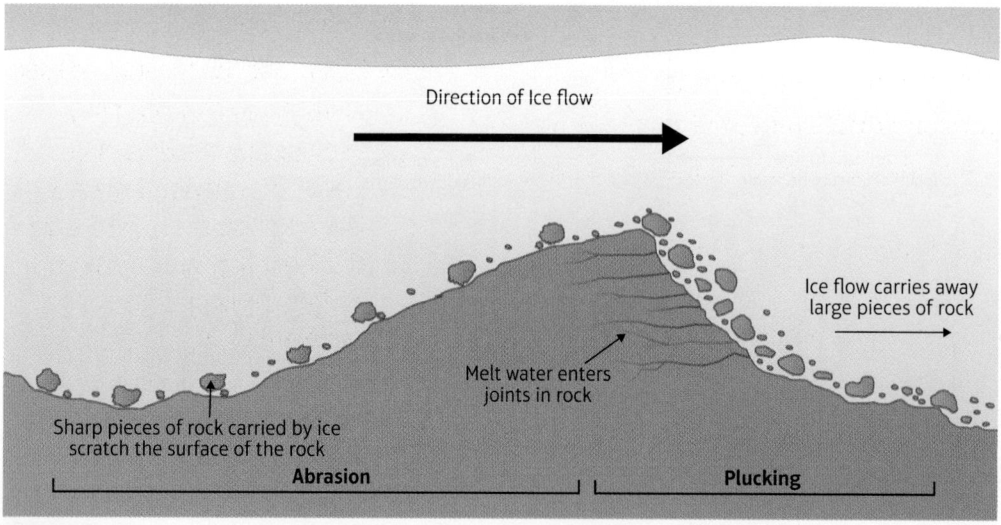

Figure 4 Processes of glacial erosion

Deposition

Most deposition occurs when the ice melts, and when it is overloaded with material. Unlike river and coastal deposits, glacial deposits are unsorted and may contain a jumble of rock fragments ranging from fine clay up to huge boulders at any one site. If a glacier moves forward again, the glacial deposits are pushed further downhill. This process is called **bulldozing**.

Post-glacial processes

Many distinctive glacial landforms can be found in upland areas of the UK. These are a product of the glacial processes acting throughout the Pleistocene Ice Age. Today, this relict glacial landscape is being modified by post-glacial processes. These include mechanical weathering and mass movement (rock falls and soil movement).

1   **Mechanical weathering (freeze thaw)** – in the upland areas of the UK, temperatures in the winter months regularly fall below freezing at night and rise again during the day. These are perfect conditions for freeze thaw weathering to attack and break down the rocks. Water enters joints and cracks in the rock. On freezing, the ice expands by about 10%, putting pressure on the rock. Repeated freeze thaw cycles widen and weaken joints, causing pieces of rock to shatter from the main rock (the term 'frost shattering' is also applied to this process). Boulder fields build up where this occurs on flat surfaces, usually on mountain summits.

2   **Rock falls** – rapid, downslope movements of rock due to gravity. They occur when frost-shattered rocks fall from steep glaciated slopes to the valley floor. Over time, the slopes become more gradual and **scree** builds up along the base of the slopes (Figure 5).

3   **Soil movement** – slow, downslope movement of soil due to gravity that occurs when soil particles are water-saturated. The soil structure has usually been weakened by frost action and the ground beneath the active soil layer may still be frozen, so acts as a slip plane.

Figure 5 The cliffs of Craig-Y-Bera, Snowdonia, Wales, with scree slopes below

Landforms of glacial erosion

Learning objectives

- To know the characteristics of landforms of glacial erosion
- To understand the role of erosion in the formation of glacial landforms
- To recognise glacial landforms in photographs

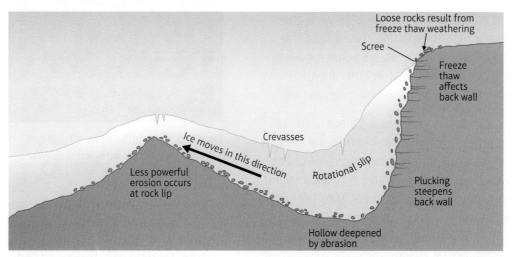

Figure 6 The formation of a corrie

The glaciated upland areas of the UK are made up of fossil landforms – landforms created when glaciers eroded the landscape that existed before the Ice Age (Figure 8a).

Corries

A **corrie** (**cirque** or **cwm**) is a deep, rounded hollow found high on the upper slopes of glaciated valleys, with a steep and rocky back wall, which in the UK can reach up to a height of 200 metres. The sides of a corrie are also steep and rocky, but the front is open and has a slightly raised rock lip. A corrie may contain a lake, called a **tarn**.

Figure 6 explains the formation of a corrie. Corries begin to form in a hollow area where snow accumulates and compresses into ice (called a **névé**). Freeze thaw weathering of the rocky outcrops above the ice supply rock fragments (scree). Water seeping down the **bergschrund crevasse** and freezing leads to freeze thaw activity in the back wall. As the weight of the ice builds, it begins to move by rotational slip. Loose rock fragments from freeze thaw and plucking are embedded in the ice and act as tools for scraping out the hollow. Erosion is greatest at the bottom of the back wall and in the base of the hollow where the ice is thickest. At the front of the corrie, the ice is thinner and so a raised lip is formed as the glacier flows out of the corrie. After glaciation, when all the ice has melted, a tarn forms in the carved-out hollow.

Figure 7 (A) Crib Goch (arête) and (B) Snowdon (pyramidal peak), Snowdonia, Wales.

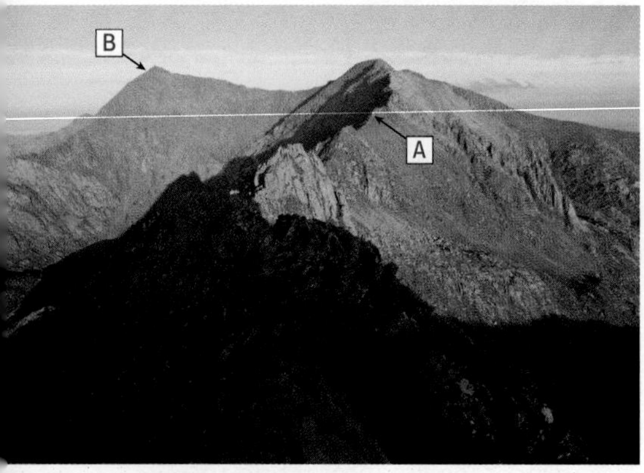

Arêtes and pyramidal peaks

An **arête** is a narrow, serrated ridge between two glaciated slopes positioned back to back (Figure 7, A). It forms when freeze thaw weathering and erosion on the back walls of two corries, one on either side of the ridge, cause them to cut back until only a narrow ridge of rock remains.

A **pyramidal peak** is a mountain with three very steep sides (Figure 7, B). It is formed when plucking and abrasion on the back walls of three or more corries cause them to cut back into the mountain from different sides to form a single, steep peak. The Matterhorn in Switzerland is a classic example of a pyramidal peak.

Glacial valley landforms

A **glacial trough** (also known as a **U-shaped valley**) is a steep-sided, wide and flat-bottomed valley. It is also usually fairly straight, its sides marked by **truncated spurs** and **hanging valleys** from which waterfalls cascade. A **misfit stream** – so-called because it is dwarfed by the size and scale of the glaciated valley – drains the valley. A **ribbon lake** – long and thin – may also fill part or all of the valley floor (see Figure 12 on page 79).

When a glacier occupies a former river valley, the ice fills the whole valley (Figure 8b). As the glacier advances, abrasion and plucking erode the floor and sides of the valley over hundreds of years, changing it from a V-shaped river valley into a U-shaped glacial valley. Unable to flow around the interlocking spurs, formed by the pre-glacial river, the powerful glacier cuts straight through them, forming truncated spurs and straight valley sides (Figure 8c). Tributary valleys are occupied by smaller, less powerful glaciers than the main glacier. As they are unable to erode down to the same level as the main glacier, the valleys are left hanging above the main valley after the ice has melted. Waterfalls often mark these landforms.

Erosion of the valley floor is usually uneven due to differences in rock type and the presence of joints or faults. The glacier erodes soft or well-jointed rock more quickly and more deeply than hard or more resistant rock, forming a hollow. Where one or more tributary glaciers join the main glacier, the thickness of the ice increases, also causing faster and deeper erosion and a hollow to form. After the ice melts, the hollow is filled with water to form a narrow ribbon lake.

A **roche moutonnée** is a small rock hill, about 10–15 metres long. It has a gently sloping side (the stoss side) facing up the valley and a much steeper lee side facing down the valley. The roches moutonnées in Snowdonia, Wales, were formed when the glacier moved over a band of resistant volcanic rock. Abrasion on the stoss side smoothed the rock, but plucking and abrasion on the lee side left a jagged slope. Striations can also be found on the stoss side.

Exam-style question

Explain why different processes combine to form an arête.

(4 marks)

Exam tip

When answering formation questions, always name processes and explain how they operate to create the landform. Using a series of sketches may help, provided they are annotated for formation.

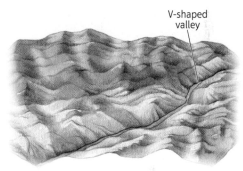

(a)

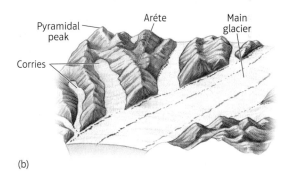

(b)

(c)

Figure 8 Upland landscape (a) before, (b) during and (c) after glaciation

Activity

1. Study Figure 6. Draw **three** simple diagrams to show the formation of a corrie at the beginning of glaciation, during and after. Add labels to describe what is happening.

2. Draw a sketch of the landforms shown in Figure 7 and annotate it to:
   a. describe the landforms
   b. explain their formation.

3. Explain how physical processes work together in the formation of a ribbon lake.

Landforms of glacial transportation and deposition

Learning objectives

- To know the characteristics of landforms of glacial transportation and deposition
- To understand the role of transportation and deposition in the formation of glacial landforms
- To recognise glacial landforms in photographs

Did you know?

The largest terminal moraine in the UK is Cromer Ridge in East Anglia. The Ridge marks the southern extent of the last ice sheet to advance over Britain and is 102 metres high and 14 km wide.

Moraine

The rock material transported and deposited by glaciers is called moraine. When a valley glacier reaches lower ground, the ice begins to melt due to warmer temperatures. As the ice thins, it is less able to carry the material it has been transporting, and so deposition occurs. The deposited material is unsorted and made up of a range of different sized rock fragments including clay, sand, stones and angular boulders. Geologists call material directly deposited by glacier ice **till** (or **boulder clay**).

Moraines have different names depending on where they are deposited.

1 **Ground moraine** – this is the material carried in the base of the glacier. As the glacier continues to move forward, melting as it does so, it leaves a trail of till behind it, forming an uneven hummocky valley floor.

2 **Lateral moraine** – this forms at the edges of the glacier from scree that has fallen from the valley sides. When the ice melts, it forms a slight ridge on the valley side (Figure 9, A).

3 **Medial moraine** – this is a line of material running down the middle of a glacier. It forms when a tributary glacier joins the main glacier and their separate lateral moraines merge. When the ice melts, the medial moraine forms a ridge down the centre of the valley (Figure 9, B).

4 **Terminal moraine** – a huge amount of till is deposited at the glacier's **snout** to form a ridge that extends across the valley or lowlands. It marks the furthest point reached by the glacier. Terminal moraines formed by ice sheets can be more than 200 metres high. Those formed by valley glaciers can be between 20 and 40 metres high, and can form natural dams behind which ribbon lakes can form.

5 **Recessional moraine** – this is a small ridge of till deposited when a glacier pauses during its retreat. Several can occur in a glacial valley, marking the history of the glacier's retreat.

Figure 9 Different kinds of moraine in and beside glaciers above Zermatt, Valais, Switzerland: (A) lateral moraines, (B) medial moraines

Included in glacial till are **erratics**. These are stones and rocks of a different rock type from the area in which they are currently found. For example, rocks originating in the Lake District and Firth of Forth have been found in North Wales.

Drumlins

A **drumlin** is a streamlined, egg-shaped hill made of till. Drumlins occur in swarms and are said to form a 'basket of eggs' topography due to the appearance of the landscape (Figure 10). In Britain, this landscape can be found in the lowland areas of south-west Scotland and north-west England. Each drumlin is typically about 30–40 metres high and 300–400 metres long. They are orientated in the same direction, with the blunt (stoss) end facing upstream and the tapered (lee) end facing downstream in the direction of ice flow.

Drumlins are formed beneath ice that is advancing across a lowland area, but is overloaded and melting. Any small obstacle, such as a rock outcrop or a mound, encourages deposition. Most deposition occurs around the upstream end of the obstacle, which forms the drumlin's blunt end. The rest of the till is then moulded and shaped by the moving ice to form the tapered end downstream.

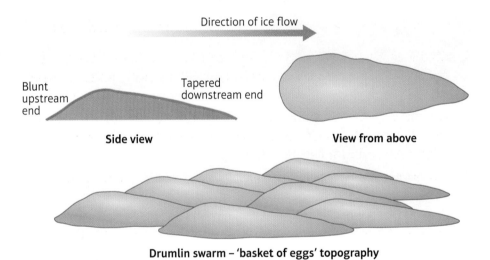

Figure 10 Drumlins

Crag and tail

A **crag and tail** is a rock hill (crag) with a tapering ridge on its lee side (the tail). They range in size from several metres to kilometres in length, with the tail pointing in the direction of ice flow. A classic example is the crag on which Edinburgh Castle sits and the Royal Mile, which forms the tail.

A crag and tail is formed by erosion and deposition. When a glacier meets a more resistant bedrock obstacle, the ice is forced to flow over and around it. Plucking and abrasion on the upstream side of the obstacle steepens the slope and makes it jagged, forming the crag. In the lee of the crag, the velocity and pressure of the ice decrease. If there is a hollow in the relatively softer rock behind the crag, deposition of glacial till occurs. Deposition decreases with distance from the crag, which explains why the tail tapers towards the end.

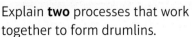

Exam-style question

Explain **two** processes that work together to form drumlins.

(3 marks)

Exam tip

The formation of landforms can often be explained with a labelled diagram. Practise drawing these diagrams for drumlins. Name the processes and explain how they operate to create the landform.

Activity

1   State **two** features of glacial till. How do these features help to explain that deposition was by ice rather than by a river?

2   State **one** difference and **one** similarity between lateral and medial moraines.

3   Describe a crag and tail feature. Explain how its shape indicates the direction in which the glacier flowed along the valley. Include a diagram in your explanation.

Investigating glacial landforms on OS maps

Learning objectives

- To recognise glaciated upland landforms on OS maps
- To identify glaciated upland landforms in photographs and find them on OS maps
- To understand how to use contour lines and symbols on OS maps to help identify glaciated upland landforms

Exam question

Identify **one** landform in the glaciated landscape shown in Figure 11. **(1 mark)**

Exam tip

If you study the photograph carefully, this type of question is usually straightforward, but make sure you use the correct terminology for the landform. For example, tarn not lake.

The spectacular landscape of the Nant Ffrancon valley in Snowdonia, North Wales (Figure 11), was carved by glaciers during the last glacial period.

Figure 11 Nant Ffrancon valley from Glyder Fach, Snowdonia, North West Wales

Identifying glacial upland landforms from contour patterns and OS symbols

OS maps showing glacial landforms, as in Figure 12, are not always easy to interpret because of the number and closeness of the contours, but if you look closely at the *shape* of the contours, you will be able to pick out some key landforms.

- **Corrie** (or *cwm* in Welsh) – shown by semi-circular or horseshoe-shaped contour lines, spaced closely together along the back wall. There may be a tarn (lake, or *llyn* in Welsh) in the centre.
- **Arête** – look for two corries back to back, where the contour lines are close together and the highest land is in the middle. The symbol for bare rock may also be present.

- **Pyramidal peak** – look for a spot height or triangulation station, with three or more corries surrounding it.
- **Glacial trough** – shown by many contour lines, closely spaced, running roughly straight and parallel to indicate the steep valley sides; the relatively flat valley floor has few contours and will look 'white' on the map.
- **Hanging valley** – look for a glacial trough first, then look for a small valley above it. They are easier to spot if the hanging valley contains a waterfall, which may be named on the map.

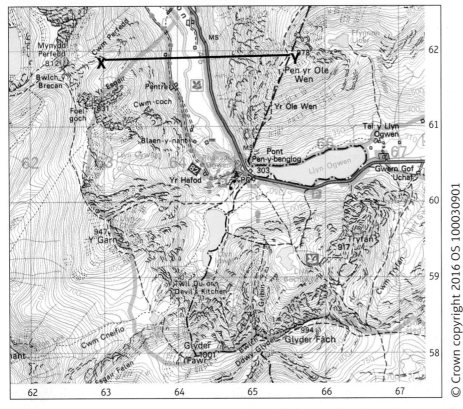

Figure 12 Extract from 1:50,000 OS map of Nant Ffrancon valley, Snowdonia, North West Wales

© Crown copyright 2016 OS 100030901

Activity

Study Figures 11 and 12.

1   Looking at Figure 12, give the six-figure grid reference for the peak at Glyder Fach (994 metres) from where the photograph (Figure 11) has been taken.

2   Identify the landforms labelled A to D in Figure 11. Name C and D.

3   Name the lake at E in Figure 11.

    a   What type of lake is this?

    b   Describe its shape and explain how it was formed.

4   In which direction do you think the glacier flowed along the Nant Ffrancon valley? Use evidence from Figure 12 to support your answer.

5   Read the tutorial on contours and drawing cross sections (page 51).

    a   Draw a contour cross section across the Nant Ffrancon valley between points X and Y shown on Figure 12.

    b   Locate and label: glacial trough, misfit stream and frost-shattered rock outcrops.

    c   Describe the physical features of Nant Ffrancon valley that show it is a glacial trough.

Tip In the exam, make sure you can give named examples for glacial landforms, such as a corrie, arête, pyramidal peak, glacial trough and ribbon lake.

Checkpoint

Now it is time to review your understanding of the development of glacial landforms and how we use OS maps to study glacial upland landscapes.

Strengthen

S1 How can you tell the direction of ice movement from studying a roche moutonnée?

S2 Draw a sketch of Figure 9 and annotate it to describe the different moraines shown.

S3 How would you identify a hanging valley on an OS map?

Challenge

C1 Describe the landforms of a glacial valley and explain how they are formed.

C2 Explain how drumlins are different from ground moraine.

C3 Identify and give the four-figure grid reference for a truncated spur in Figure 12. Describe the shape of the contours.

Case Study – Changes to the glaciated uplands of Snowdonia

Learning objectives

- To know how people and the environment interact in Snowdonia
- To know how human and physical factors cause change to Snowdonia
- To understand the impact of farming, forestry and settlement in Snowdonia

The changing physical landscape of Snowdonia

Snowdonia in North Wales was designated a National Park in 1951 – the first in Wales (Figure 13). It covers 2176 square kilometres and is home to about 26,000 people.

The region has a complex **geology**. Snowdon (1085 metres, the tallest mountain in Wales), for example, is formed from volcanic rock with some sedimentary rock and **igneous intrusions** folded into a **syncline**. The Harlech Dome (the oldest physical feature in Snowdonia), originally formed from muds and sands, was later altered by volcanic activity to form the slates and grits of today.

In more recent geological times (18,000 years ago), an **ice cap** covered Snowdonia (Figure 13 inset). Centred over Migneint Moor and with a depth of 1400 metres, the landscape would have looked similar to Antarctica today – a sea of ice with only the highest mountain peaks exposed. Under gravity, glacier ice flowed from the ice cap down pre-existing river valleys, eroding the landscape as it moved. When temperatures started to rise, the ice cap began to melt. Gradually the snouts of the glaciers retreated up the valleys until eventually the ice completely melted, leaving behind rocky corries (cwms) and steep-sided U-shaped valleys. Upland areas were stripped to bare rock while the lower slopes were covered in moraines and till.

Snowdonia continues to be a dynamic landscape, constantly changing due to natural processes. It is a harsh environment to live in. The climate is wet and cold, with average annual rainfall exceeding 3000 mm and average annual maximum temperature reaching 12°C. In winter, the **diurnal variation** in temperature can be as much as 8°C. Climatic conditions deteriorate with height. It becomes colder and there is more precipitation

which also means more cloud cover and less sunshine. Glacial erosion has increased the steepness of the land and the height of the valley sides, making access more difficult.

Activity

1   What physical processes might operate on the landscape of Snowdonia today? Explain how each process operates and describe any changes in the landscape.

Tip Processes can often be explained with a simple, labelled diagram.

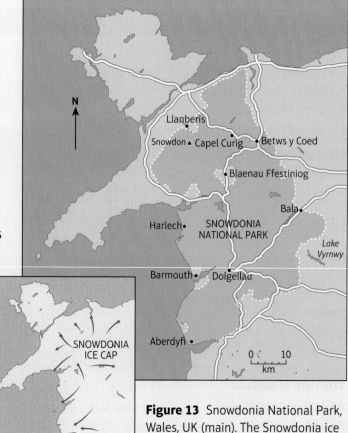

Figure 13 Snowdonia National Park, Wales, UK (main). The Snowdonia ice cap, about 18,000 years ago (inset)

However difficult the conditions, people have used Snowdonia's resources for centuries. Settlements, farming, forestry and quarrying have changed the landscape as well as affecting natural processes.

Settlement

Glaciated upland areas tend to be sparsely populated, with only 12 people for every square kilometre in Snowdonia. Most settlements are scattered along the valleys, where access by road and rail is easier. Snowdonia is very popular for recreational activities and one in seven houses in is now owned by visitors. In winter, these villages are extremely quiet as the holiday homes are empty, and there is some conflict between the permanent residents and the visitors.

Farming and forestry

Around 80% of the land in Snowdonia is farmed, with 14% of the population working in jobs related to farming. Farmers have been modifying Snowdonia's landscape for centuries. In the past, natural woodlands were cleared for farmland in the valleys, and land on higher ground was used to feed livestock. Valley floors in glaciated upland areas are the most productive farming land, being wide, relatively flat and quite fertile due to till deposits from when the glaciers retreated. Today they are used for growing crops and making hay and silage. Away from the valley floor, the land is only suitable for livestock farming. Cattle are kept in the valley, while sheep use the rough grazing on the steeper slopes.

Poor soils and wet weather here mean that farming is often **marginal**, meaning it is difficult for farmers to make a profit. Many farmers have chosen to **diversify** – they look to create new and additional sources of income.

Planting coniferous trees on north-facing slopes and lower slopes too steep for farming is one example of diversification. When these forests are mature, they are sold for timber and wood pulp. Other farmers run their farmhouses as bed and breakfast accommodation, convert farm buildings into holiday cottages or have camping sites on their land (Figure 14).

Human impacts on natural processes

As well as changing the landscape, humans affect natural processes, particularly in rivers. In upland areas such as Snowdonia impermeable rocks, thin soils and

Figure 14 Camping in a field near Capel Curig, Snowdonia, Wales

steep slopes cause the high rainfall to run off rapidly into rivers. Human activities can change the rate of runoff and increase the risk of flooding downstream (see pages 52–55).

Farming and forestry
- Trees collect, store and use water and their roots encourage water to pass into soil and rock, so they reduce or slow runoff. Past **deforestation** of the valley floors and sides has increased runoff. Drainage of the valley floors also increases runoff. By contrast, planting trees, or **afforestation**, is one type of land-use management which reduces the flood risk (see page 59).
- In some UK upland areas, overgrazing by sheep has been blamed for compacting the soil and increasing runoff and erosion.

Settlements
- In the bigger settlements, rainwater cannot infiltrate the hard, impermeable concrete and tarmac surfaces, particularly the bare rocks of Snowdonia's large old slate quarries. Rain water runs off immediately into drains and river channels.

Activity

1 Draw a sketch of Figure 14. Label the possible land uses and annotate them to explain the physical problems of living in Snowdonia. Add annotations to show how human activities affect runoff.

2 What impacts might there be if farming in Snowdonia continues to decline? Try to think of one example for each economic, environmental and social factor.

Development in the glaciated uplands of Snowdonia

Learning objectives

- To know how development can lead to change in Snowdonia
- To know the advantages and disadvantages of development, and how it is managed in Snowdonia
- To understand the effects of climate change on development in Snowdonia

Figure 15 Dinorwic slate quarry on the slopes of Elidir Fawr, with the glaciated upland of Snowdonia in the background

Activity

Study Figure 15. Describe how the quarry landscape differs from the glaciated upland landscape.

Tip An annotated sketch of Figure 15 might be a good way of comparing the two landscapes.

Activity

Study the information about the resources of Snowdonia.

a Make **three** lists of resources: economic, environmental and social (some may be in more than one category).

b Describe the impact a growing tourist industry may have on the resources of Snowdonia.

Snowdonia's natural landscape attracts millions of visitors each year. The land is also a rich resource, used for farming and **renewable energy** supply today, and once exploited for its slate. It provides many economic, environmental and recreational opportunities.

Water storage and supply

Snowdonia receives over 3000 mm of rainfall a year. High rainfall combined with deep glacial valleys favour the capture and storage of water. While ribbon lakes and tarns can provide areas of natural water storage, glacial valleys have also been developed to create man-made stores. Lake Vyrnwy just to the south of Snowdonia is a glacial valley that once contained a misfit stream, but a dam was built in 1888 to flood the valley. The **reservoir** took two years to fill. An **aqueduct**, 110 km long, was built to carry water from Lake Vyrnwy to Liverpool. Today, pipelines carry up to 210 million litres of water a day to Cheshire and Merseyside.

Quarrying and mining

Quarrying and mining were once important industries in Snowdonia. Copper and gold were mined, but slate quarrying had a greater impact on both the economy and the landscape. Small villages such as Llanberis developed into industrial towns to accommodate some of the 17,000 quarry workers. Over 485,000 tons of slate were produced to be used for roofs and in the construction of dams, such as at Lake Vyrnwy.

Dinorwic quarry on the side of Elidir Fawr, overlooking Llyn Peris, was one of the largest slate quarries in Snowdonia. Figure 15 shows the derelict man-made faces of the quarry in contrast with the glaciated upland in the background. This industrial 'eyesore' can also been seen on OS maps (Figure 16, grid square 5960), marked as rock outcrops and slag/spoil heaps. As well as terraces and waste-tips, dams, water courses, tramways and railways were built in and around the quarry.

Renewable energy

Dinorwic slate quarry closed in 1969 and remained derelict until the 1980s when Dinorwig power station was built on the site (Figure 16). Dinorwig is a pumped storage **hydro-electric power (HEP)** station.

- Water released from Marchlyn Mawr Reservoir (north-east of the power station) falls through tunnels built deep below Elidir Fawr to the power station and flows through turbines, generating electricity.

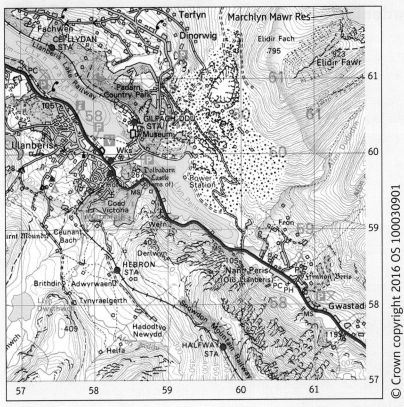

© Crown copyright 2016 OS 100030901

Figure 16 Extract from 1:50,000 OS map showing Dinorwic slate quarry, Snowdonia, Wales

- Off-peak electricity is then used to reverse the turbines and pump water back from Llyn Peris to the reservoir.

- The power station generates 1728 MW of electricity and supplies power to homes and businesses throughout the UK.

Wind farms for generating electricity are found in some glaciated upland areas of the UK, but they are not permitted in Snowdonia. In the Lake District, there are plans to build 400 new wind turbines.

Recreation, tourism, conservation

Snowdonia National Park attracts over 4 million visitors a year, contributing about £400 million to the local economy. Over 8000 people work in the tourist industry here. Tourists visit Snowdonia for its natural picturesque scenery and variety of year-round activities (Figure 17). The National Park is within two hours travelling time from several large urban areas. Mountaineers and rock climbers are attracted to the area's steep rock faces, while hikers explore the arêtes and valleys. Snowdon is one of many **honeypot sites** in Snowdonia, attracting 400,000 walkers every year. A further 100,000 visitors reach the summit by the Snowdon Mountain Railway. Visitors are also drawn to places of cultural and historic interest, such as Harlech Castle, and towns like Betws y Coed. Around 20% of Snowdonia is specially designated by law to protect its distinctive wildlife, such as the Snowdon Lily and the Rainbow Beetle. Three areas – the Dyfi Estuary Biosphere Reserve, Cwm Idwal and Llyn Tegid – are **Ramsar** sites. There are also 17 National Nature Reserves in Snowdonia.

Figure 17 Places of interest and activities for visitors to Snowdonia, Wales

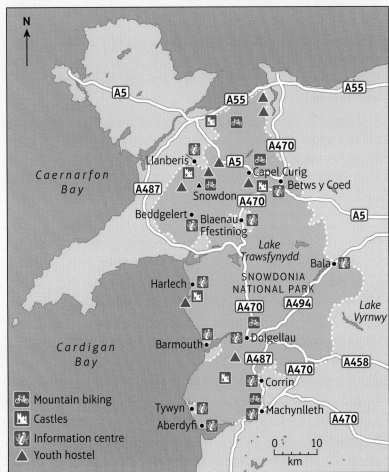

The impact of development in Snowdonia

Developments in water supply, renewable energy, tourism and conservation have all played their part in changing the landscape of Snowdonia. While some of these changes may benefit the area, they can also create social and environmental problems for the region.

Figure 18 Maintained footpath, Snowdonia National Park

Table 1 Advantages and disadvantages of development in Snowdonia

Advantages	Disadvantages
Water storage and supply – e.g. Lake Vyrnwy (just south of Snowdonia)	
Supplies water to parts of the UK that are without their own freshwater supplies nearby. Hard impermeable rocks in glaciated uplands provide natural conditions for rainwater storage in lakes and reservoirs. Large areas of surrounding catchment may be managed as part of the scheme and provide recreational opportunities, e.g. woodland walks, bird hides and local crafts.	Many nearby hill farms have no treated, clean water piped to them. Lakes and reservoirs have to be protected from pollution. Man-made reservoirs displace people and submerge farms, e.g. the creation of Lake Vyrnwy involved relocating Llanwyddn village. Man-made reservoirs displace natural vegetation and wildlife.
Renewable energy – e.g. Dinorwig power station	
HEP and wind farms are clean, **sustainable** methods of producing energy; they don't pollute the environment. Power stations can be built on **brownfield sites**, e.g. Dinorwig power station was built on the site of a derelict slate quarry. HEP stations create local jobs and encourage investment into the local area. Reservoirs and lakes that are used for HEP generation provide opportunities for water sports such as fishing. Salmon, trout and freshwater lamprey still thrive and spawn in Llyn Peris and Marchlyn Mawr.	Low rainfall/light winds can mean no electricity is produced (average annual rainfall at Llanberis is over 2600 mm, so this is unlikely). There needs to be enough water in the reservoirs/lakes to protect habitats. HEP can displace wildlife and disturb spawning grounds. Llyn Peris was home to a rare fish, the Welsh Arctic Charr; this has been relocated. Pipelines may run overland – they are unsightly and can prevent access to the land, e.g. at Cwm Dyli, but not at Dinorwig. Wind farms are unsightly, create noise pollution and can kill birds.
Recreation and tourism – e.g. Snowdonia National Park	
Provides jobs for local people and income for the local economy. Allows farmers and others to diversify to improve their incomes. Helps to preserve local services such as buses, shops and post offices. Increases the demand for local food and crafts. Encourages improvements in local infrastructure and services, such as healthcare. Tourists come to see and use the landscape so there is pressure to conserve it and its habitats.	Jobs are mainly seasonal, low paid and with long hours. Traffic congestion and pollution. Littering, footpath erosion, fires, vandalism and disturbance of livestock. Shops can pander to tourists, stocking goods for them rather than meeting locals' needs; goods can be expensive. Demand for holiday homes can make housing expensive for locals. Pressure to develop more facilities: hotels, shops, outdoor centres.

Advantages	Disadvantages
Conservation – e.g. Snowdonia National Park	
Protects the **fragile environment**, including native vegetation and wildlife. Encourages outdoor recreation and appreciation of the landscape and historic heritage. Natural areas can help to regulate the effects of erosion, flooding and climate change. Grants are available for repairing dry-stone walls and for planting deciduous trees.	Conservation projects can be expensive to set up. Projects can take a long time to complete due to limited manpower and the large areas to cover. Non-native species of plant can be well-established and difficult to clear.

Managing development in Snowdonia

Economic pressures for development in Snowdonia are strong, but the Snowdonia National Park Authority is safeguarding against any threat to what makes it special. It has three overarching aims:

- to conserve and enhance the natural beauty, wildlife and cultural heritage of the area
- to promote opportunities to understand and enjoy the area's special qualities
- to foster the economic and social wellbeing of the area's communities.

Although the Authority does not promote tourism as such, it does recognise its value and is working towards making tourism in Snowdonia more sustainable. It does this by:

- promoting understanding of the area through the use of leaflets, information centres, events and guided walks. Education staff meet school groups to explain about the National Park
- managing footpaths by diverting footpaths and fencing off old paths to allow time for the vegetation to recover; by making artificial paths, using stone, steps and raised boards (Figure 18)
- encouraging visitors to leave their cars behind and use greener travel, such as Green Key – an integrated bus service for the north of Snowdonia
- supporting outdoor activities that do not damage the landscape or harm wildlife
- making policy decisions such as new houses restricted to locals only and not allowing wind farms. Instead the Authority encourages small-scale renewable energy schemes
- asking local communities for their views and ideas on managing the National Park by setting up forums, groups and consultations.

Inevitably, there are conflicts between the groups of people who use Snowdonia – between farms and visitors about access to land, letting dogs off the lead and damage to walls; and between local residents and visitors over holiday homes and the price of housing and goods.

Exam-style question

Examine the ways human activities can change glaciated upland landscapes.
(8 marks + 4 SPAG)

Exam tip

The answer should be focused on specific examples through the use of relevant case study points.

Activity

1 Why do you think the Snowdonia National Park Authority does not allow wind farms to be built within the Park? Do you think this is the right decision? Explain your answer.

2 In what ways has Dinorwig power station tried to reduce its environmental impact?

Tip Think about its construction as well as its energy production.

3 Explain why management of visitor activities is needed in Snowdonia.

The impact of climate change on development in Snowdonia

Climate change is already having an effect on the landscape, wildlife and communities of Snowdonia. Warmer weather encourages more visitors to the area, creating more traffic problems and releasing more carbon dioxide (a **greenhouse gas**) into the atmosphere. The risk of wild fires has also increased. Fires will spread more quickly if the weather is drier and warmer. Some species and habitats are not adapting quickly enough to changing weather. The Snowdon Lily (Figure 19) and other alpine plants, for example, depend on the cold to survive and could be lost in Wales if temperatures continue to rise.

Figure 19 The Snowdon Lily

Many scientists agree that climate change is happening. The world is getting warmer and the weather is getting more extreme. Modelling techniques have been used to predict the changes in the climate of Snowdonia by the end of the century. It is expected that although annual averages will not change by much, there will be significant variations in seasonal weather patterns. Summer droughts and periods of heavy rainfall during the winter are expected. Climate change will have varying impacts on the activities that take place in Snowdonia. It will bring new opportunities for the visitor economy but may alter traditional farming methods.

The impact of climate change on forests is not really known but, like farming, there are possible threats from an increase in pests and diseases, forest fires and invasive species. Forests could, however, increase as trees store carbon dioxide and would therefore help to **mitigate** global warming. The interest in and opportunities for renewable energy schemes is expected to increase as the century progresses. However, the scale of the operations may change as the disadvantages of large-scale HEP and wind farm operations cause more conflict in communities.

Table 2 Possible impacts of climate change on farming in Snowdonia

Positive	Unknown	Negative
More possibilities for diversification as the number of visitors to the area increases	Changes in traditional farming methods to mitigate the effects of climate change and adaptation to it	Increase in wild fire events, threatening farms, livestock and infrastructure
Opportunities to grow new varieties of crops if topography, access and soil quality are not **limiting factors**		Increase in flood risk, threatening livestock, leading to degradation of soil/land and infrastructure
Increase in grass yields, reducing the cost of buying extra feed during winter		Possibility of heat stress among some livestock breeds during long periods of hot weather
Livestock reared outside for longer if milder winters/warmer springs – energy costs reduced		Likely increase in pests and diseases, including water-borne pathogens

Table 3 Possible impacts of climate change on recreation and tourism in Snowdonia

Positive	Negative
Increasing air fares may encourage domestic tourism.	If fuel prices increase, tourist numbers may decrease as other destinations may be easier to reach than Snowdonia by public transport.
Warmer, drier summers/milder winters will make Snowdonia a more attractive holiday destination.	Wetter winters may reduce out-of-season visitor numbers, particularly those interested in outdoor activities.
Outdoor activities such as mountain biking will increase due to warmer, drier summers.	Some summer days could become too hot for outdoor activities.
Higher temperatures may encourage more beach holidays, such as to Harlech, and may lead to an increase in number of foreign tourists as Mediterranean resorts become too hot.	Rising sea level could have an impact on coastal and beach holidays to the detriment of tourist businesses and holiday accommodation.

Activity

1 On balance, do you think climate change will have a positive or negative impact on Snowdonia? Explain your answer.

2 Look back at your learning in this topic. Examine how the glaciated upland landscape of Snowdonia was formed and the most significant factors in its change.

Checkpoint

It is now time to review your understanding of how physical and human processes interact to change glaciated upland landscapes.

Strengthen

S1 State two ways in which farming changes the glaciated upland landscape.

S2 State one environmental issue in glaciated upland areas and explain the causes.

S3 Explain how tourism can become more sustainable in glaciated upland areas.

Challenge

C1 Explain why farmers in Snowdonia are choosing to diversify.

C2 Many walkers visit glaciated upland areas. Explain how they can damage the environment.

C3 Examine the advantages and disadvantages of renewable energy developments in glaciated upland areas. Overall, do you think it benefits the areas, or not? Explain your answer.

Glaciated Upland Landscapes and Processes

Around 18,000 years ago, ice covered much of Britain. Glaciers flowed down pre-existing river valleys, eroding the landscape as they moved. When temperatures started to rise, the ice melted, leaving behind rocky upland areas and lower slopes covered in moraines and till. Human activities can lead to changes in these glaciated upland landscapes which affect people and the environment. While some of the changes may benefit the area, they can also create problems.

Checklist

You should know:

- [ ] the glacial processes that once operated in the glaciated upland landscape – erosion, transport and deposition
- [ ] the processes that operate on the relict glacial upland landscapes of today – mechanical weathering and mass movement
- [ ] how climate in the past affected processes operating in the glaciated upland landscape
- [ ] how the UK's weather and climate affect processes operating on the relict glacial upland landscapes of today
- [ ] the role of erosional processes in the development of truncated spurs, corries, glacial troughs, tarns, arêtes, hanging valleys and roches moutonnées
- [ ] the role of depositional processes in the development of ground and terminal moraines
- [ ] the interaction of depositional and erosional processes in the development of drumlins and crag and tail landforms
- [ ] how farming, forestry and settlement have affected glaciated upland landscapes
- [ ] the advantages and disadvantages of development in glaciated upland landscapes
- [ ] how development can lead to change in glaciated upland landscapes
- [ ] how one upland glaciated area in the UK has been formed and the most significant factors in its change.

Which key terms match the following definitions?

a   Materials deposited by ice, with different names according to where they are deposited.

b   A body of land-based ice that moves under its own weight due to gravity.

c   A process of glacial erosion where individual rocks are pulled away from the valley floor or sides by ice flow.

d   A tributary valley, high above the main valley floor, with a waterfall.

e   A high ridge running across the valley representing the maximum advance of a glacier.

f   An egg-shaped hill found on the floor of a glacial valley.

g   Creating new and additional sources of income.

h   Pieces of rock with sharp edges, lying towards the foot of a slope.

i   A natural source of power that will never run out.

j   A sharp-edged two-sided ridge on top of a mountain.

k   A place where wildlife and landscape are easily damaged by outsiders or climate change.

To check your answers, look at the Glossary on pages 296–301.

Glaciated Upland Landscapes and Processes

Question 1 Explain **one** way that tourism has a negative effect on glacial upland landscapes. *(2 marks)*

Student answer

Walkers that visit areas like Snowdonia can cause footpath erosion due to the high footfall, this creates a scar on the landscape.

Verdict

The answer has identified a correct impact, 'footpath erosion', and explained how this affects the glacial upland landscape.

Exam tip

In questions worth only a few marks, make sure that you write answers that are to the point. This answer clearly specifies one impact of tourism and explains why it will damage the landscape.

Question 2 Describe how freeze thaw weathering influences the formation of a landform. *(3 marks)*

Student answer

Freeze thaw weathering is when water freezes in a crack in the rock, and at night it expands and pieces of rock break off.

Verdict

The answer is poor – it has described what freeze thaw weathering is, rather than explaining how the process can affect the formation of a landform.

Exam tip

When asked to 'explain how' a process operates, you should discuss the role of the process. In this instance, you should give an example of a glacial landform, and explain the action of freeze thaw, providing material for abrasion and leading to plucking.

Question 3 Examine how physical processes work together in the formation of a terminal moraine. *(8 marks + 4 SPAG)*

Student answer

A terminal moraine is a pile of rocks found at the point reached by the end of a glacier. The material will have been transported from further up the valley. Freeze thaw weathering will break pieces of rock off from the valley sides and deposit them on the glacier. As the glacier moves downslope due to gravity the material will be moved down the valley. When the glacier melts the rock debris is deposited.

Verdict

This answers the question by explaining how different processes have been involved in the formation of a terminal moraine. It could, however, improve on the description of the landform.

Exam tip

'Examine' questions ask you to break something down into its different parts or processes. You will need to learn the key features of landforms, the physical processes and how these cause the formation. Good answers will also include accurate use of geographical terms.

Pearson Education Ltd accepts no responsibility whatsoever for the accuracy or method of working in the answers given.

Writing geographically: a clear, well-structured answer

Every response you write needs to be clearly written and clearly structured. To achieve this, you need to **signal that your answer is relevant** and **signal the sequence and structure of your ideas**.

Learning objectives

- To understand how to use key noun phrases and verbs from the question to make sure you answer it
- To be able to write a clear opening sentence beginning with a subject–verb construction
- To understand how to use adverbials to link your ideas and signal their sequence and structure.

Definitions

Noun: a word that describes an object, idea, person, place, etc., e.g. *wind*.

Noun phrase: a phrase including a noun and any words that modify its meaning, e.g. *south-westerly, prevailing wind*.

Verb: a word that describes an action (Chemicals *poured* into the river), incident (Something *happened*) or situation (The rock *is* sedimentary).

Adverb(ial): a word or phrase that can modify a verb, adjective or another adverb; often used to link ideas in a text, e.g. *suddenly, all of a sudden, therefore, firstly*.

How can I make sure I am answering the question?

Look at this exam-style question in which key noun phrases, verbs and adverbials are highlighted:

> Suggest how physical processes work together to form a spit. **(8 marks)**

Now look at the first sentences of two different responses to this question:

> **Student A** *The formation of a spit occurs due to a number of physical processes working together.*

> **Student B** *First, the wind moves the waves up the beach at an angle.*

1. Which student signals most clearly that their response is going to answer the question?
2. Write a sentence or two explaining your choice.

How can I signal the structure and sequence of my answer?

When explaining, describing or analysing a concept, you can use adverbials to link your ideas:

> *Similarly... For example... However... Therefore... Consequently... In conclusion...*

When you explain or describe a process, such as the formation of a spit, you can use adverbials to signal a series of events over time:

> *Firstly... Secondly... Then... Next... Meanwhile... After several years... Over a period of time... Eventually... Finally...*

3. Now look at Student A's response to the exam-style question on page 90. How many adverbials have they used to link their ideas and explain the process they are describing? Make a note of them all.

> The formation of a spit occurs due to a number of physical processes working together. Firstly, the south-westerly prevailing wind causes the waves' swash to push sediment up the beach at an angle. The backwash then brings material back down the beach at right angles to the coast, under the force of gravity. The swash and backwash process results in a zigzag movement of material along the coastline, known as longshore drift. The direction of longshore drift transports sediment from west to east over a period of time.
>
> When there is a change in the direction of the coastline, usually because of an estuary, the transported material is deposited offshore. Over time this build-up of material causes a spit to form, stretching across from the headland in an easterly direction. The estuary limits the growth of the spit due to the deep waters and currents. As the spit grows, sheltered waters develop behind the spit causing finer sediments to settle and these begin to fill in the area, eventually leading to the development of a saltmarsh. Finally, the spit becomes curved towards the north of the estuary due to the river currents and secondary wind direction.

Did you notice?
Adverbials can be positioned at a number of different points in a sentence.

4. At which point in Student A's sentences are most of the adverbials positioned?

5. Choose one sentence from Student A's answer in which an adverbial is used. Experiment with repositioning the adverbial at different points in the sentence. What impact does it have on the clarity of the sentence?

Improving an answer
Look at Student B's response to the exam-style question on page 90.

> First, the wind moves the waves up the beach at an angle. The swash pushes the sediment onto the beach and the backwash brings the sediment back down the beach. The sediment moves in a zigzag pattern along the coastline in an easterly direction. At the end of the coastline the material is deposited and builds up to form a spit. Winds cause the spit to curve and a saltmarsh develops behind it.

6. Rewrite Student B's response aiming to:

• use key words in the first sentence to signal clearly that the answer is relevant to the question

• use adverbials to signal clearly the sequence of events you are describing.

THINKING
GEOGRAPHICALLY

Using the mean, median and mode

What you need to know about mean, median and mode

In geography we use them to give us an overall summary of a set of values and to compare different sets of data with each other.

- The **mean** is the sum of the data values divided by their number, often called the average.
- The **median** is the middle value when a set of values in a data set is written in order.
- The **mode** is the most frequent value in a data set.
- To calculate the mean, add up all the values then divide by the number of values.
- To calculate the median, arrange the data in rank order (lowest to highest): the median is the middle value. If there are two middle values, add them together and divide by two.
- To find the mode, you can make a tally chart to see which value occurs most often.

Sample question

Some students were investigating whether a river's discharge increased downstream. At five sites they drew cross sections of the river. At each site they measured the width and sampled the depth by measuring every 50 cm across the river. The results for one site are in Figure 1.

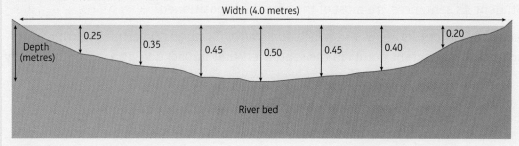

Figure 1 River investigation: channel cross section

Calculate the mean depth of the river.

> The mean depth
>
> = (0.25 + 0.35 + 0.45 + 0.50 + 0.45 + 0.40 + 0.20) ÷ 7
>
> = 2.60 ÷ 7
>
> = 0.37 metres (to 2 decimal places).

Apply your knowledge

1. The students measured river velocity by timing how long an orange took to float 10 metres. They did this ten times to try to eliminate error. Their results are shown below, in metres per second.

0.2	0.3	0.5	0.5	0.3	0.6	0.6	0.5	0.4	0.1

   Calculate the mean of the students' ten results to give an average for the river's velocity.

2. One student argued that using the mode would be better. What do you think?

92

Command word

When asked to **calculate**, you must show your working and remember to include the unit(s) (e.g. m/sec or cumecs) in your result.

What you need to know about modal classes

- In geography we sometimes organise data into classes (groups) to help make sense of it.
- The **modal class** is the most frequent class in a data set.
- The **range** is the difference between the smallest and biggest values.

Example

Some students were investigating a beach to see if the sediments were bigger in some places than others.

They sampled 40 pebbles at Sites A and B and measured the longest axis (side) of each. They recorded their results on a tally chart for each site, divided into five classes and started drawing a graph to show the data for Site A (Figure 2).

The students went to Site C but they only had time to measure nine pebbles. They quickly recorded the pebble sizes as shown in Figure 3.

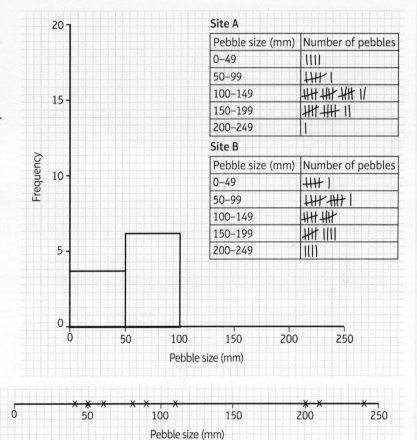

Site A

Pebble size (mm)	Number of pebbles
0–49	IIII
50–99	HHT I
100–149	HHT HHT HHT II
150–199	HHT HHT II
200–249	I

Site B

Pebble size (mm)	Number of pebbles
0–49	HHT I
50–99	HHT HHT I
100–149	HHT HHT
150–199	HHT IIII
200–249	IIII

Figure 2 Pebble sizes at Sites A, B and C: tally for Sites A and B; pebble distribution for Site A

Figure 3 Pebble distribution for Site C

Apply your knowledge

1. Copy and finish the graph in Figure 2, then draw a similar one showing the data for Site B.
2. Label the modal class on each graph.
3. The mean pebble size at Site A is 125 mm, and 118 mm at Site B. Discuss why drawing graphs and finding the modal class may be better than using the mean for this data.
4. Use Figure 3 to identify the median pebble size, and the range of values for the pebbles at Site C.
5. If the mean pebble size at Site C is 120 mm, discuss whether you think using the median or the mean pebble size would be better for this data.

Using quartiles and the inter-quartile range

What you need to know about the inter-quartile range

In geography we sometimes need to know about how spread out are the values in a dataset around the median (The median is the middle value: it divides a set of data into two halves.). One advanced method is to find out the inter-quartile range.

Example

Some students measured the size of pebbles on the outside and inside of a meander bend to see if there was a difference. The students plotted diagrams of the pebble sizes, from smallest to largest, on graph paper. Their results for the outside of the meander bend are below.

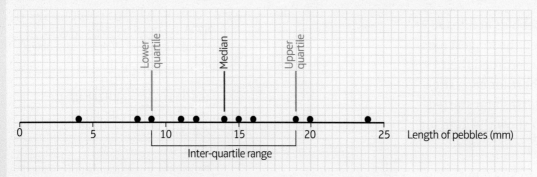

Figure 4 River investigation: pebble sizes on the outside of a meander

The students found the **median** pebble size and marked it on their diagram = 14 mm.

They now had a set of values divided into two halves. Next they split each half in half again and marked these on their diagram. These are called the **lower quartile** and **upper quartile**.

- The **lower quartile** divides the bottom half of the data in two halves = 9 mm.

- The **upper quartile** divides the top half of the data in two halves = 19 mm.

- The **inter-quartile range** is the difference between the two quartiles = 10 mm.

Apply your knowledge

1. Study the record of pebble sizes on the inside of a meander below.

5	3	2	16	12	10	8	11	6	14	7

2. On graph paper, draw a scale from 0 to 25 mm. Mark on the values of the pebbles on the inside of the meander, in size order.

   (a) Mark on the median, lower quartile and upper quartile.

   (b) Mark on and calculate the inter-quartile range.

   (c) Use your findings about the median and inter-quartile range to write a comparison of the pebbles on the outside and inside of this meander bend.

2 | Weather Hazards and Climate Change

Climate change is a process that has affected our planet for millennia and continues to do so today. What is it that causes these changes across our world and how will they affect us? The weather is becoming increasingly extreme around the world, with reports of storms, hurricanes, droughts and flooding. Are these the result of natural processes or are we responsible? Will our weather in the UK change, and if so, will it be for better or for worse? Does the weather affect countries differently depending on how developed they are? It is questions such as these that we need to investigate in order to understand our weather, our climate and how it affects us all.

Your learning

In this section you will investigate key learning points:

- what drives our climate and why it varies across the world
- what climate change is and how it has affected our planet in the past
- the natural and human causes of climate change
- how we can prove past climate change
- the possible impacts that climate change can have on us and the world
- the climate of the UK
- why there are regional variations in climate across the UK
- how the climate of the UK has changed over time
- tropical cyclones and how they form
- the problems created by tropical cyclones and how they can affect areas at different levels of development
- the causes and effects of drought across the world
- the impact of drought in areas at different levels of development.

Global climate

Atmospheric circulation

The Earth's atmosphere is constantly in motion. While these wind movements are variable from one moment to another, over time their trends form a global circulation pattern that can be clearly defined, as shown in Figure 1.

Key

- **P** Polar Cell
- **F** Ferrel Cell
- **H** Hadley Cell
- — Cold air
- — Warm air

Cold air sinking and flowing south

Warm air rising at polar front

Tropical air flowing north

Air flowing south

Warm moist air rising near Equator

Tropical air carrying heat south

Air sinking over subtropical desert zone

Cold air flowing north

Figure 1 Global circulation cells

Figure 1 shows the circulation cells that make up the global circulation pattern. The movement of air within the cells is controlled by heating and cooling. The Earth receives all of its heat from solar radiation from the Sun. The radiation passes through the atmosphere and heats up the ground directly. As the ground heats up it warms the air above it, providing the heat in our atmosphere. As the Earth is roughly spherical in shape, not all areas receive the same amount of radiation from the Sun (Figure 2). This is because the surface of the planet is curved, therefore the radiation

from the Sun hits the Earth's surface at differing relative angles. The Equator receives the most concentrated radiation, because the Sun's rays hit the surface closest to a right angle. This is the hottest part of the surface. In polar areas, the Sun's rays reach the surface at a lower angle and therefore have a larger surface area to heat.

As air is heated by the ground, it rises, causing low pressure. In other places air sinks, which leads to high pressure. Differences in pressure cause winds, which redistribute heat from the tropics across the planet.

Other factors affect wind direction around the Earth. One is the **Coriolis effect** (Figure 3). As the air moves above the surface of the Earth, the planet continues to rotate. This means that if a mass of air moves north from the Equator over a large distance, it will appear to have been deflected to the

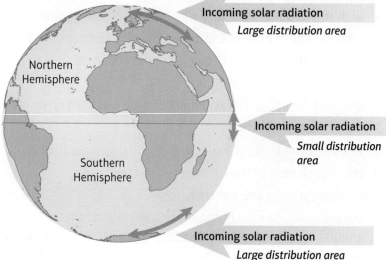

Figure 2 Distribution of solar radiation across the Earth's surface on 21 March and 23 September

right and not travelled straight north. This is because the Earth has rotated below the air, making it appear that the air has travelled in a curve. In the Southern Hemisphere, winds are deflected to the left.

Jet streams can also have an impact on air movement. Jet streams form mostly at the boundaries of the main circulation cells (e.g. at the boundary of a **Polar cell** and a **Ferrel cell**) where there is a significant temperature difference (Figure 4). These streams can affect the movement of other weather systems and can therefore change the **weather** for different areas.

Oceanic circulation

The oceans are just as effective at redistributing heat around the Earth as the air is. Surface ocean currents are driven by the movement of wind across the top of the water, whereas deep ocean currents are driven by water sinking and rising as a result of temperature changes. Both types of current are deflected by the Coriolis effect. Some ocean currents that play a part in heat redistribution include the Gulf Stream, which brings warm water from the Caribbean Sea across the Atlantic Ocean to the UK, and the Humboldt Current, which takes cold water from the southern tip of Chile north to Peru and supports a large amount of marine life.

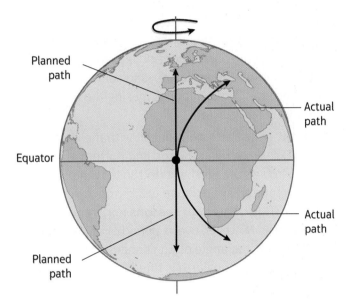

Figure 3 The Coriolis effect

Activity

1. Identify **two** ways in which heat at the Equator can be redistributed around the world.

2. How do ocean currents affect the climate of an area?

3. How can the Coriolis effect and jet stream affect the weather of an area?

4. In mid-winter the Northern Hemisphere is tilted away from the Sun. Use Figure 2 to explain why Europe is colder in winter than in summer.

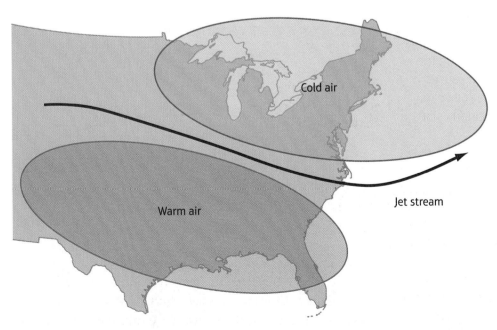

Figure 4 The northern Polar jet stream

Global climate change

Learning objectives

- To know how the Earth's climate has changed over time
- To understand the different causes of climate change and their impact on the Earth
- To use past climate data to describe and understand patterns over time

Climate change refers to how the average climatic conditions of the planet vary over time. At some points in our planet's history the Earth has been comparatively warm and during other periods it has been significantly colder (Figure 5). The planet's history is divided into **periods** and the **climate** during the **Quaternary period** has changed many times.

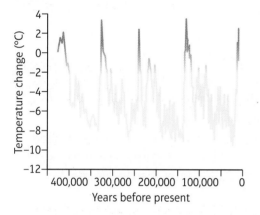

Figure 5 Average surface temperatures over the last 450,000 years

Climate change can occur through both natural and human causes. Natural causes have been responsible for most climate change during the majority of Earth's history, with human causes having a greater impact over the last 250 years compared with natural causes, particularly since the Industrial Revolution.

Natural causes of climate change

There are several natural processes that can lead to climate change. One such process is Milankovitch cycles. These are natural changes to the Earth's orbit and position that affect how much radiation we receive from the Sun. Sometimes these cause us to receive more radiation than normal, resulting in global warming, and sometimes lead to us receiving less than normal, leading to global cooling. There are three types of cycle that vary.

- **Eccentricity** – the orbit of the Earth changes shape over long periods of time, approximately every 100,000 years. This means that sometimes the Earth's orbit around the Sun is more circular, making us slightly warmer (**interglacial**), and sometimes the orbit becomes more elliptical, making the Earth slightly cooler (**glacial**).

- **Axial tilt** – the Earth does not sit with the North and South Poles exactly at the top and bottom of the planet. In fact, the Earth is tilted so that the poles are actually rotated approximately 23° from a vertical position. This creates our **seasons** north and south of the Equator. However, over a period of approximately 40,000 years, the angle of tilt changes. This means that sometimes the Earth is tilted further away from the Sun, which makes the difference in the seasons more pronounced (summers are warmer and winters are colder). When it is tilted closer to the Sun, the difference in the seasons is less.

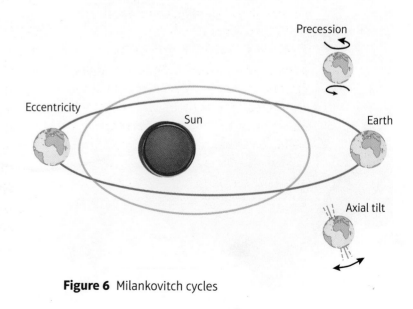

Figure 6 Milankovitch cycles

- **Precession** – as the Earth rotates on its axis (which is, of course, what gives us day and night), it does not do so perfectly. In fact, the Earth 'wobbles' on its axis, in a similar way to a spinning top as it slows down. As this happens, the direction the axis is facing changes. This affects our seasons and creates either greater or smaller differences between summer and winter. This occurs over a period of approximately 24,000 years.

The other main natural causes of climate change are shown in Table 1.

Table 1 Natural causes of global climate change

Cause	Description
Solar variation	The amount of radiation the Sun produces varies over time. Periods of lower solar activity are likely to lead to glacial periods and those with higher activity lead to interglacial periods.
Volcanism	Large-scale volcanic eruptions can eject huge volumes of ash and dust into the atmosphere. Some eruptions can produce so much that the volcanic material can partially block out solar radiation, reducing temperatures and causing glacial periods.
Surface impact	Large cosmic material, such as asteroids and comets, can impact the Earth's surface. This can eject large volumes of dust into the atmosphere, partially blocking solar radiation and leading to glacial periods. Climate change that is caused by surface impact can have dramatic effects on life. One such impact approximately 65 million years ago is considered to be responsible for the extinction of the dinosaurs. It is not the force of the impact that is thought to have wiped them out however, but rather the massive climate change that was created by the impact.

Exam-style question

Explain how the climate of the Earth can change because of natural causes. **(3 marks)**

Exam tip

Read the question carefully. The question asks about natural causes, therefore it is only information about these that will earn marks. Don't go off topic.

Command word

Remember to check the command word in the question. **Explain** means that you have to give reasons for your answers, not just identify the correct points.

Checkpoint

Now it is time to review your understanding of global climate and climate change.

Strengthen

S1 How has global climate changed over the last 1000 years?

S2 What processes control the distribution of heat around the Earth?

S3 How can volcanoes affect the global climate?

S4 How do surface impacts lead to climate change?

Challenge

C1 How does the relative angle of the Earth's surface affect how warm an area will be?

C2 Describe and explain in your own words how Milankovitch cycles can affect the climate of the Earth.

C3 Which natural cause of climate change do you think would have the greatest impact on global climates? Explain your answer.

C4 Natural events can cause global warming or global cooling. Which do you think would have a greater impact on humans? Justify your answer.

Evidence of natural and human climate change

Learning objectives

- To know what natural climate change is and how it can be proven
- To understand how the enhanced greenhouse effect is generated by human activity
- To be able to explain how different human activities impact on climate change

As climate change has been occurring since before the development of the thermometer, scientists and geographers need to look for other evidence that there has been global climate change occurring naturally over geological time periods. This evidence comes from a number of sources.

Figure 7 Variations in tree rings, representing different climatic conditions

Since trees can live for hundreds, and in some cases thousands, of years, they can experience the impact of climate change. As trees grow they produce **growth rings** that can be seen in a cross section of a trunk (see Figure 7). Growth rings tend to be wider in warmer, wetter climates and thinner in colder, drier climates. Analysing the rings can tell us what the climate was like throughout a tree's history.

While this is very helpful, we can only get this data for the length of time that the tree has been alive. To gather data from further in the past, we can use **ice cores**. Ice cores are drilled sections of ice from sheets in locations such as Antarctica and Greenland. As snow falls it is compressed into ice layers and these layers capture information about the climate at the time they were formed. This is because they can contain volcanic ash, microbes, pollen and even bubbles of air trapped when the ice formed. All of this can give invaluable information on past climates.

Did you know?

One of the oldest trees in the world is thought to be around 5000 years old and is found in California's White Mountains.

Pollen is also useful. Pollen is produced by all flowering plants and the distinct shapes and structure of pollen allow us to identify which plant the pollen has come from. Pollen can become trapped in ice and in sedimentary rocks. Since certain plants can only grow in certain conditions, this gives us information about what the climate must have been like when the rock or ice in which the pollen was trapped was formed.

We can also use historical documents, such as personal diaries and religious records, to examine more recent historical climates. These documents include descriptions of what the climate was like during the past.

The greenhouse effect

The greenhouse effect is a natural process which keeps the Earth warm. Greenhouse gases in the atmosphere, such as carbon dioxide and methane, trap some of the heat that is radiated from the surface which would otherwise have been lost into space. Without this effect, the average temperature of the Earth would be significantly cooler (Figure 8).

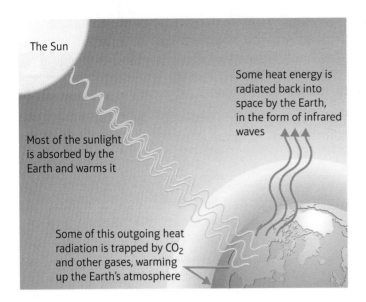

Figure 8 The greenhouse effect

Human causes of climate change

Human activity has resulted in a large increase in the production of greenhouse gases, leading to the **enhanced greenhouse effect** and global warming. The sources of these gases are illustrated in Figure 9.

All greenhouse gases

Industrial processes 17%
Power stations 21%
Transportation fuels 14%
Waste disposal and treatment 4%
Land use and biomass burning 10%
Agricultural by-products 13%
Fossil fuel retrieval, processing and distribution 11%
Residential, commercial and other sources 10%

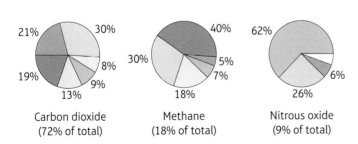

21% 30% 8% 19% 9% 13%	40% 30% 5% 7% 18%	62% 6% 26%
Carbon dioxide (72% of total)	Methane (18% of total)	Nitrous oxide (9% of total)

Figure 9 Sources of greenhouse gases

The main human activities that have caused the enhanced greenhouse effect are shown in Table 2.

Table 2 Human activities that produce greenhouse gases

Cause	Description
Industry	As levels of disposable income rise, increased demand for the production of consumer goods leads to industry growth and the need for more energy, resulting in more fossil fuels being burnt.
Transport	With cars becoming more affordable and more people taking flights over long distances, huge quantities of fuel are used. Almost all transport relies on burning fossil fuels in some way, again increasing the amount of greenhouse gases released.
Energy	The demand for electricity is growing because of increasing population and new technologies. Most of our energy is produced through burning fossil fuels (coal, oil, natural gas), which produce greenhouse gases.
Farming	Population growth has led to a higher demand for food production. Mechanisation means more fuel is burnt, and intensive farming of cattle and rice results in increased production of methane, which is a greenhouse gas.

Activity

1 Describe **three** ways in which scientists can identify past climate change.

2 Explain how natural processes can lead to global climate change.

3 Why might some people say that our growing population is the key cause of modern climate change? Suggest an alternative key cause.

Negative impacts of climate change

Learning objectives

- To know how food production and glacial retreat will be affected by climate change
- To understand how climate change can lead to sea level rise
- To be able to explain how climate change can affect a specific location

As we are aware, climate change is beginning to have an impact on our planet and cause serious issues and problems for people across the world.

Food production

Plants are able to produce their own food through the process of **photosynthesis**. Animals eat plants (herbivores) or other animals that have eaten plants (carnivores) or they eat both plants and animals (omnivores). This makes plants a vital food source. Photosynthesis is a complicated process and can be negatively affected by increases in temperature or decreases in sunlight, both of which can occur because of global climate change. With lower **crop yields**, large sections of the population could suffer from malnutrition, a problem that will be worse in developing countries.

Sea level rise: The Maldives

The most commonly known impact of climate change is a likely rise in sea level. An increase in temperature will result in land-based ice, particularly on the continent of Antarctica, melting and adding to the amount of water in the oceans. Another cause of sea level rise is **thermal expansion**. Warm water occupies a greater volume than colder water. A rise in global temperatures will cause the oceans to expand in volume, further adding to sea level rise.

The Maldives is a country located in the Indian Ocean which is made up of nearly 1200 small coral islands. The Maldives is the flattest country on Earth, the highest point being only 2.4 metres above sea level. Predictions of how much global sea levels will rise before the end of the century vary from 20 cm to more than 1 metre.

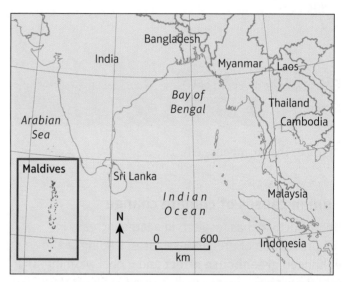

Figure 10 Location of the Maldives

This puts large areas of the Maldives at serious risk. As a developing country, the Maldives relies heavily on tourism. The main attractions of the islands are its sandy beaches, clear seas and coral reefs teeming with fish. Almost all of the country's infrastructure is under threat from sea level rise. For example, the country's international airports, vital to the tourism industry, are built within 50 metres of the coastline. Table 3 summarises the main impacts.

The Maldives is responding to the threat of sea level rise with various plans to mitigate the impacts on the country. These include increasing rainwater harvesting to reduce reliance on groundwater supplies as well as trying to protect the **groundwater** supplies from sea water infiltration. Another plan includes raising key infrastructure to higher levels. The possibility of mass migration away from the country has also been discussed.

Table 3 Possible impacts of sea level rise on the Maldives

Impact on the Maldives	Description
Social	Higher sea levels and more regular storms lead to periodic flooding of coastal areas. In 2007, more than 1600 people had to be evacuated because of coastal flooding.
Economic	The key attractions of beaches and coral reefs will become inaccessible, leading to a loss of employment in tourism. Cost of evacuations and rehousing will continue to increase.
Environmental	Groundwater supplies are contaminated with sea water flowing onto the islands. The soil is also contaminated. Temperature increases in the surrounding ocean may lead to bleaching and death of the islands' coral reefs.

Retreating glaciers and melting ice sheets

Glaciers and ice sheets account for most of the land-based ice around the world, as well as approximately 10% of the planet's total land area. With increasing global temperatures, many glaciers are showing a pattern of retreat, meaning that they are becoming smaller, and ice sheets are thinning.

Figure 11 The Grinnell Glacier, Montana, has retreated by over 40% since 1966

Melting of high mountain glaciers, such as those in the Himalayas upon which farmers in India and Pakistan rely for irrigation water, can lead to flooding of the local area in the short term. However, in the long term, with a smaller volume of ice available in the glacier, there may be water shortages because less water is produced by the glacier on a regular basis. On a global scale, melting ice sheets will add more water to the oceans, leading to sea level rise.

Exam-style question

Explain the negative effects of climate change.

(4 marks)

Exam tip

Remember to use key words in your answers. You need to have detailed knowledge of the topics and correct use of key words helps to demonstrate this.

Checkpoint

Now it is time to review your understanding of global climate and climate change.

Strengthen

S1 How can tree growth rings be used to evidence global climate change?

S2 Describe two other methods as evidence for global climate change.

S3 How do humans contribute to global climate change?

S4 What problems could be caused by climate change?

Challenge

C1 Explain the enhanced greenhouse effect and how it can lead to global climate change.

C2 Describe and explain in your own words how we can prove past global climate change.

C3 What do you think is the biggest threat we face from global climate change? Justify your answer.

C4 Describe and explain how the Maldives will be affected by an increase in global temperatures.

The UK climate

The UK is located between 50°N and 60°N of the Equator. Distance from the Equator has an impact on climate: locations further north and south from the Equator receive less solar radiation than areas closer to the Equator. The UK's climate is best described as temperate. Extremes of weather are uncommon and extreme weather events such as tornadoes and prolonged **droughts** are rare. As a result of the meeting of major air masses over the UK, particularly cool air from the north and warmer air from the south, **frontal rainfall** is quite common throughout the year.

UK climate over time

Over the last 1000 years, the UK's climate has been through two major changes.

The Medieval Warm Period occurred between approximately 950 and 1100. During this period, the temperatures in the UK were high enough to support the growth of grape vines as far north as York and also allowed greater crop yields across the UK. The population increased significantly because of milder winters and a greater availability of food. This period has been attributed to increased solar activity and a possible period of low volcanic activity (see Table 1) across the world.

The Little Ice Age was the period between the Medieval Warm Period and the modern climate, between 1600 and 1850, when temperatures in the UK were low enough on occasion for the River Thames to freeze to a sufficient thickness for people to walk on. The extended winters caused widespread crop failures. This period has been attributed to some extreme volcanic eruptions as well as a decrease in solar activity.

UK climate and location

While there are key factors, discussed below, that control the climate of the UK, there are also significant regional variations within the UK (Figures 12 and 13).

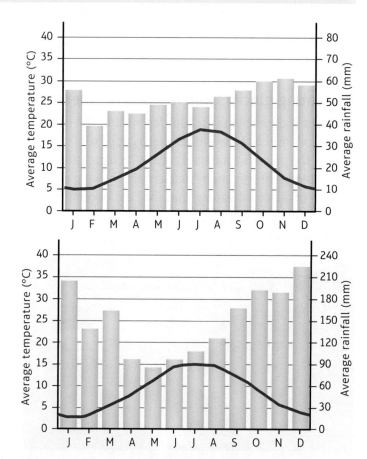

Figure 12 Climate graphs for London (top) and Fort William (below) showing temperature (red) and rainfall (blue)

Did you know?

The first recorded Thames Frost Fair in London, when people could walk and skate on the frozen river, was in 1607 and the most recent was in 1814.

Activity

1 What were the causes of changes to climate between 950 and 1850?

2 What were the effects of climate change on people?

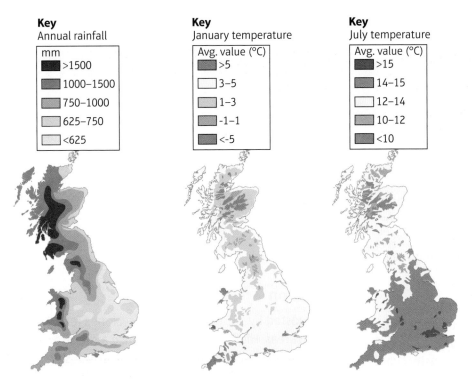

Figure 13 Temperature and rainfall maps of the UK

Significance of the UK's location on climate

Maritime influence – As the UK is surrounded by sea, most of the air that reaches us contains a large amount of moisture, resulting in consistent rainfall throughout the year.

Prevailing wind – The prevailing wind is the most common wind direction, which in the UK is from the southwest. It has travelled over large expanses of warm ocean, so this air is warm and contains a lot of moisture. As Figure 13 shows, the prevailing wind reaches the western areas of the UK first and releases this moisture as rain there. This leaves the eastern side of the UK relatively drier.

North Atlantic Drift – A warm ocean current (see page 97) called the North Atlantic Drift brings warm water north to the UK from the Gulf of Mexico, driven by the prevailing wind. This current of warm water has a particular effect during the winter, making the UK climate milder than would be expected for our latitude.

Circulation cells – The UK is located near the 'boundary' between the northern Ferrel and Polar circulation cells (see page 96). At this boundary, warm air from the south and cooler air from the north meet, leading to the formation of depressions and unsettled weather.

Altitude – The higher the altitude of an area, the cooler it will be: 1°C lost for every 100 metres higher above sea level. Also, as the air is forced to rise over the high land it is cooled, causing more of the moisture in the air to condense and fall as **precipitation** on the hill tops. For example, Scafell Pike (978 metres) averages 178 days of rain per year, whereas London (35 metres) receives just 98 days.

Tropical cyclones

Learning objectives

- To know the key features of tropical cyclones across the world
- To understand the formation and impact of tropical cyclones
- To be able to describe and explain the impacts and responses to tropical cyclones in different regions of the world

Tropical cyclones are large, rotating storms that form over the oceans in tropical areas. Depending on where in the world they form, they are known as hurricanes, cyclones or typhoons. They can be devastating if they move over land.

Tropical cyclones are easily identifiable because of their distinctive features. The most well-known of these features is the **eye**, located at the centre of the storm. Surrounding the eye is the **eye wall**; high density cloud covers the remaining area of the storm.

The global atmospheric circulation (see pages 96–97) has an impact on the formation of tropical cyclones. As air moves around the planet it moves away from the Equator and begins to rotate because of the need to disperse the high levels of heat at the Equator across

the planet's surface. This movement, a result of the Coriolis effect, combined with the **evaporation** caused by higher temperatures, leads to the formation of tropical storms.

Formation

As suggested by the name, tropical cyclones form in tropical areas. High temperatures cause air to rise away from the ocean surface. The rising air causes thunderstorms, which are only local in their effects. However, sometimes these storms group together, creating a strong flow of warm, rapidly rising air, which in turn produces an area of extreme low pressure at the centre of these converging storms.

However, in order for these storms to converge fully into a tropical cyclone, several trigger conditions need to be present. These include:

- a source of moist, warm air, normally warmer than 27°C (which is why they form in the tropics)
- the time of year (season) when ocean water is at its warmest
- winds converging at the ocean surface, causing the air to rise
- formation some distance from the Equator so the Coriolis effect will cause the storm to rotate.

As the storm rotates, the winds accelerate inwards and upwards, making the depression stronger and forming a tropical cyclone. The eye of a cyclone is dry and calm, because it is the only place for kilometres around where the air is sinking.

Movement

Tropical cyclones do not remain where they are formed. Cyclones follow the direction of the local prevailing winds and ocean currents. The **track** of the tropical cyclone

Figure 14 Satellite photograph of a tropical cyclone

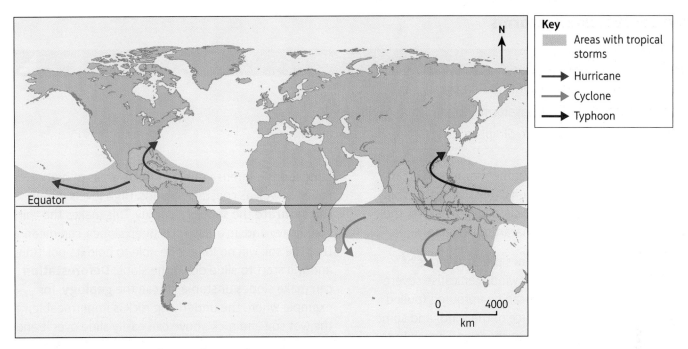

Figure 15 Location map of tropical storm formation

affects how strong it becomes. The further it travels over the ocean, the more heat and moisture it collects, so increasing its strength. When the cyclone reaches dry land, it is cut off from its energy source. It can no longer extract heat from the ocean, loses strength and slows.

The formation of tropical cyclones can be forecast; certain areas of the planet are more likely to produce the favourable conditions that trigger them. Once formed, dedicated centres, such as the National Hurricane Centre in Florida, USA, will use various methods to predict the track of the cyclone so that preparations can be made at potential landfall locations. The use of satellite imagery and statistical modelling is key to predicting the track of a tropical cyclone, along with other weather data, such as wind conditions.

Location

In order for tropical cyclones to form, there needs to be a rotation force, therefore areas immediately around the Equator do not experience tropical cyclones. However, areas further north and south, such as the Caribbean Sea, parts of the South China Sea and parts of the Indian Ocean, are regularly affected (Figure 15).

Frequency

Because a tropical cyclone requires specific conditions for its formation, they are more likely to occur in some periods of the year than in others. For example, because of the temperatures required for formation, tropical cyclones are more likely to form between June and November in the northern tropics and between November and April in the southern tropics. These periods when tropical cyclone formation is more likely are referred to as seasons.

It is impossible to predict how many tropical storms will be formed in a season and how many will become cyclones. In warmer years more cyclones are likely than in cooler years, but exact numbers will vary. For example, there were nine named hurricanes in the Atlantic Ocean in 2009, but there were 28 named hurricanes in 2005. Since 1968, an average of 12 named hurricanes have formed each season.

Activity

1   Describe **two** specific features of a tropical cyclone.
2   Explain the formation of a tropical cyclone.
3   Should tourists be banned from travelling to areas that are likely to be hit by tropical cyclones during the 'season'? Give reasons for your answer, including possible impacts on the countries involved.

Impacts of tropical storms

Learning objectives

- To know the key impacts of tropical storms
- To understand how tropical storms can affect areas differently
- To be able to use the Saffir–Simpson scale to classify tropical storms

Tropical cyclones are severe weather hazards that can bring loss of life and damage on a massive scale. While a tropical cyclone itself can be classed as a hazard, the storm also produces specific hazardous effects.

- **High winds** – Tropical cyclones produce winds of over 119 km per hour. These winds can cause severe damage to buildings. Trees can be uprooted (pulled out of the ground by the force of the wind) and some smaller constructions, such as sheds and beach huts, can be moved. These become dangerous as they can impact on people and buildings, causing damage, injury and loss of life.

- **Intense rainfall** – As tropical cyclones move over the ocean they take up a large amount of water and this results in a large release of rain. Weather forecasters can estimate how much rain may fall based on how fast the storm has been travelling over the water. The intense rain created by the tropical cyclone can lead to flooding, damage to property and injury, as fast-flowing water can knock people over, even if it is not particularly deep.

- **Storm surges** – A tropical cyclone creates a large area of low pressure, which allows the level of the sea to rise. When this is combined with the high winds produced by the storm, a large mass of water can be forced towards land by the strength of the wind. When the surge hits land, it does so with severe force. Storm surges can erode beaches and coastal habitats, damage coastal defences and flow inland, contaminating farmland and freshwater areas such as lakes.

- **Coastal flooding** – The combination of intense rain and storm surges puts coastal areas at severe risk of flooding. Not only does this put people and property at risk, but it can also affect the farming and tourism industries. The environmental impact of flooding by salt water will also be very damaging.

- **Landslides** – Intense rainfall affects areas of high **relief** as well as coastal lowlands. High levels of rain can **saturate** the soil very quickly. This makes the soil very heavy and, in areas with steep slopes, can mean that the soil will no longer be able to hold its position and will start to slide down the slope. **Deforestation** can make slopes unstable, as can the **geology**, for example where the underlying rock is impermeable, the wet soil and rock above can easily slide over it and downhill. This can cause massive devastation to any settlements at the base of the slope, and cause river flooding if the landslide blocks river channels.

All of these hazards pose a severe risk to people, property and the local environment. However, the probable level of damage a tropical cyclone will cause if it reaches land is determined based on the wind speeds.

Exam-style question

Explain the impacts tropical cyclones have on inhabited areas. **(4 marks)**

Exam tip

Focus on explaining two impacts specifically, including why they are a risk to human life and how they are linked to tropical cyclones.

In the Northern Hemisphere, the Saffir–Simpson Hurricane Wind Scale is used to classify tropical cyclones, and these are specifically referred to as hurricanes. It is based on the wind speed generated by the storm, but does not take into account rainfall or storm surges and so does not predict exactly what damage will occur when a hurricane reaches land. However, you can use rainfall and storm surge data to estimate the category of a hurricane.

Table 4 The Saffir–Simpson Hurricane Wind Scale

Scale number (Category)	Sustained winds (km/h)	Damage	Storm surge (metres)
1	119–153	Minimal: Unanchored mobile homes, vegetation and signs.	1.2–1.7
2	154–177	Moderate: All mobile homes, roofs, small crafts, flooding.	1.8–2.6
3	178–208	Extensive: Small buildings, low-lying roads cut off.	2.7–3.8
4	209–249	Extreme: Roofs destroyed, trees down, roads cut off, mobile homes destroyed. Beach homes flooded.	3.9–5.4
5	More than 250	Catastrophic: Many buildings destroyed. Vegetation destroyed. Major roads cut off. Homes flooded.	Greater than 5.4

Activity

Using the information in this topic, calculate which category each of the following cyclones would fall into.

a   Winds of 160 km/h, heavy rain and a storm surge of 2.4 metres.

b   A storm surge of 4.2 metres and wind speeds of 210 km/h.

c   Sheds destroyed and some roads flooded.

d   A storm surge of 6 metres predicted.

e   Small trees uprooted and winds measured at 125 km/h.

Checkpoint

Now it is time to review your understanding of tropical cyclones, their formation and the effects they have.

Strengthen

S1 What climatic conditions are needed for a tropical cyclone to form?

S2 How do we categorise tropical cyclones?

S3 What impacts does a tropical cyclone have?

Challenge

C1 Which effect of a tropical cyclone is the most damaging: a storm surge or high winds? Justify your answer.

C2 Do developed countries cope with the effects of a tropical cyclone better than a developing country? Why?

C3 Is the Saffir–Simpson Scale the best way of categorising tropical cyclones? What other means could we use to categorise them?

Case Study – Hurricane Sandy, USA 2012, tropical cyclone in developed country

On 24 October 2012, a storm that had formed earlier in the month was officially registered as a hurricane (Category 1) on the Saffir–Simpson Scale. This hurricane, officially named as Hurricane Sandy, swept through the Caribbean Sea, making landfall on the island nations of Jamaica, Cuba and the Bahamas before moving north and eventually reaching the USA (Figure 16).

Hurricane Sandy made landfall in the state of New Jersey in the USA on 29 October. Its wind strength had varied during its journey across the Caribbean and North Atlantic, but when it made landfall wind speeds of 129 km/h were recorded. Much of the damage, however, was not caused by the wind speed but by the storm surge that was produced by the hurricane.

Although the storm had been forecast and preparations had been made in states from Florida up to New Jersey, the damage and death toll were still high. Floodwater from the intense rain and storm surge rapidly moved inland across various states. In New York City, several subway stations and road tunnels were flooded and were unusable, power lines were damaged, tall buildings swayed with the force of the wind and a tanker ship ran aground near Staten Island. Many other states across the eastern USA suffered power outages, disruption to transport and property damage.

Figure 16 Path of Hurricane Sandy

110

Table 5 Impacts of Hurricane Sandy

Impact	Description
Social	More than 150 people were killed by the hurricane, making it the most deadly in the USA since Hurricane Katrina. Millions of people were left without electricity for days. Transport links, including roads, railways and airports, were closed or faced severe disruption. Schools were closed for many days and homes and businesses were damaged from either flooding or high winds.
Economic	Total property damage was estimated at US$65 billion across all the affected states. Additionally, the New York Stock Exchange was forced to close for several days because of a loss of power. Petrol was in short supply and had to be brought into the affected states at a cost to the government. The New York Marathon, scheduled for 4 November, was cancelled, affecting tourist income.
Environmental	Several coastal nature reserves, such as Prime Hook National Wildlife Refuge in the state of Delaware, were damaged by the storm surge. The flooding also led to the release of millions of gallons of raw and untreated sewage into the waters around New York and New Jersey.

In response to the hurricane, the media played a large part in raising funds for the victims. Charity concerts were organised and broadcast on television and online, along with telethons and corporate donations to raise millions of dollars for the relief effort. Charities such as the American Red Cross were involved in providing relief to people in the affected areas, funded through some of these media events. The US government also voted in legislation to provide billions of dollars to the affected states to help with rebuilding and supporting victims. The state of New York set up a new local government office to co-ordinate rebuilding efforts to make sure that all areas would be helped. Some of this money was paid directly to homeowners to help with reconstruction, the rest went to businesses, infrastructure and other community support schemes.

Both during and after the storm, people posted images and descriptions of the impacts of Hurricane Sandy on social media sites. People across the world could see and assess the impact of the storm in real time as information was uploaded to the internet. This allowed both the general public and local government bodies to begin to assess the damage being caused, even before the storm had passed. Government agencies were also able to use satellite images. By comparing older satellite photographs with those taken soon after the storm, the changes that had occurred to the area as a result of the hurricane could be observed and a plan for how to respond based on the specific needs of an area could be formulated. The impact of the storm on different areas was also analysed by the use of socio-economic data. By assessing the impact on sectors such as health care, education and public services, the areas suffering most deprivation as a result of damage to each of these sectors could be identified. Local government could then respond to the worst-affected areas quickly to restore these services as soon as possible. This approach can be applied to both developed and developing countries.

Did you know?

Owing to the level of damage from this hurricane, the name 'Sandy' has been removed from the list of names used to identify hurricanes so no hurricane will ever be called Sandy again.

Exam-style question

Describe the effects of a tropical cyclone on a developed country.   **(3 marks)**

Exam tip

It is important to identify your case study in your answer. Make sure that you provide specific detail about the example you have chosen to show your depth of knowledge.

Case Study – Typhoon Haiyan, Philippines 2013, tropical cyclone in emerging country

Typhoon Haiyan, also known as Typhoon Yolanda in the Philippines, was the equivalent of a Category 5 on the Saffir–Simpson Scale, and so one of the strongest tropical cyclones on record. Typhoon Haiyan formed on 2 November 2013 in the South Pacific Ocean, close to the Federated States of Micronesia (Figure 17).

Wind speeds continued to increase over the following days, and the typhoon was classified as equivalent to a Category 5 hurricane by 6 November. With winds reaching gusts of over 306 km/h, the typhoon made landfall in the Philippines on 7 November. The force of the high winds destroyed or damaged nearly every building in the area of Guiuan, which was the first location to be hit. Flooding from the storm surge caused huge damage to coastal areas and continued further inland in lower lying areas. Most of the damage was on the islands of Samar and Leyte. There were reports of widespread flooding and landslides across the area and power outages across the country. The city of Tacloban, on the island of Leyte, was severely damaged, with widespread destruction of buildings, trees uprooted, and roads and communications blocked for many days.

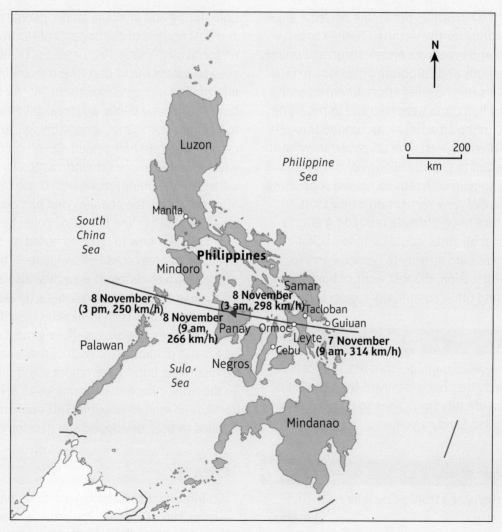

Figure 17 Typhoon Haiyan: location map and affected areas of the Philippines

Table 6 Impacts of Typhoon Haiyan on the Philippines

Impact	Description
Social	More than 6000 people were confirmed dead, with many others missing. Power to the affected islands was cut off and many areas were isolated by debris or landslides, preventing aid from reaching them swiftly. Tens of thousands of people were made homeless. There were also reports of a loss of law and order as people panicked because of the lack of communication and support, but this was restored quickly once aid began to arrive.
Economic	The cost of the damage was estimated to be approximately US$2 billion. Transport across the islands was disrupted, making the provision of aid and support difficult. Foreign aid agencies were able to provide support for the effort.
Environmental	Across the islands, coastal areas of mangroves were damaged and thousands of trees were uprooted. Several areas were evacuated because of chemical leaks from damaged industrial facilities. A tanker also ran aground, which caused an oil spill.

In response to Typhoon Haiyan, seven provinces in the Philippines were placed under a 'state of national calamity', which allowed the government to redirect funds to help address the problems created by the typhoon. The relief effort was slowed considerably because of the damage to local infrastructure. With roads blocked and some local airports severely damaged, some areas remained isolated for days. Infrastructure failure and contamination from sea water meant that many people were without safe drinking water for a long time. It was decided to try to evacuate as many people from affected areas as possible, particularly Tacloban. However, because there was no electricity in the area, the evacuations could only happen during daylight hours, which further slowed the rescue effort. This, in turn, caused people to panic and rush at the evacuation planes. They had to be held back by police and military personnel. The focus of relief efforts on Tacloban City resulted in people in other affected areas feeling abandoned, because aid was reaching them even more slowly despite the fact they were also suffering huge devastation.

Exam-style question

Identify the correct geographical term for the red line joining 7 November and 8 November on Figure 17.
- ☐ A Typhoon path
- ☐ B Typhoon track
- ☐ C Typhoon eye
- ☐ D Typhoon surge **(1 mark)**

Exam tip

In multiple-choice questions, watch out for choices which are nearly, but not quite, right and make sure you tick only one box.

Checkpoint

Now it is time to review your understanding of the impacts and responses to tropical cyclones across the world.

Strengthen

S1 What examples can you give of tropical cyclones affecting developed and developing countries?

S2 Which areas of each country were directly affected by the tropical cyclones?

S3 What effects did the tropical cyclones have in each country?

Challenge

C1 Look back at your answer to C2 from the Checkpoint on page 109. Having studied two examples, do you still agree with your original answer? Why?

C2 How could each country have prepared for the tropical cyclone, had they known in advance that it would make landfall in their country?

C3 Which country responded better to the tropical cyclone? Justify your answer.

Drought

Drought is a hazard that can affect any area, regardless of its level of development. While the cause and the impact may vary from place to place, areas that are susceptible to drought share some similar characteristics.

Arid environments (Figure 18) do not suffer from drought, as aridity (low precipitation) is already the normal climate for the area. This is because they are located in regions which normally have high pressure. This is where dry air (air with very little or no moisture stored in it) descends towards the ground, such as where **Hadley cells** and Ferrel cells meet (see page 96). As the air is dry, clouds are unlikely to form and so the area will have low levels of precipitation throughout the year.

A key factor that can affect whether an area is likely to suffer from drought is how it receives its precipitation. Countries such as the UK have rainfall throughout the year and do not rely on a particular 'rainy season'. Other parts of the world receive the majority of their annual precipitation during particular months, for example in the Sahel in central Africa and the 'monsoon' season in India. This makes these areas significantly vulnerable to drought. Drought results if changes in global circulation mean the rains are delayed or weaker than normal, they do not produce as much precipitation or may even fail completely.

Another key issue is when the precipitation occurs. If the 'rainy season' is during winter months, when there are lower temperatures and less intense sunlight, then the water is absorbed by the soil with relative ease. The water is stored underground and will be available during the drier months. However, if the majority of the precipitation falls during the summer months, then the water is not as easily absorbed by the soil. This is because the precipitation falls on soil that is likely to have been baked hard by intense sunlight and therefore it is more difficult for the rain to soak in. There will also be higher rates of evaporation because of the higher temperatures and so water is more likely to evaporate

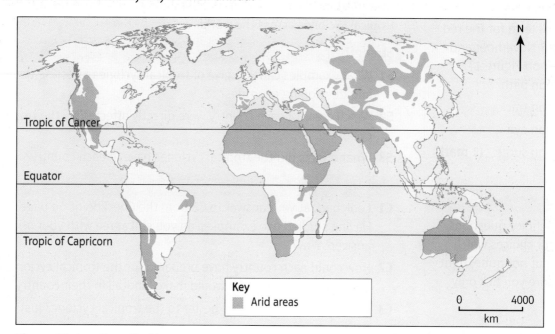

Figure 18 Location of arid areas

away before it can soak in, reducing water supplies. Where these two factors combine, drought is likely to be a regular occurrence.

Drought also varies in severity. The UK is less susceptible to drought but can have drought conditions. For example, in 1995 drought conditions led to hosepipe bans and to **reservoirs**, such as Haweswater in the Lake District, drying up. These impacts are in stark contrast to those caused by drought conditions in areas such as the Sahel, where drought causes life-threatening conditions for many people.

Causes of drought and their great impacts

Meteorological
Meteorological drought refers simply to the level of dryness in an area, that is, when an area receives less precipitation than normal. This is the most significant cause of drought across the planet.

An area can be classed as being in drought despite receiving more precipitation than an area not in drought – it depends on how much precipitation is normal. This means that an arid area such as the Great Australian Desert would not be classed as being in drought because its normal climatic condition is that it receives a very low level of precipitation. However, an area such as the Sahel, which has long periods of low precipitation and a rainy season that provides the majority of the annual rainfall, is much more vulnerable to drought as slight changes to circulation patterns can cause the rainy season to fail or be delayed. This will mean that the area is at risk of drought as a result of only small meteorological variations.

This type of drought is caused by a change in the usual weather patterns of an area.

Atmospheric and oceanic circulation (see pages 96 and 97) control much of the climatic patterns of an area and so changes in these patterns can have a large impact. As our planet gets warmer, the temperatures of the ocean and atmosphere change and this affects where heat is redistributed to. Climate change is already having an impact on these processes, and in some parts of the world is leading to more frequent or more severe droughts.

Investigation of the El Niño event would help your understanding of meteorological causes further.

Figure 19 Desiccation cracks caused by drought

Jet streams (see page 97) can also have a limited impact as they can cause weather systems, such as low pressure systems bringing rain, to be diverted from their usual path. This affects areas that rely on a rainy season. As the path of a jet stream is not constant, this can happen at any time.

Hydrological
Hydrological drought refers specifically to the impact of low precipitation on a hydrological system (a river basin, for example). While this will have the same cause as a meteorological drought, it is possible that the effects of the drought may not be readily obvious.

Although the surface effects of a drought may be noticeable straightaway, the impact on groundwater and reservoir levels may take more time to become obvious. A farmer may notice a loss of soil moisture quite quickly, but a water company may not feel the effect on its water supply from a reservoir for several months.

As less water enters the soil because of a lack of precipitation (meteorological drought), surface water, such as that in rivers, becomes difficult to access as levels drop. This will then lead to an over-reliance on groundwater and reservoirs.

Activity
1 Explain why places like the Sahara or Great Australian Desert do not suffer droughts.

2 Why is drought more likely if the rainy season is normally in the summer months?

Human causes and impacts of drought

Learning objectives

- To know the key human activities that can cause drought
- To understand the main impacts of drought on an area
- To be able to group impacts of drought into different categories

Human activity can also cause drought, often through agriculture or the diversion of water from its normal path.

Figure 20 Lake Mead, Nevada and Arizona, USA. The paler areas show the previous level of the reservoir

Dams

Dams are built on rivers to act as flood defences, to create reservoirs as stores of water for industrial, agricultural and recreational use, and also to provide electricity through hydroelectric power. However, restricting the flow of water in the river can lead to a drop in water levels further downstream. This can leave an area in drought as it no longer receives the same amount of water as before the construction of the dam.

Deforestation

Deforestation can also contribute to drought, and on different scales. On a global scale, removing trees results in less carbon dioxide being absorbed from the atmosphere, which in turn will lead to an increase in the greenhouse effect. This will cause global warming and climate change, which will result in changes to atmospheric and oceanic circulation.

But deforestation can also have an impact on a more regional scale. Large tropical forests like the Amazon create their own weather systems. As well as evaporation from the ground, trees absorb rainwater through the soil and release water vapour back into the atmosphere through **transpiration**. As this water vapour enters the air, the warm air rises and cools, the water vapour condenses and falls daily as rain. The rising air creates low pressure, which in turn pulls moist air in from surrounding areas.

Deforestation for timber, fuel and to create farmland is a serious threat to tropical forests. Without trees to intercept rainfall and return it to the atmosphere, the local water cycle is disrupted, the drop in pressure is reduced and there is less rainfall, sometimes leading to drought.

Agriculture

Agriculture can suffer because of drought, resulting in low yields, crop failures and loss of livestock. However, it can also contribute to drought when water is taken from wetter areas to irrigate agriculture in others, or pumped from rivers and groundwater. This may leave water supplies even lower and worsen the effects of drought.

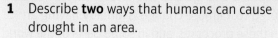

Activity

1 Describe **two** ways that humans can cause drought in an area.

2 Why are some areas more at risk from drought than others?

3 Do you think the UK is at risk from drought? Why?

Impacts of drought

Since water is such a valuable resource, droughts are extremely problematic. Like most natural hazards, the key impacts of drought can be grouped into economic (linked to jobs and money), social (linked to people) and environmental (linked to wildlife, habitats, etc.) hazards. As shown in Table 7, drought can have both immediate impacts on the area, and impacts that are not directly created by the drought.

Table 7 Examples of the impacts of drought

Type of impact	Examples
Social	Ill-health among the population caused by low supply or poor quality supply of water.
	Depression and anxiety over economic impacts.
	Safety risks as fires and dust storms are more likely.
	Migration as people move away from affected areas, but doing so without adequate supplies for the journey.
Economic	Industries, such as farming and forestry, unable to support jobs, leading to mass unemployment.
	Water companies have to spend large amounts of money on new supplies and pipe systems, leading to higher bills for customers.
	Food prices increase as farm production decreases, putting the poorest at risk of malnutrition.
	Related industries (e.g. those building fishing equipment, farming equipment, power companies) see a drop in income, possibly leading to job losses.
Environmental	Wild animals suffer from a loss of water.
	Habitats, particularly river habitats, damaged or lost.
	Soil becomes dry and cracked, so it no longer supports plants.
	Endangered species could become extinct.
	Wildlife may migrate away from the area.

Checkpoint

Now it is time to review your understanding of the causes and effects of drought.

Strengthen

S1 What is a drought?

S2 What different types of drought are there? Can you describe them?

S3 Classify droughts into those with natural causes and those with human causes.

Challenge

C1 Why are some areas more likely to suffer from drought than others?

C2 Which impacts are worst: social, economic or environmental? Justify your answer.

C3 Use your knowledge to explain why drought is not a common problem in the UK.

Case Study – California, USA, 2012 to present, drought in developed country

Location

California is one of the wealthiest states in the USA and is famous for its major cities of Los Angeles, San Francisco and San Diego. Its location on the west coast of the continent, bordering the Pacific Ocean, has made it a popular destination for foreign and domestic tourists. With several large universities and industrial areas such as Silicon Valley, it is also a popular destination for study and work. However, California suffers from frequent severe droughts.

In January 2014, a state of emergency was declared by the state governor in response to a drought that had been affecting the state for the previous few years. This meant that new laws and regulations could be put in place to help deal with the impact of the drought.

Causes

A period of lower than normal rainfall and snowfall across the western side of the USA caused a distinct drop in water supplies for California. But this was made worse by the fact that most of California's water comes from the Colorado River, which also provides water for six other states. Also, states had been allowed to extract more water from the river than it receives, leading to a reduction in availability. Combined with a very high level of wastage and over-use, water was becoming a very scarce commodity.

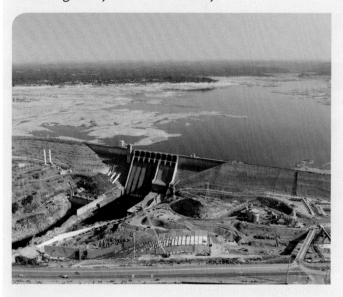

Figure 21 Effects of drought in California

Key effects

As water became scarcer in the state, several impacts began to show. One of these is **subsidence**. As surface water flows decrease, water is increasingly extracted from groundwater and **aquifers** to maintain supplies. This changes the structure of the land and can cause it to settle to a lower level. This can cause infrastructure and building damage in affected areas, such as the San Joaquin Valley.

Some coastal areas, such as Santa Barbara, are suffering from seawater intrusion. This occurs when the natural groundwater flow, which is towards the sea, is reversed because of a lack of flow pressure. This means that groundwater supplies become contaminated with seawater, making them unusable or costly to use for domestic or agricultural purposes.

So that water can be diverted for domestic or agricultural use, wetlands and rivers receive less water. Therefore, these environments suffer from the lack of water faster than other areas because the amount of water they receive is being reduced artificially as well as naturally. This will have an adverse effect on the birds and fish that rely on these environments to survive.

Did you know?

Protesters in California have been campaigning against companies bottling water for sale in the state during the period of drought.

The drought has been accompanied, and was possibly caused by, a period of very warm, windy weather across the state. This has also lead to the problem of **wildfires**. Warm windy weather dries out vegetation and makes it very easy for a fire to start, either naturally through a lightning strike for example, or by human activity, either deliberate or accidental. These fires spread very quickly because the vegetation is dry and the winds fan the flames and push them into new areas. Not only do the fires themselves cause environmental damage and put people's lives and property at risk, ash and debris from the fires also gets into water supplies, contaminating them. It can also block streams and rivers, causing mudslides and flooding.

California's drought has had a significant impact on one of the world's most productive farming regions. California is a major supplier of fruit, vegetables and dairy products to the USA. In a dry climate this is made possible by a huge network of irrigation pipelines and canals.

Some farmers have adapted by taking land out of production or pumping groundwater from ever-deeper supplies. Others conserve irrigation water and focus on higher value crops. In 2015, California farms lost an estimated US$1.8 bn and 10,000 jobs because of the drought, with some increases in food prices. In addition, some farms are affected by saltwater contamination and wildfires.

California's power supplies are also affected by drought, especially where lower water levels reduce the output of its hydro-electric power stations. In addition, its thermal power stations require large amounts of cooling water. With a growing demand for energy, the state is looking for new sources, including renewable energy.

Key responses

Since the state of emergency was declared, various state and national government departments, including the Department of Water Resources, US Bureau of Reclamation and the State Water Resources Control Board, have introduced new measures to try to deal with the drought:

- limiting flows during winter months to try and build up reserves for later in the year when demand is higher
- warning some areas that they will be given limits on how much water they will receive because river levels are too low
- reducing water supplies down to the minimum allowed for public health and safety
- installing salinity control points in crucial areas to prevent seawater intrusion
- running education and information programmes to encourage people to use as little water as possible at home, particularly on gardens
- increased monitoring of some rivers to check on levels of endangered species and the effects of the drought on them.

Summary

State of emergency declared in January 2014 as a result of the drought.

Subsidence caused by groundwater reserves being used.

Natural environments being starved of water and wildfires more common.

Increased monitoring and education to reduce wastage, water limits set.

Figure 22 Photo showing a public awareness message in California

Case Study – Ethiopia, 1983 to present, drought in developing country

Location

Ethiopia is a developing country in eastern Africa. Since the 1980s, Ethiopia has suffered from multiple droughts across various areas of the country. This has led to famine and huge loss of life. The cycle of drought and famine is still continuing. The worst periods have been during 1984, 1994, 2004 and 2014–16.

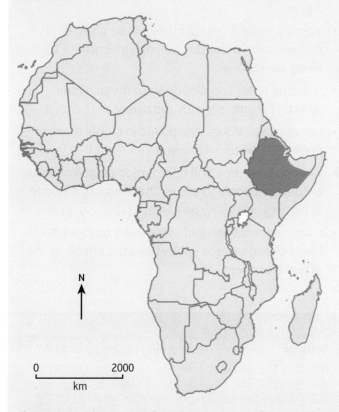

Figure 23 Location map for Ethiopia within Africa

Causes

Ethiopia relies on two periods of rain throughout the year, one longer than the other. Since the 1980s, the short rain season has been getting shorter, and increasingly delayed. The long rain season has become equally unpredictable. A likely cause is warming of the Indian Ocean, where rising air loses more moisture as rainfall. Dryer air moves westward and descends over East Africa, causing drought.

Key effects

Although Ethiopia's cities are booming, 85% of the population live in the countryside and depend on farming. They are most vulnerable to drought and climate change.

For farmers, more unreliable rains make planning very difficult. It is harder for them to know when to plant, and some types of crop they have used for generations no longer do well. For livestock farmers, when land becomes too dry to support vegetation, there is less food and water for their animals. People in rural areas also rely on local plants and trees for building materials, for example timber for their houses and grass for thatched roofs. Drought reduces their availability or increases their cost.

As agriculture becomes more difficult across the country, reduced food supplies lead to increases in prices, particularly affecting the poorest and marginal people. This can lead to hunger and malnutrition and in the past has caused famine.

Drought also affects water supplies, particularly in rural areas. Only 57% of Ethiopians have access to an improved water source – others rely on a natural source such as a spring, river or lake. When these dry up, people may have to walk many kilometres to find water. This has particular effects on older people who cannot make the journey, and women and children who do. The time spent fetching water takes children out of school and prevents women from working. Water sources can also become polluted so people have no alternative but to use unsafe water, with the risk of diseases such as cholera, typhoid, dysentery, diphtheria and others. Without access to medical care, these diseases can all be fatal.

So drought also has an impact on education, health and development in the countryside. It is an important cause of migration from rural areas to cities.

Key responses

The issues created by the drought in Ethiopia were brought to global attention in the 1980s through a large charity event called 'Live Aid'. This event was organised to make people aware of the crisis caused by the drought and to try to raise money for people affected. Today, Ethiopia is developing rapidly and in times of hardship the government organises its own relief programmes.

NGOs from across the world like UNICEF and Oxfam often work with Ethiopian experts in remote areas of the country to support those worst affected by drought. As the cycle of droughts has continued, NGOs have been working to provide clean water, food and medical care for people affected by the droughts and food shortages. Longer term, they also work to help people become more resilient to drought in future, for example by developing new farming techniques and crop varieties, and improving access to safe water, education and training.

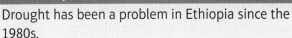

Summary

Drought has been a problem in Ethiopia since the 1980s.

Drought affects people's livestock, food supply and the vegetation used as a building material.

Food prices rise rapidly, preventing people from being able to afford enough food.

Aid agencies are working in Ethiopia to support people and provide water supplies.

Education charities are trying to improve people's chances of getting jobs in urban areas.

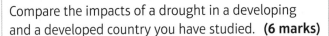

Exam-style question

Compare the impacts of a drought in a developing and a developed country you have studied. **(6 marks)**

Command word

Compare means that you should include both similarities and differences in your answer.

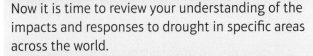

Checkpoint

Now it is time to review your understanding of the impacts and responses to drought in specific areas across the world.

Strengthen

S1 List the causes of drought in California and Ethiopia.

S2 Which place is suffering more because of drought? Explain your answer.

S3 Compare the responses to drought in each place.

Challenge

C1 Do you think the response in California was enough to reduce the impact of drought? What else could be done?

C2 Explain why climate change may be an underlying cause of drought in Ethiopia.

C3 Which hazard is worse: a tropical cyclone or a drought? Justify your answer.

Weather Hazards and Climate Change

The Earth's atmosphere is a global system that transfers heat and energy. This system causes great differences in climate, and influences the weather in places such as the UK. The global climate has changed in the past and is continuing to change today as a result of human activity. Changes in atmospheric circulation patterns sometimes cause extreme weather events, including tropical cyclones and droughts. Some places are more vulnerable to these hazards than others, and the way people respond can be different in developed, emerging and developing countries.

Checklist

You should know:

- [ ] how heat is redistributed by the atmosphere and oceans
- [ ] why some areas of the Earth receive more heat than others
- [ ] the impact of the Coriolis effect and the jet stream on atmospheric circulation
- [ ] how the world's climate has changed over time
- [ ] how climate change can occur naturally
- [ ] how we can prove historic climate change
- [ ] how human activity can cause climate change
- [ ] the negative impacts of global climate change
- [ ] what the climate of the UK is like and how it has changed over time
- [ ] variations in the climate of different regions of the UK
- [ ] the formation and hazards of tropical cyclones
- [ ] how different countries can be affected by, and respond to, tropical cyclones
- [ ] the distribution and causes of drought
- [ ] how different countries can be affected by, and respond to, drought.

Which key terms match the following definitions?

a   Circulation cell near the Equator responsible for storms at the Equator and desert belts north and south of the Equator.

b   The deflection of air movement by the Earth's rotation.

c   A period of time with lower average temperatures causing widespread glaciation.

d   A section of ice drilled from a glacier showing the layers of ice created over time.

e   The increase in volume created when a fluid (e.g. seawater) is heated and expands.

f   The centre of a tropical cyclone; an area of clear conditions created by cooler air sinking.

g   The path followed by a tropical cyclone.

h   A region with little or no regular precipitation.

i   The collapse of land because of a lack of support underneath, often caused by a reduction in water levels.

j   Permanently removing forest so the land can be used for something else.

To check your answers, look at the Glossary on pages 296–301.

Weather Hazards and Climate Change

Question 1   Describe **two** negative impacts of global climate change.   (4 marks)

Student answer

A possible negative impact is sea level rise. With ice at the poles, particularly around the South Pole, melting due to higher temperatures, more water will enter the oceans and this will cause sea levels to rise. Another possible impact is the drop in food production that will occur.

Verdict

Part one is accurate and clear. There is correct identification of a possible impact and a clear and accurate description. This shows a good level of understanding. Part two does not provide a complete answer. A different possible impact of global climate change is identified but no further detail is provided.

Exam tip

Always check the number of marks available for each question. This question is worth four marks and asks for two impacts. This means that two marks are available for each impact discussed. You will not achieve two marks for just identifying a feature or impact.

Question 2   Assess how effective responses to tropical cyclones are in developed and developing or emerging countries..   (8 marks + 4 SPAG)

Student answer

Hurricane Sandy hit New York in mainland USA in October 2012. Over 150 people were killed. Typhoon Haiyan was responsible for over 6000 deaths in the Philippines.

The response to these disasters was quite different. Aid was able to reach the areas affected by Sandy much faster. Also, the efforts in the USA were distributed over the whole affected area. With Haiyan, efforts were focused on one city. This meant that other people felt abandoned and some rioting occurred in various areas. Also, the USA did not need to rely on foreign aid agencies to provide support and so was able to act without having to wait for aid to arrive.

Verdict

The first paragraph briefly mentions the impacts of tropical cyclones, but not the responses to it and so does not answer the question set. Paragraph two does discuss responses and so would receive credit. The key point about this paragraph is that it compares the responses between two different tropical cyclones, in two differing parts of the world. The information is accurate but lacks some detail, including information on timescales and names of specific locations, which would show a deeper level of knowledge and understanding.

Exam tip

The question states that it wants responses for both developed and developing or emerging countries, which means the answer will need to compare as well as assess the responses. The student discusses the similarities and differences between the responses. However, not all of the answer is focused on the responses and the student has not summarised the effectiveness in countries at different levels of development.

Proportion, ratio and percentage

What you need to know

In geography we use proportion, ratio and percentage to break down data sets to describe and understand them better, and to compare them to other data sets.

- **Proportion** expresses one part as a fraction of the whole. For example, the proportion of all tropical storms in a year (80) that develop into hurricanes (30)

  $= 30 \div 80 = \frac{3}{8}$.

- **Ratio** states how many parts make up a whole. Map scales are often shown as ratios. For example, a scale of 1:200 means that the distance shown on the map is $\frac{1}{200}$th the distance in real life.

  5 cm on the map

  $= 5 \times 200$ cm in real life

  $= 1000$ cm

  $= 10$ metres.

  You can use a ratio to describe how two or more quantities make up the whole, e.g. A village population made up of a ratio of 3:4 males to females means there are 3 males for every 4 females in the village.

- **Percentage** is the proportion or ratio expressed as a fraction of 100, e.g. the percentage of days with air frost (40) in a year (365 days)

  $= \frac{40}{365}$

  $= \frac{40}{365} \times 100\%$

  $= 10.96\%$ (to 2 decimal places).

Example

Students wanted to investigate the amount of sunshine in summer compared with winter where they lived. They measured the hours of sunshine over a year (Table 1).

Table 1 Hours of sunshine over one year

Season	Winter			Spring			Summer			Autumn		
Month	D	J	F	M	A	M	J	J	A	S	O	N
Hours of sunshine	35	70	85	140	222	188	228	202	170	170	94	36

Calculate the annual total hours of sunshine (S_a).

$S_a = (35 + 70 + 85 + 140 + 222 + 188 + 228 + 202 + 170 + 170 + 94 + 36)$

$= 1640$ hours.

Calculate the totals for the summer (S_s) and winter (S_w) subsets.

$S_s = 228 + 202 + 170$ and $S_w = 35 + 70 + 85$

    $= 600$ hours $= 190$ hours.

The decimal proportion of the annual sunshine in summer $S_s \div S_a$

$= 600 \div 1640$

$= 0.37$ (to 2 decimal places).

As a percentage this is:

0.37×100

$= 37\%$.

In winter the proportion would be $S_w \div S_a$

$= 190 \div 1640$

$= 0.12$

As a percentage this is 12% (to 2 significant figures).

Therefore 37% of the annual sunshine occurs in the summer compared with just 12% in the winter.

An alternative way to present this is using a ratio.

The ratio of summer to winter sunshine, $= S_s : S_w$

$= 600 : 190$.

$= 60 : 19$.

So, for every 60 hours of sunshine in summer there are only 19 hours in winter.

Apply your knowledge

Students investigating the seasonal distribution of rain falling in parts of the UK were testing the statement that 'Most rain in Wales falls during the winter season'. They had a set of average rainfall data for Valley in Anglesey from the Meteorological Office, from Climate data for 1981–2010 (Table 2).

Table 2 Average rainfall data for Valley in Anglesey

Month	D	J	F	M	A	M	J	J	A	S	O	N	Annual
Rainfall (mm)	91	76	55	63	55	48	54	54	70	72	101	104	843

1. Calculate the proportion of annual rain falling in each season by adding together the averages for each season and dividing by the total annual rain.

2. Express the proportion of rain in each season as a percentage by multiplying by 100.

3. Express your answer as a four-part ratio – winter rain:spring rain:summer rain:autumn rain.

4. Which season was wettest? Does this data support the statement the students were testing or not?

THINKING GEOGRAPHICALLY

Magnitude and frequency

In geography we use magnitude and frequency to help us find out how often or how meaningful an event or its effect is or how geographical conditions differ.

- **Frequency** is the number of times a data value occurs: how often it happens, e.g. the number of storms in a year.

- **Magnitude** is the quantifiable size of an event or piece of data: how large it is, e.g. the force of a wind. It can be numerical or ranked.

- Both can be measured and recorded using a variety of scales, e.g. arithmetic scales to plot frequency of monthly temperature and rainfall; ranked order of magnitude scales such as the Richter Scale for earthquakes and storm surges.

- Ranked scales do not always use equally spaced increases of obvious data values. The Saffir–Simpson Hurricane Scale describes the observed damage (rank 2 is roughly 4 times as damaging as rank 1) but does not imply equal increments of wind speed.

Apply your knowledge

1. Some students were studying whether the frequency and magnitude of hurricane winds and their effect have changed during the last 50 years. Using GSI to access the National Oceanic and Atmospheric Administration (NOAA) database they collected data for hurricane strength on landfall at New Orleans.

(a) Complete the frequency for 2000–2009 in Table 3 by converting the following wind speeds to their equivalents on the Saffir–Simpson Scale: CINDY (2005) 121 km/h, KATRINA (2005) 236 km/h, GUSTAV (2008) 158 km/h.

Table 3 Hurricane wind speed magnitude (Saffir–Simpson Scale)

Decade	1	2	3	4	5
1960–1969	1	1	0	2	1
1970–1979	1	0	0	0	0
1980–1989	1	1	1	0	0
1990–1999	1	0	0	0	0
2000–2009					
2010–	1	0	0	0	0

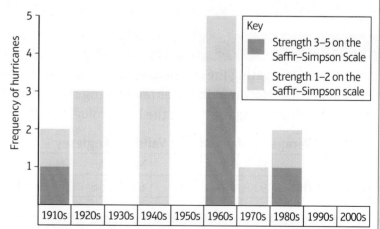

Figure 1 Frequency of hurricanes from 1 to 5 on the Saffir–Simpson Scale making landfall at New Orleans from 1910 to 2009

(b) Copy and complete the graph in Figure 1.

(c) What is the frequency of hurricanes making landfall in New Orleans from 1960 to 2009?

(d) What is the frequency of hurricanes of magnitude 3 and above from 1960 to 2009?

(e) Describe how the frequency and magnitude of hurricane storms appears to have changed during the last 50 years.

3 | Ecosystems, Biodiversity and Management

Deserts, tropical rainforest and tundra are examples of large-scale ecosystems. Climate has a huge influence on where these large-scale ecosystems are and what they are like. Tropical rainforests, for example, occur where warm temperatures and high precipitation (rainfall) all year round produce the most biodiverse ecosystem on Earth, comprising millions of different species of plants and animals. Scientists have developed models for ecosystems that help us to understand the processes that make them like they are and explain the differences between them. Humans depend on ecosystems, but humans have a destabilising impact on many large-scale ecosystems. Human activities also change the natural processes that keep ecosystems in balance. Many ecosystems are under threat. What is likely to happen to large-scale ecosystems as a result of these threats? What can humans do to reduce their impact by managing ecosystems sustainably?

Your learning

In this section you will investigate key learning points:

- what the world's large-scale ecosystems are like, and where they are
- how climate influences large-scale ecosystems
- what the biosphere is and why it is so important for people
- what ecosystems the UK has – including the marine ecosystems around the UK's coasts – what these ecosystems are like and where they are
- what the special features of the tropical rainforest ecosystem are and how the different parts of the ecosystem work together and depend on each other
- why tropical rainforests are important and why they are under threat
- how sustainable management can help protect tropical rainforests
- what the special features of the deciduous woodland ecosystem are and how the different parts of the ecosystem work together and depend on each other
- why deciduous woodlands have less biodiversity than rainforests
- how deciduous woodland plants and animals have adapted to their environment
- why deciduous woodlands are important and why they are under threat
- how sustainable management is used to help protect deciduous woodlands.

The world's ecosystems

Learning objectives

- To learn what the world's large-scale ecosystems are and where they are distributed
- To describe these large-scale ecosystems and know their characteristics
- To explain how the distribution of large-scale ecosystems is influenced by climate and other factors

Distribution

Figure 1 shows the distribution of the world's large-scale **ecosystems**. Distribution is a key geographical concept that describes how something is spread out over an area. For example, the distribution of the tropical rainforest ecosystem on the map in Figure 1 shows that this **biome** is restricted to a belt either side of the equator.

Characteristics

Characteristics are typical features that allow us to identify and distinguish one thing from another. Table 1 shows how climate differences produce different biome characteristics.

Explaining ecosystem distribution

Climate is the key factor influencing the distribution of the world's large-scale ecosystems. The Earth's climate system is driven by the Sun's energy.

- Temperature decreases with latitude. The equator receives the most heat from the Sun because the Sun is directly overhead and therefore its rays are most intense here. Further away from the equator, temperatures decrease.

- The high surface temperatures at the equator all year round power a convection cell of rising air. As this air rises it cools, the moisture it contains condenses and a lot of rain falls.

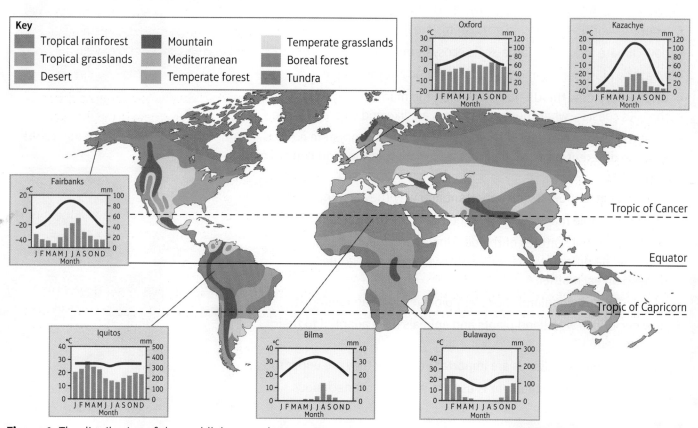

Figure 1 The distribution of the world's large-scale ecosystems

Table 1 Differences between biomes

Biome	Climate characteristics	Distinctive vegetation
Tropical rainforest	Hot all year (27–30°C). Wet all year (average annual precipitation 2000–3000 mm)	A huge variety of broadleaved plants. Trees dominate, with other plants competing for light
Tropical grasslands	Hot all year (25–35°C), 500–1000 mm of rainfall a year but always with a dry season	Tall grasses with scattered, drought-adapted trees and shrubs
Deserts	Very hot all year (above 30°C), very low rainfall (less than 250 mm annual average)	Plants have water-storing features, spines instead of leaves and extensive root systems
Temperate grasslands	Hot in summer (25°C), very cold in winter (as low as –40°C), 500–900 mm of rainfall a year, most in late spring and summer	Grasslands with very few trees or shrubs
Temperate forest	Warm summers (around 18°C), cool winters (around 5°C), precipitation all year (1000 mm)	Deciduous trees, which drop their leaves in autumn
Boreal forest	Warm summers (16–30°C), very cold winters (well below 0°C), low precipitation (less than 500 mm) mainly in summer	Coniferous trees with needles instead of leaves to survive cold and reduce water loss
Tundra	Temperatures below 0°C for most of the year, and only reaching around 10°C in summer, low precipitation (often less than 250 mm)	Very few plants can live here, mostly lichens and mosses. Trees are rare and stunted (short height)

- The cooled air falls over the tropics of Cancer and Capricorn, which creates high pressure zones of clear skies. As the air falls, it warms. This means that temperatures are high but **precipitation** is low here.

- The tilt of the Earth on its axis creates seasons, these often have different precipitation patterns. The equator is least affected by the tilt of the Earth, so precipitation here is similar all year round.

- The Inter-Tropical Convergence Zone (ITCZ) shifts northwards in June, following the overhead Sun, to bring a wet season to the tropical grasslands of the Northern Hemisphere. These grasslands are dry in winter when the ITCZ has moved into the Southern Hemisphere.

- In the interior of the world's continents, summer temperatures are much higher and winter temperatures much lower than in locations nearer the coast, where the sea moderates temperature extremes. Temperate grasslands and deserts are influenced by this effect.

- High mountains force air to rise and cool as it passes over them. This means that precipitation is high in the mountains. When the air has passed over the mountains it has lost its moisture. This is called a rain shadow effect and it influences the location of some desert and temperate grassland ecosystems.

Local factors
- **Altitude (height)** – because temperature drops by 1°C for every 100 metres gain in height, high mountains in the tropics can have cold temperature ecosystems.

- **Soils** – the characteristics of an ecosystem can change when the underlying geology or relief produces different types of soil or soil conditions. The vegetation in a poorly drained, swampy area will be different from that of a well-drained area, for example.

- **Humans** – if you look out of a window in the UK, do you see a temperate forest? Centuries of human activity have altered the local characteristics of large-scale ecosystems.

The biosphere

Activity

1 Using Figure 2 to help you, identify biosphere resources that you use in your daily life.

2 Now think about someone your age from one of the world's poorest countries. How might their reliance on biosphere resources be different from yours?

The biosphere is a vital system that provides us with some of our most essential resources: the food we eat and many of our medicines, building materials and sources of fuel.

Modern technologies have reduced our day-to-day dependence on the biosphere, but they have led to an increase in the **exploitation** of the biosphere.

- The huge demand for water around the world (for rapidly growing cities, for industry and for agriculture) means that other parts of the biosphere are deprived of water. One example is the Hamoun wetlands in Iran. Here a combination of drought, rapid population growth, dam-building in neighbouring Afghanistan and wasteful irrigation practices have caused the wetlands to dry up.

- Biofuels are a valuable alternative to fossil fuels because they provide renewable energy. However, commercial production of biofuels means that huge areas of land are devoted to biofuel crops instead of food crops. Forest land has also been cleared for biofuel crops. This makes vital resources from the biosphere – food and fuel – more expensive for local people, and impacts on biodiversity. For example, a sharp decline in the number of orang-utans in Malaysia and Indonesia has been linked to the increasing number of plantations producing the biofuel palm oil.

- Mineral resources are not part of the biosphere, but increasing demand for minerals has major impacts *on* the biosphere. An extreme example is mountain-top removal mining, in which coal is mined by removing the tops of mountains to allow easier access to coal seams. This type of mining was developed in the Appalachian mountains in the east of the USA.

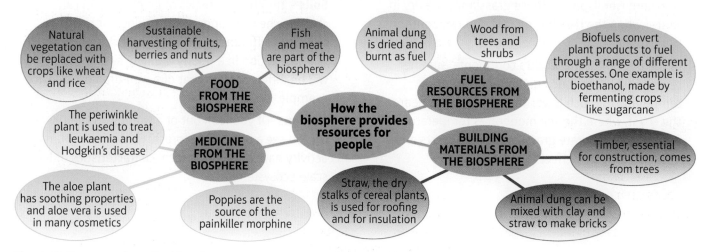

Figure 2 Resources from the biosphere

The nutrient cycle

The **nutrient cycle** describes how **nutrients** are transferred around an ecosystem. A scientist called Philip Gersmehl used a model based on nutrient cycles to explain differences between ecosystems. A model is a scientific theory that allows complex systems to be understood more easily.

Gersmehl's model said that all ecosystems have the same three basic compartments: soil, **litter** and **biomass**. Each is a store for nutrients. Nutrients are transferred between the stores. The size of these stores is different in different ecosystems, as is the amount of nutrients transferred between stores.

Abiotic and biotic

The living parts of an ecosystem are called its **biotic** components ('bio' means life). Nutrients allow the biotic components to survive and grow, but nutrients are not biotic components. The parts of the ecosystem that are not living but which are essential to life are called **abiotic** components. Examples of abiotic components are water, light, temperature, atmosphere and soil. Biotic and abiotic components are interdependent – they are closely connected and interlinked.

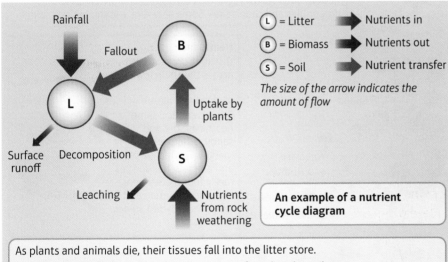

The size of the arrow indicates the amount of flow

An example of a nutrient cycle diagram

As plants and animals die, their tissues fall into the litter store.
As living tissue decomposes, nutrients are transferred to the soil store.
Some nutrients are lost from litter by surface runoff.
Plants take nutrients from the soil. Soil loses nutrients by leaching, but gains nutrients from the weathering of the rock beneath it.

Figure 3 Nutrient cycles

Exam-style question

In ecosystems, abiotic and biotic components are interdependent. Define the term 'biotic'. **(1 mark)**

Exam tip

Make sure you know key terms for all your topics very well. Then you can answer questions like this one quickly and easily.

Checkpoint

Now it is time to review your understanding of the world's ecosystems and reasons for their location; the biosphere; and the nutrient cycle.

Strengthen

S1 What types of tree are characteristic of the boreal forest large-scale ecosystem?

S2 Name three resources from the biosphere that you or your family rely on.

S3 Complete this list of the three basic nutrient stores: Soil, L_____ and B_____.

S4 Temperature drops by 1°C for every 100 metres of altitude. Use this fact to explain why mountains often have different ecosystems from the lowlands surrounding them.

Challenge

C1 Explain in your own words how the distribution of large-scale ecosystems is related to climate.

C2 In Astana, the capital of Kazakhstan, summer temperatures can reach 35°C while winter temperatures can drop to −30°C. How does Astana's location in the middle of a continent (Asia) help explain its extreme climate?

C3 A tropical rainforest ecosystem has a huge biomass store, but only a small store of nutrients in its soil. In desert ecosystems, most nutrients are stored in the soil. What could explain this? Think of possible explanations.

The UK's ecosystems

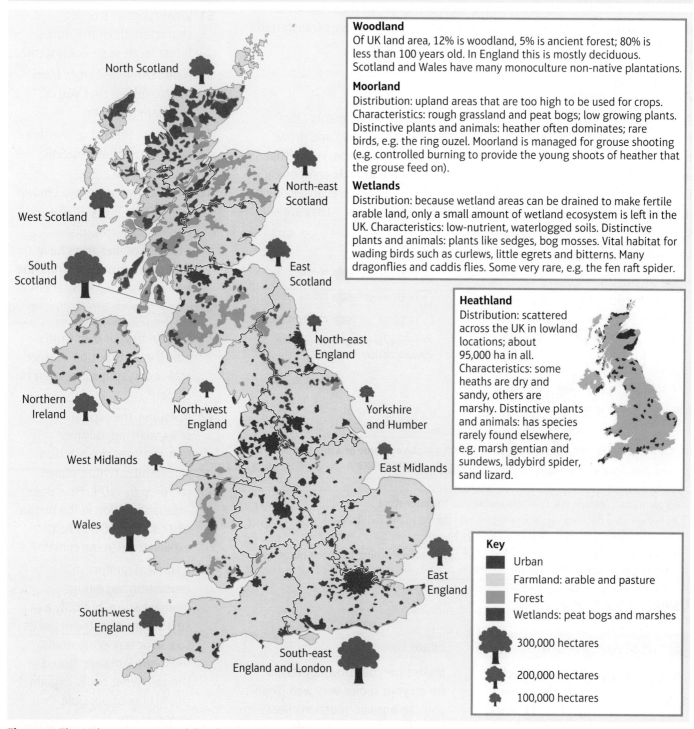

Woodland

Of UK land area, 12% is woodland, 5% is ancient forest; 80% is less than 100 years old. In England this is mostly deciduous. Scotland and Wales have many monoculture non-native plantations.

Moorland

Distribution: upland areas that are too high to be used for crops. Characteristics: rough grassland and peat bogs; low growing plants. Distinctive plants and animals: heather often dominates; rare birds, e.g. the ring ouzel. Moorland is managed for grouse shooting (e.g. controlled burning to provide the young shoots of heather that the grouse feed on).

Wetlands

Distribution: because wetland areas can be drained to make fertile arable land, only a small amount of wetland ecosystem is left in the UK. Characteristics: low-nutrient, waterlogged soils. Distinctive plants and animals: plants like sedges, bog mosses. Vital habitat for wading birds such as curlews, little egrets and bitterns. Many dragonflies and caddis flies. Some very rare, e.g. the fen raft spider.

Heathland

Distribution: scattered across the UK in lowland locations; about 95,000 ha in all. Characteristics: some heaths are dry and sandy, others are marshy. Distinctive plants and animals: has species rarely found elsewhere, e.g. marsh gentian and sundews, ladybird spider, sand lizard.

Key

- Urban
- Farmland: arable and pasture
- Forest
- Wetlands: peat bogs and marshes
- 300,000 hectares
- 200,000 hectares
- 100,000 hectares

Figure 4 The UK's main terrestrial (land) ecosystems

The UK's marine ecosystems

Marine ecosystems around the UK together make up an area that is three and a half times as big as the whole of the UK's land area. Marine ecosystems can be divided into inshore and offshore.

- Inshore habitats are those close to the shore and the coastal margins. These are very important for recreation and tourism in particular.

- Offshore ecosystems are found away from the shoreline and are important for commercial fishing and energy production. They have a vital role in buffering the impacts of global warming.

Marine ecosystems provide the following benefits.

- **Tourism** – 250 million people visit the UK's coasts, supporting 200,000 jobs in coastal tourism, which brings about £3 billion into the UK's economy.

- **Fishing** – the UK fishing fleet is the seventh largest in the European Union with around 6400 fishing boats. 12,000 people work on the fleet and 14,000 more work in fish processing.

- **Energy: oil** – the UK has oil reserves of around 24 billion barrels in the North Sea (off the east coast of the UK), enough for another 30 years of production. The industry employs 450,000 people.

- **Energy: offshore wind farms** – the London Array in the Thames Estuary, 20 km from the Kent coast, is the world's biggest wind farm, with 175 turbines.

Human activities and damage to marine ecosystems

Human activities damage marine ecosystems in many different ways.

An example of direct damage is overfishing of fish species. Although the UK has many thousands of small boats in its fishing fleet, one-half of the UK catch each year is made by just 4% of the fleet which is made up of very large vessels that are extremely efficient at catching fish. In 2011 there was a collapse in cod stocks in some UK marine areas. The removal of an important species such as cod has a big effect on the whole ecosystem.

Other examples of human activities that can damage marine ecosystems include:

- **eutrophication**, which is caused by fertilisers used on farmland being washed into the sea; it may also be caused when the sea is used to break down and detoxify sewage

- the construction of deep-water ports and navigation channels, essential for global trade

- economic development of the coastline, which often removes coastal ecosystems such as salt marsh

- the construction of large windfarms interferes with bird migration routes and the noise they make may disturb animals that rely on sound, such as dolphins.

Tropical rainforests

Tropical rainforest (TRF) is the most productive biome on Earth, and has the greatest variety of lifeforms. Consistently high temperatures and precipitation create the perfect conditions for plant life.

Tropical rainforest characteristics

- Although rainforest trees are deciduous, different species lose their leaves at different times (and only for a few weeks), so the forest always looks green.
- Trees grow very tall – 30 to 40 metres. Although they are very tall, the trees only have shallow roots.
- **Stratification** – the rainforest has different layers. The tree **canopy** is one layer. Above that is the emergent layer – very tall trees that grow another 10 metres above the canopy. Beneath the canopy, where there is less light, is the understorey: shorter trees of around 20 metres. The air is still here and the humidity very high. Beneath that is the shrub layer. Only around 3% of light reaches this layer through the canopies above. The final layer is the dark forest floor.
- Where there is rich and abundant plant life, you would expect soils to be very fertile. But in fact the tropical rainforest soils are very low on nutrients. Why is this?

Activity

Use information from Figure 5 to explain the key characteristics of the TRF.

Biotic
The nutrient cycle diagram is the key to understanding the TRF ecosystem. The biggest store is biomass (B), which is all the living things in the TRF (biotic characteristics). When leaves fall or branches drop into the litter store (L), they decompose very quickly. As soon as the nutrients are released into the soil (S), the plants of the TRF hoover them up. The trees have shallow roots because the only fertile part of tropical rainforest soils is a very thin nutrient layer right at the surface. The nutrient cycle returns nutrients to the biomass store very quickly.

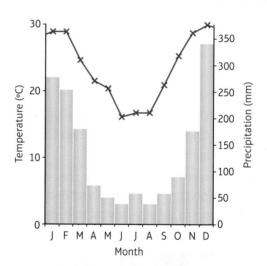

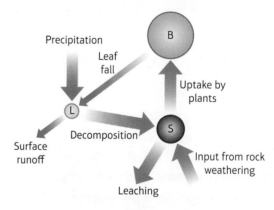

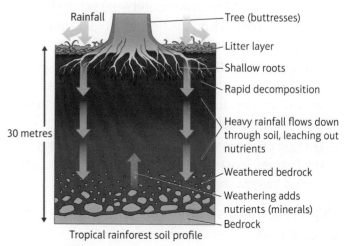

Tropical rainforest soil profile

Figure 5 Climate graph, nutrient cycle diagram and soil profile of the TRF

Another biotic factor is human activity. Humans play an important role in many TRF ecosystems. People hunt animals for food, spread the seeds of rainforest plants through the fruits, nuts and seeds that they eat, and affect the ecosystem through their use of fire.

Abiotic

The warm temperatures and moist conditions are perfect for chemical weathering of the bedrock, which releases minerals into the soil. However, tropical rainforest soils are often 30 or 40 metres deep so these nutrients do not reach the upper layers. The constant rainfall means that a lot of water travels down through tropical rainforest soils. As it trickles through the soil, the water takes nutrients and mineral salts with it. This is called leaching. Leaching makes tropical rainforest soils low in nutrients.

Food webs show the interactions between species in an ecosystem – who eats who. Rainforests have very complex food webs (Figure 6).

Why is rainforest so biodiverse?

The TRF is the most biodiverse ecosystem on Earth. Why is this?

- Rainforests offer optimum conditions for plant growth, which then supports very high animal biodiversity.

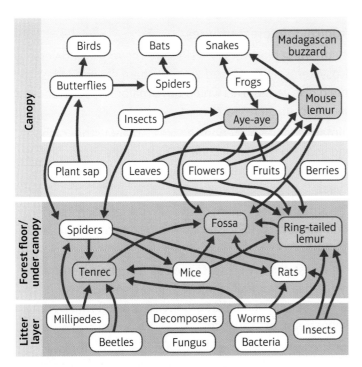

Figure 6 A food web for a Madagascan tropical rainforest ecosystem

- Rainforests are usually very old, resulting in a lot of evolutionary variation in species.

Plants and animals have adapted to TRF conditions.

- The canopy layer is extremely humid (hot and wet). Almost all plants here have 'drip tip' leaves, which means water runs off them quickly. This is important because otherwise moss and algae would quickly grow over the leaf surface, cutting off its light.
- The trees also have 'buttress' structures at their base. Because nutrients are concentrated in the top level of the soil only, rainforest trees only need shallow roots and the buttresses have evolved to keep their tall, slender trunks anchored upright.

In the Madagascan rainforest, 80% of creatures live in the canopy.

- The different tree species produce flowers, leaves and fruit at different times, and some animals travel through the canopy to eat them as they appear. In Madagascar lemurs have gripping hands and feet, strong legs and long tails that enable them to leap from tree to tree.
- Hundreds of bird species live in the canopy, including the Madagascan serpent eagle which flies through the canopy. Its wings are adapted for fast manoeuvring and it uses its powerful legs to grab lemurs, frogs, birds and snakes that it spots with its extremely good eyesight.

Up in the canopy, many species use different forms of camouflage to avoid being eaten. Some insects mimic sticks and leaves, birds have colouration and barring (stripes) that make them hard to see. The chameleon (there are 70 species in Madagascar) is the ultimate camouflage specialist as some species can change skin colour to fit their surroundings.

Exam-style question

Explain **two** ways in which animals have adapted to living in a tropical rainforest. **(4 marks)**

Exam tip

For this question you need to do two things. First, identify two adaptations. Second, explain what each one is for.

The importance of tropical rainforest ecosystems

Learning objectives

- To describe the goods and services provided by TRF ecosystems
- To explain different ways in which climate change threatens the TRF ecosystem
- To use photographs to identify differences between forest ecosystems

Activity

The photos in Figure 7 are taken at ground level rather than being oblique or aerial photos.

1 What are the advantages of ground level photos for showing the characteristics of these two forest ecosystems?
2 Would aerial or oblique photos have other advantages?

Rainforest goods and services

Economists divide outputs into goods and services. Goods are physical things, while services are 'intangible' – that is they are not physical resources you can touch. Table 2 summarises them.

Climate change and the TRF ecosystem

There is evidence in some tropical areas that climate change is making these places drier and hotter. These changes could have a big impact on rainforest structure, function and biodiversity.

Changes to TRF structure

The vegetation cover in many areas currently covered by TRF is likely to change to seasonal tropical forest, similar to that in the more wooded areas of tropical grasslands. This happens when the dry season starts to last for several months.

- Most trees drop their leaves in the dry season to avoid water loss through transpiration.

Table 2 Examples of goods and services relating to the rainforest

Tropical rainforest goods	Tropical rainforest services
More than 7000 drugs have their origins in TRF plant and animal products. An example from Madagascar is the rosy periwinkle, which is the basis for a drug used to treat childhood leukaemia.	Maintaining biodiversity – TRFs are the most biodiverse ecosystems on Earth and without them life would be much less varied. This would have major impacts for pharmaceutical research.
Oxygen – rainforests have been called 'the lungs of the world' as the huge amount of plant life produces oxygen as a by-product of photosynthesis.	Climate change buffering services – plants store carbon and soak up carbon dioxide (CO_2) from the atmosphere. The Amazon rainforest soaks up 2 billion tonnes of CO_2 a year.
Hardwood timber, such as ebony and rosewood, has valuable properties for furniture manufacture. Timber is used for construction and wood for fuel.	The amazing ecosystem of the TRF brings tourists and their money to TRF locations. It provides recreation and inspiration.
By preventing soil erosion and encouraging infiltration, forests help produce clean water supplies that would otherwise be polluted by silts.	The forest canopy protects the soil from being eroded by the heavy rainfall, and the vegetation reduces surface runoff that could otherwise cause flash flooding downstream or landslides.
For the people who live in or near the forest, the ecosystem is a source of food (e.g. meat, fruit) and its soils are used to grow crops.	For the indigenous peoples of the forest, the forest is their home and the basis of their culture and sense of identity.

- There is no canopy in the dry season and thick underbrush can grow among the trees.
- The lack of vegetation in the dry season means animals are adapted to live on stored food or go into a sort of hibernation. Biodiversity is still high but much lower than in the TRF.
- Trees have deep roots to reach groundwater (no buttresses) or are adapted to store water, for example the baobab trees in Figure 7(b), with their swollen trunks.
- The falling leaves make a deep litter layer, but decomposition is very slow in the dry season so the soil becomes a bigger store of nutrients and the biomass store is smaller.

Changes to TRF function

The vital services provided by TRFs could be significantly impacted by hotter, drier conditions.

- Less vegetation cover means that when it does rain, surface runoff will increase because of a reduction in infiltration. More sediment will be carried into drainage systems, polluting water quality. Increased silt in rivers harms some freshwater fish species.
- The TRF ecosystem itself influences precipitation because of the vast amounts of water vapour that are pumped out by the extensive vegetation. Less dense forest means lower rainfall in surrounding areas.
- TRF on mountains is known as 'cloud forest'. These forests have a function called 'cloud stripping' where they soak up moisture from passing clouds like a giant sponge. The slow release of this water into the drainage system provides areas downstream with a steady supply of water all year. Drier conditions could stop this 'cloud stripping' function.
- Drier forest emits more CO_2 than it soaks up, and if dry forest burns in forest fires, the added increase of CO_2 is colossal. Droughts in the Amazon TRF in 2005 and 2010, for example, are estimated to have each added 5 billion tonnes of CO_2 to the atmosphere.

Changes to TRF biodiversity

TRF plant species cannot tolerate drier conditions – they cannot survive prolonged drought or forest fires. Temperatures in TRF ecosystems are very similar all year round and species cannot cope with fluctuations. For example, researchers have reported seeing the deaths of whole colonies of flying fox bats as heat levels spiked above the limits they could tolerate.

As conditions become drier and warmer, other plant species suited to the new conditions would spread and out-compete TRF species. This may also include the spread of pests and diseases that TRF species are not immune to.

Not all areas of the TRF ecosystem would be affected in the same way, however. As temperature drops by one degree with every 100 metres, TRF on hills and mountains would not heat up so much. Some biodiversity would be preserved if species were able to migrate to these higher areas.

Figure 7 (a) TRF in eastern Madagascar

Figure 7 (b) Dry seasonal forest in western Madagascar

Activity

1 Give **two** examples of a tropical rainforest 'good' and two of a tropical rainforest 'service'.

2 Using Figure 7 to help you, draw and label a picture to show the structure of the TRF ecosystem and then the structure after the TRF has become a seasonal tropical forest.

3 Scientists think that climate change could trigger a feedback loop, with the TRF ecosystems starting to contribute to rises in atmospheric CO_2. Using the information on pages 136 and 137, explain how this might happen and what the evidence is for this theory.

Deforestation in the TRF

Learning objectives

- To explain the economic and social causes of tropical rainforest deforestation
- To describe the factors involved in the sustainable management of rainforest
- To identify key facts about rainforest management from a case study of Madagascar

Deforestation happens when forest is converted to farmland, when trees are cut down to sell as timber and because of mining, especially **open-cast** mining. Around the world, 7.3 million hectares of rainforest are cleared each year.

Deforestation in the Madagascan TRF

Madagascar is the world's fourth largest island, located off the east coast of the African continent. Deforestation has been extensive since the 1950s. Now only about 20% of Madagascar's land area is forested – one-half the amount that there was in 1950. Each year 1400 hectares is deforested.

Tavy *and deforestation*

Around 80% of deforestation in Madagascar is due to *tavy*, which is a type of 'slash-and-burn' agriculture. Trees are cut down on a small plot and the undergrowth burned, and then crops are planted. The nutrients in the soil are quickly exhausted and weed growth takes over. At this point the farmer often decides to clear another plot.

Population growth and deforestation

In the 1940s, inoculation programmes resulted in a big drop in Madagascan infant mortality. This produced a rapid rise in the population, from 4 million people in 1950 to 20.7 million in 2010. Over the next ten years, Madagascar's population will increase to 30 million.

Madagascar's population puts pressure on the amount of land available for agriculture. The pressure to feed growing families means that farmers try to get more from their *tavy* plots, but this exhausts the soil fertility faster, meaning that more plots have to be cleared.

Logging and deforestation

The second main cause of Madagascan deforestation is commercial logging. In the 20th century the Madagascan government sold rainforest timber to get money to pay the interest on international debt. There are now strict controls on logging, but a lot of illegal TRF logging still goes on. This is because:

- there is high demand for rosewood, a rainforest timber that is very dense, pink-coloured and fragrant
- Madagascan people are very poor and illegal logging pays well
- there is corruption – police and government officials often allow illegal logging in return for money.

Case Study – Sustainable rainforest management in Madagascar

Government policies (governance) – Most rainforest in Madagascar is owned by the government. Twenty years ago the Madagascan government set up a scheme for local communities to manage their own resources sustainably. International advice was that sustainable rainforest management (SRFM) would only succeed if local people were in charge. One very successful project is Association Mitsinjo.

Ecotourism – Association Mitsinjo started 15 years ago when a group of local wildlife guides, employed to take tourists round the Analamazoatra reserve, planned a community-based nature tourism association. Money from tourism brings in one-third of the association's income each year. Its members patrol the 10,000 hectares of their reserve area to look out for illegal logging and snares for animals. This has been very successful in preventing illegal logging and hunting.

Rainforest services – Association Mitsinjo also manages a rainforest restoration project, which began in 2002. In return for help with improving their crop yields, local farmers agree to set aside some of their land as a nursery for growing young rainforest trees. More than 1 million new trees have been planted, from 150 local species, on an area of 1000 hectares.

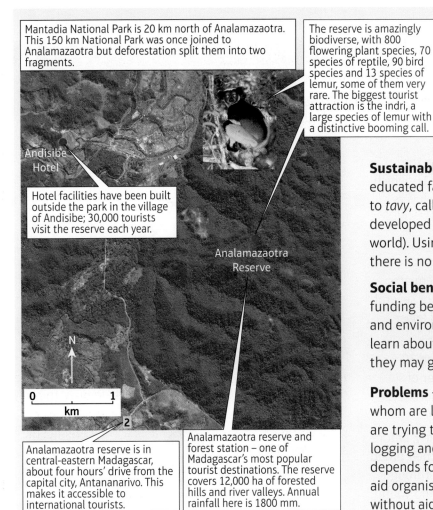

Mantadia National Park is 20 km north of Analamazaotra. This 150 km National Park was once joined to Analamazaotra but deforestation split them into two fragments.

The reserve is amazingly biodiverse, with 800 flowering plant species, 70 species of reptile, 90 bird species and 13 species of lemur, some of them very rare. The biggest tourist attraction is the indri, a large species of lemur with a distinctive booming call.

Andisibe Hotel

Hotel facilities have been built outside the park in the village of Andisibe; 30,000 tourists visit the reserve each year.

Analamazaotra Reserve

Figure 8 The location of the Analamazaotra reserve in Madagascar

Analamazaotra reserve is in central-eastern Madagascar, about four hours' drive from the capital city, Antananarivo. This makes it accessible to international tourists.

Analamazaotra reserve and forest station – one of Madagascar's most popular tourist destinations. The reserve covers 12,000 ha of forested hills and river valleys. Annual rainfall here is 1800 mm.

Sustainable agriculture – Association Mitsinjo has educated famers about a sustainable alternative to *tavy*, called System of Rice Intensification (SRI – developed in Madagascar and now used all over the world). Using this technique, more food is grown and there is no need to clear more land.

Social benefits – Association Mitsinjo is involved in funding better healthcare, including a health clinic, and environmental education in the area. If children learn about the importance of the rainforest now, then they may grow up to care for it in the future.

Problems – The area has 14,000 inhabitants, most of whom are living in poverty. Those not in the association are trying to make a living from activities such as logging and *tavy* agriculture. The association also depends for two-thirds of its income on international aid organisations. It is not financially sustainable without aid.

Exam-style question

Assess the following statement.

'Population growth is the most important cause of tropical rainforest deforestation.' **(8 marks + 4 SPAG)**

Exam tip

You should consider all the factors involved and identify which of them is or are the most important, and explain why.

Checkpoint

Now it is time to review your understanding of features of TRF ecosystems: their goods and services; climate change and the TRF; causes of TRF deforestation; and the sustainable management of rainforest

Strengthen

S1 Describe two characteristics of the TRF ecosystem.

S2 Explain why rainforest plants often have 'drip tips'.

S3 Give an example of how ecotourism can contribute to sustainable rainforest management.

Challenge

C1 Read the case study on Madagascar. Identify factors for management that are political (to do with the government), economic (to do with money) and social (to do with how people live).

Deciduous woodland

Deciduous woodland ecosystems are located in the temperate forest biome (see page 128 [Figure 1]), which has cool summers and mild winters, with rain all year.

Key characteristics of the deciduous woodland ecosystem

- The tree species that dominate this ecosystem are deciduous and shed their leaves each year for several months to cope with reductions in light and lower temperatures.
- Woodland has a canopy layer between 20 and 30 metres above the ground, a sub-canopy layer of saplings and shade-tolerant bushes and a herb layer of plants such as bluebells, brambles and ivy.
- In spring, species in the herb layer flower early, before the trees of the canopy come into leaf and their broad leaves block out much of the available light through the summer. The canopy is not continuous and young trees grow up where there are canopy gaps.
- Deciduous woodland trees have deep root systems so they can access groundwater and nutrients.
- Deciduous woodland soil has a well-developed humus layer at the top, where there is a lot of biological activity in spring and summer that breaks down the leaf litter from the previous autumn.

Study the information about the deciduous woodland ecosystem shown in Figure 9.

Biotic
Deciduous woodland is a productive ecosystem with a large biomass because there is plenty of precipitation and summer warmth. However, the biomass store is much smaller than in the tropical rainforest (TRF), where optimum conditions for plant growth are present all year.

The soil and the biomass stores are of similar size in the deciduous woodland ecosystem. In the TRF, nutrients from the litter layer are very quickly cycled back into

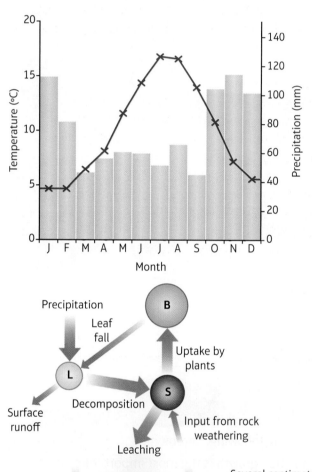

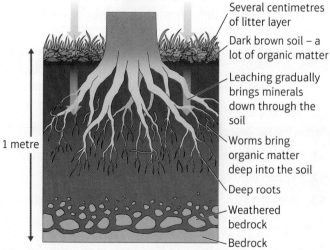

Figure 9 Climate graph, nutrient cycle diagram and soil profile for the deciduous woodland ecosystem

biomass. In the deciduous woodland the annual leaf fall adds a lot of nutrients to the soil. While temperatures are too low in winter for soil bacteria to function and for much decomposition to occur, in the spring decomposition becomes rapid as temperatures rise. These processes make deciduous woodland soils very fertile.

Another biotic factor is human activity. Humans manage many deciduous woodlands, which has a big impact on these ecosystems.

Abiotic

Woodland soils are not as deep as TRF soils as they have not existed for so long and the processes of soil formation are slower. The deep roots of the trees (biotic) help to break up the bedrock, and weathering of this rock adds nutrients to the soil (abiotic). There is much less leaching than in the TRF soils and it happens more gradually because rainfall is not as high or continuous as in the TRF. The leaf litter and ground layer of plants and tree roots prevents much surface runoff.

Food webs

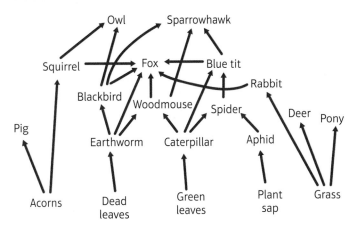

Figure 10 A food web for a deciduous woodland ecosystem: the New Forest, southern UK

Figure 10 shows an example of a simplified food web for the New Forest, a deciduous woodland in the southern UK.

Different food and animal species are closely interlinked. Humans and their livestock have had a very significant role in this woodland ecosystem for at least 1000 years, too. People have rights to keep livestock in the forest, and these animals have a significant impact. There are 3000 New Forest ponies, which live wild in the New Forest. They graze selectively, meaning they eat tall grasses but leave flowers behind. In autumn they also eat bracken, a plant which is toxic to most other species. This means the herb layer of the ecosystem is less dense, allowing more species to grow. Pigs also roam freely in the New Forest, eating acorns and nuts from trees. When they root around for food they mix up the leaf litter, aiding decomposition.

Activity

1 Write a description of a short walk through a deciduous woodland ecosystem in spring, as the trees are just coming into leaf. What can you see, hear and smell?

2 Compare the climate graph, nutrient diagram and soil profile for the woodland ecosystem with those for the tropical rainforest ecosystem on page 134.

   a The two ecosystems have different characteristics. Describe **three** differences in their characteristics.

   b The two ecosystems have some similar characteristics. Describe **three** ways in which they are similar.

   c Use the information from the climate graphs, nutrient cycle diagrams and soil profiles to explain the differences and similarities.

3 The New Forest ponies are sometimes called the 'architects' of the New Forest ecosystem. Because the ponies are only there because of humans, does that mean that the New Forest is not a natural ecosystem? Give reasons for your answer.

Biodiversity in deciduous woodland

Learning objectives

- To explain why deciduous woodland is less biodiverse than tropical rainforest
- To identify ways in which plants and animals are adapted to deciduous woodland ecosystems
- To understand the goods and services provided by deciduous woodland ecosystems

Deciduous woodland ecosystems have only moderate biodiversity compared with tropical rainforests. They have fewer species than other tropical biomes too, for example tropical grasslands. This is because of the low-temperature conditions that slow down the production of food in winter.

Deciduous woodlands are often dominated by three or four species that are particularly well adapted to climatic conditions. In the UK the dominant deciduous woodland tree is the oak.

- Oaks are large, strong trees which spread their branches horizontally, ensuring their leaves capture as much of the available light as possible.
- Oak leaves are broad and soft – their width maximises the amount of solar energy the oak can access and they are soft because they do not need a waxy coating to protect them from excess water loss.
- In autumn the supply of water to the leaves is cut off by a seal that forms between the leaf and the twig it is attached to. This causes the leaf to die and fall off. This enables the oak to survive through the short days and weak sunlight of the cold winter.
- The leaves and acorns contain a lot of the acid tannin. Tannin is poisonous for some animals, for example horses, and tastes bitter to others, such as deer. This gives the tree some protection from grazing.
- Oaks have an enormous root system, securely anchoring the tree against winter gales and enabling it to access groundwater in drier conditions.
- Oaks are mini-ecosystems in themselves, supporting 200 insect species. Their fruit, acorns, are large and packed with energy that the oak sapling uses as it starts to grow, and these are a valuable food source for animals. So that they do not support ever-increasing populations of animals who eat all their acorns, oaks only produce a big crop of acorns every few years.
- Oaks drop their leaves later in autumn than many other deciduous species, gaining the maximum advantage from their large canopies, but then are later to grow new leaves in spring than some other species.

The dominance of oaks and other deciduous species such as beech and ash means that plant species in the subcanopy and herb layer have to be adapted to shady conditions for most of the **growing season**. Plants such as the bluebell are adapted to flower at the very start of spring, before the trees come into leaf, to maximise both light and access to pollinating insects.

Animals in the deciduous woodland are adapted to survive in cold winters when there is not much food to eat. There are three main adaptations.

- Migration – many bird species move south to warmer winter conditions. For example, the swallow leaves the UK in September to spend the winter in central Africa.
- Hibernation – some animals spend the winter in a deep sleep in which their metabolic rate drops very low, meaning they require only a little energy to keep them alive. Hedgehogs, dormice and bats all hibernate, as do reptiles such as adders and grass snakes, amphibians such as frogs, newts and toads and many insects including bumblebees, wasps, ladybirds, butterflies, moths and snails.
- Food storage – storing food to survive on through the winter is an adaptation that squirrels use. Some species store nuts in piles on the forest floor (red squirrels), while others (grey squirrels) bury their nuts to hide them from other nut-eaters (including other squirrels). Because squirrels do not always remember all their buried nut locations, this helps some acorns to germinate.

Deciduous woodland goods and services

Like all ecosystems, the deciduous woodland ecosystem provides us with a range of goods (physical products) and 'intangible' services (see page 136). Table 3 shows some of the key goods and services.

Table 3 Deciduous woodland goods and services

Deciduous woodland goods	Deciduous woodland services
Timber – the UK produced 13 million tonnes of timber in 2014, which is mainly used in building. Most of this wood, however, comes from coniferous woodland as this type of timber is quicker to grow. Only about 500,000 tonnes is hardwood from UK deciduous woodlands.	Recreation – deciduous woodlands are a very popular location for many different recreation activities, including cycling, horse-riding, dog-walking and nature walks. For example, the New Forest, which became a National Park in 2005, has around 15 million visitors each year.
Fuel – air-dried fuel wood is used in the UK for wood-burning stoves and charcoal for barbecues (though 80% of charcoal is currently imported). Some UK power stations are being converted to burn biomass – much of it wood pellets from deciduous and coniferous woodland.	Carbon capture – like the TRF, deciduous woodland also acts as a store of carbon. It is estimated that the UK's woodland captures 1 million tonnes of carbon from the atmosphere each year. About half the UK's forests are deciduous woodland.
Non-timber forest products (NTFP) – these include such goods as forest moss (used by florists), edible fungi, venison (deer meat) and game shooting. Rearing birds such as pheasants and partridge for shooting is big business in the UK, and around 40% of these shoots take place in woodland. Successful shoots require active, sustainable management of the woodland ecosystem, which benefits other animal species and plants.	Conservation – forest areas often preserve rare plant and animal species that are protected by law. For example, the New Forest is a very important habitat for woodland birds – 75% of the UK's Dartford warblers live there, as well as rare birds such as the nightjar and honey buzzard. Recent surveys have shown a 95% decline in woodland bird numbers in the UK, so conservation of habitat is very important.

Figure 11 The New Forest deciduous woodland

Exam-style question

Explain **two** ways in which plants have adapted to living in deciduous woodland. **(4 marks)**

Exam tip

For each of the two adaptations you use in your answer, make sure you identify what the adaptation is and explain how it is an adaptation to characteristics of the ecosystem.

Checkpoint

Now it is time to review your understanding of the features, biotic and abiotic characteristics, biodiversity, adaptations and goods and services of the deciduous woodland ecosystem.

Strengthen

S1 Describe the location of temperate forest (deciduous woodland) on the global scale.

S2 Explain, with examples, how each of the following are adaptations to the deciduous woodland ecosystem: migration, hibernation, food storage.

Challenge

C1 Outline ways in which climate, soil, water, plants, animals and humans are linked together in the deciduous woodland ecosystem.

C2 Explain why deciduous woodland soil makes fertile farmland when cleared, while tropical rainforest soil quickly loses its fertility after being cleared.

Threats to deciduous woodland ecosystems

Learning objectives

- To explain the threat of climate change to deciduous woodland
- To identify causes of deforestation of deciduous woodland
- To assess different approaches to the sustainable use and management of the New Forest deciduous ecosystem

Climate change and the deciduous woodland ecosystem

In the UK, deciduous woodland ecosystems are already under a lot of pressure. Most woodland is found in small blocks rather than big forests. This makes them vulnerable to climate change.

The threats to deciduous woodland come from three main factors.

1 Milder winters

Plants and animals in the deciduous woodland ecosystem are adapted to cold winters.

- Key processes, such as seed germination, are triggered by cold temperatures. Without this trigger, the processes become disconnected.
- New tree species that are not adapted to cold winters are able to out-compete native deciduous trees if winters become milder.
- Pests and diseases that do not survive cold winters can spread if winters become milder.

2 Increased risk of drought

More frequent droughts would put a lot of stress on deciduous woodland trees. They are not adapted to survive drought conditions year after year. Beech trees are particularly vulnerable to drought stress. Stressed trees are less able to fight disease and pest attack.

3 Increased risk of fire

High temperatures and drought make forest fires more likely. Deciduous woodland is not adapted to forest fires. However, other ecosystems are adapted to fire, and benefit from the way fire releases nutrients. Plant species from these ecosystems could start to replace some deciduous woodland plants.

Biodiversity and climate change

Deciduous woodland species may be able to migrate to the cooler north of the UK. However, the rate of change may be too rapid for many species to succeed in doing this. Species in the south of the UK that are already vulnerable would be likely to become extinct in this country, reducing biodiversity.

Deforestation of deciduous woodland

The UK is in the temperate forest biome, but only 13% of its land area is covered by woodland. The UK is one of the least wooded countries in the European Union. This is because of deforestation that happened many centuries ago.

After the First World War, woodland was reduced to just 5% of the UK's land area. The government decided that a national reserve of timber was needed. Landowners were encouraged to plant more woodland. This is why the amount of woodland has increased to 13% today.

Coniferous versus deciduous woodland

However, most of this growth has been of coniferous woodland, not deciduous woodland. Of the 3 million hectares of woodland in the UK, only 1 million is native deciduous woodland. The most precious deciduous woodland of all is ancient deciduous woodland (woodland that has been around since at least 1600, 1750 in Scotland). Only around 2.3% of the UK's land area is ancient woodland (500,000 hectares), and it is still being deforested – 1000 hectares have been lost in the last ten years.

Figure 12 A conifer plantation in Norfolk

Economic causes of deforestation: timber extraction and agricultural change

Recent deforestation of deciduous woodland occurred in the 20th century when it was cut down and replanted as coniferous forest: 38% of ancient woodland was lost this way.

- Instead of using native conifer species, the coniferous plantations were mostly **non-native** species such as Sitka spruce.
- The plantations were also **monocultures** – only one species was grown rather than a mix.
- The dense evergreen canopy meant there was no light for undergrowth, so the plantations had very low biodiversity. The plantations were not popular with many people as they looked ugly.

Coniferous trees produce softwood, which grows faster than the hardwood of deciduous trees. This meant timber could be extracted sooner from coniferous plantations, generating money more quickly. The non-native conifer species are also faster-growing than native conifers, and planting the trees as a monoculture plantation made it much easier to grow and manage the plantation.

Most of the land in the UK that is suitable for farming was cleared of woodland centuries ago. Only a small amount of ancient woodland (7%) was cleared in the last 100 years for agricultural use. However, farming continues to have some negative impacts on deciduous woodland. Because woodland mostly exists in small blocks rather than as big forests, woodland is usually surrounded by farmland. The edges of the woodland are affected by the pesticides and herbicides that are sprayed on crops to control weeds. Woodland species are damaged by these.

Social causes of deforestation: urbanisation

The UK's population has increased significantly over the last 50 years, as Figure 13 shows.

The increasing numbers of people are linked to the clearing of deciduous woodland areas for both new housing (urbanisation) and new road construction.

- Experts say that the UK needs to build 240,000 new houses each year to keep up with the demand for

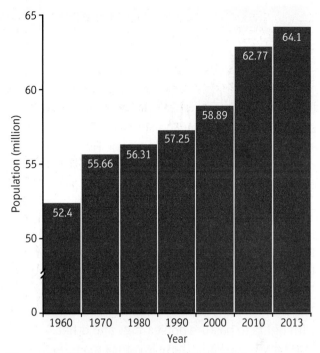

Figure 13 UK population growth, 1960–2013

housing; in 2014 less than one-half of that number were built. Developers would like to end greenbelt restrictions, which currently protect a lot of deciduous woodland near to cities and towns, to build new houses to meet this demand. Houses in semi-rural locations can be sold for a lot of money.

- The number of vehicles in the UK has increased every year since the Second World War (except in 1991). In 2013 there were 35 million vehicles on the UK's roads. There is great pressure to reduce congestion by widening carriageways, providing relief roads and bypasses, and to provide more service stations for road users. Deciduous woodland can often be lost as a result.

Activity

1 Identify **two** ways in which the causes of deforestation in deciduous woodland are different from the causes of deforestation in the TRF.

2 Discuss the threat of climate change for deciduous forest. Do you think deciduous forest is less at risk than TRF from climate change, more at risk, or the same?

3 Explain **three** ways in which the biodiversity of UK deciduous woodland is under threat.

Case Study – The New Forest: sustainable deciduous woodland management

The New Forest is a National Park on the south coast of England. It covers 480 km². About 175,000 people live in the area and it is very popular with tourists.

Tourism is worth £500 million to the region each year, but the 15 million people who visit the New Forest annually also pose some sustainability problems for the Forest's ecosystems.

- The visitors can do damage by trampling delicate plants; causing erosion by walking, cycling, horse-riding and car parking on verges; starting fires with barbeques; scaring wildlife and farm animals with their dogs; and dropping litter.

- The New Forest is used by people (called verderers) with rights to pasture ponies, pigs and other livestock in the Park. These livestock roam freely and are a popular tourist attraction. However, sometimes animals are run over by visitors driving too fast through the Forest. The ponies can also be dangerous to approach if they have young foals.

- Timber is extracted from the New Forest, both softwood from conifer plantations and hardwood from deciduous trees. Some forestry operations are not compatible with visitors using the woodland for recreation and access has to be controlled.

- Half the woodland in the New Forest is privately owned and about 40% of that is not managed. It becomes very overgrown, with rotting timber on the forest floor, and is not so attractive to visitors.

Sustainable woodland management

Forestry in the New Forest is very carefully organised so that deforestation does not occur and conservation of the deciduous woodland ecosystem is promoted. The New Forest produces 50,000 tonnes of timber each year.

- When conifers in conservation areas are cut down for timber, they are replaced by native-species deciduous trees. Deciduous trees are always replaced by more deciduous species. This means the percentage of deciduous trees is increasing in the New Forest.

- Pesticides and herbicides are used sparingly to avoid damaging the ecosystem.

- The foresters cut down timber, plant new trees and cull deer in winter, when there are the fewest visitors. Work in deciduous woodland between April and August is minimised so nesting birds are not disturbed.

- Half the forestry in the New Forest is managed by the Forestry Commission. This organisation runs courses in sustainable woodland management for private woodland owners and supports volunteers in conservation work.

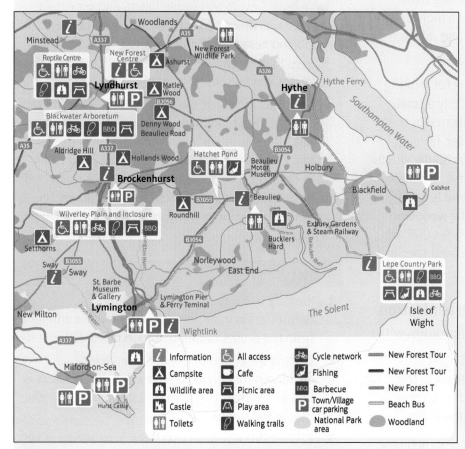

Figure 14 A map designed to help tourists navigate the New Forest and plan their visit

Sustainable use of the New Forest

The National Park promotes sustainable use of the New Forest by encouraging visitors not to damage the Park and by organising tourism to benefit local people.

- Different systems are used to control where visitors go: there are a lot of car parks in the New Forest so that people do not park on roadside verges; special cycle routes and paths have been set up through the Park, which guide visitors away from vulnerable areas; barriers are used to stop access to areas, for example for forestry work.

- Hotels and campsites in the New Forest are encouraged to join in sustainable transport schemes, such as the New Forest tour – an open-topped bus – and electric vehicle and bike hire. Electric vehicle charge points are provided through the National Park.

- A visitor leaflet called '5 ways to love the Forest' explains why visitors should drive slowly through the Forest or leave the car behind, about Green Leaf business and about the Forest Marque.

- Green Leaf businesses are local businesses that have signed up to a scheme to use local products where possible, to encourage walking and cycling, to set aside 10% of their grounds for local wildlife and generally to support sustainable use of the Forest.

- The Forest Marque certifies that local wood products are made from sustainable Forest timber.

- Conservation schemes are funded by the National Park authority and other sources. Local landowners can get grants to help improve biodiversity in their woodlands through planting native species and using traditional techniques such as coppicing to manage tree growth in the way the New Forest ecosystem has been managed for many centuries.

Exam-style question

Assess the approaches used to achieve sustainable use of a deciduous woodland in a named region. **(8 marks + 4 SPAG)**

Exam tip

Make sure you are clear on what sustainable use means and use that as the core of your answer. To assess the approaches you must do more than describe them – you need to consider their value in terms of sustainable use of the deciduous woodland.

Checkpoint

Now it is time to review your understanding of threats to deciduous woodland and approaches to the sustainable use and management of deciduous woodland.

Strengthen

S1 Describe two ways in which climate change could affect deciduous woodland biodiversity.

S2 Explain how population growth is linked to deforestation of deciduous woodland in the UK.

S3 Design a poster for use in the New Forest that explains ways in which visitors can help use the Forest sustainably.

Challenge

C1 Explain why some people who use the New Forest might oppose moves to encourage more tourists to come to the region. What sustainable approaches might help meet these people's needs?

C2 Which do you consider to be the main driver for deforestation in both TRF and deciduous woodland: economic factors or social factors? Explain your answer.

C3 Which one of the following would you argue was the most important approach to get right for the sustainable management of the New Forest: conservation, forestry, recreation, local people's needs? Give reasons.

Ecosystems, Biodiversity and Management

Ecosystems describe a network of connections between biotic and abiotic components. Evolution has produced these complex interdependencies and humans evolved as part of natural ecosystems, too. However, humans have had major impacts on ecosystems for many thousands of years. Very recently, these impacts have developed into some major threats to biodiversity within ecosystems. In order to reduce the impact of these threats, people use their knowledge of ecosystem processes to minimise the damage done by human activity and to conserve and protect biodiversity within the ecosystem.

Checklist

You should know:

- [ ] what the characteristics are of the world's large-scale ecosystems
- [ ] the distribution of the large-scale ecosystems and how climate and local factors affect this distribution
- [ ] how the biosphere provides resources for people and how it is being exploited
- [ ] the UK's ecosystems: moorlands, heathlands, woodlands, wetlands – distribution and characteristics
- [ ] the UK's marine ecosystems: why they are important and how human activities are damaging them
- [ ] the nutrient cycle and the interdependence of biotic and abiotic characteristics in ecosystems
- [ ] what the distinguishing features of tropical rainforests are
- [ ] why tropical rainforests have high biodiversity and how plants and animals are adapted to the tropical rainforest environment
- [ ] why tropical rainforests are important and the different ways in which they are under threat, through climate change and deforestation
- [ ] how a case study of a rainforest in Madagascar shows the different factors involved in sustainable rainforest management
- [ ] what the distinguishing features of deciduous woodlands are
- [ ] why deciduous woodlands have medium biodiversity and how plants and animals are adapted to the deciduous woodland environment
- [ ] why deciduous woodlands are important and the different ways they are under threat, from climate change and deforestation
- [ ] how a case study of the New Forest shows different ways in which deciduous woodland can be sustainably used and managed.

Which key terms match the following definitions?

a The living parts of an ecosystem (compared with the non-living components).

b Substances that enable plants and animals to grow.

c Permanently removing forest so the land can be used for something else.

d A community of plants and animals that interact with each other and their environment.

e The non-living parts of an ecosystem (as compared to the living components).

f A layer made up of leaves, twigs and other dead material that fall onto the soil surface.

g Transfer of nutrients between living and non-living parts of an ecosystem.

To check your answers, look at the Glossary on pages 296–301.

Ecosystems, Biodiversity and Management

Question 1 Study Figure 15. Explain why there are differences in these nutrient cycles. **(4 marks)**

Student answer

The biomass store is much bigger in the TRF than in the deciduous forest. Strong sunshine and high precipitation all year make the rainforest biome perfect for plant growth.

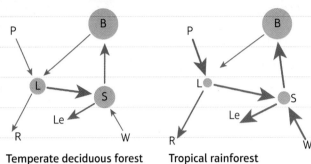

Temperate deciduous forest   Tropical rainforest

Figure 15

Verdict

The question asked for differences: a second difference should have been added to the answer and explained clearly.

Exam tip

Always look at the number of marks for each question. This will guide you in how much is expected from your answer.

Question 2 Assess the importance of ecotourism in the sustainable management of a rainforest in a named region. **(8 marks + 4 SPAG)**

Student answer (extract)

[The student's introduction has been omitted.] Ecotourism is vital to the Analamazoatra reserve. It was only because local people could earn money showing people round the rainforest that they wanted to keep the rainforest rather than cut it down.

Money from ecotourism provides one-third of Association Mitsinjo's budget. It uses this money for a wide range of sustainable rainforest management projects, including training local farmers in a rice-growing system that improves yields and reduces dependence on tavy.

Two-thirds of Association Mitsinjo's budget comes from international aid. Although aid makes sustainable rainforest management possible, it is ecotourism that makes the rainforest more valuable as it is rather than cut down for timber or farming.

Verdict

The student has explained ecotourism's importance and has considered one other factor: international aid. Although the student has said which of the two factors they think is most important, they should have spent more time at the end of the answer making an overall assessment that clearly explains which factor is most important and why.

Pearson Education Ltd accepts no responsibility whatsoever for the accuracy or method of working in the answers given.

Writing geographically: developing your answer

When you are asked to write an explanation, discussion, assessment or evaluation, you need to support, explain and develop your ideas.

Learning objective

- To understand how to link and develop ideas using subordinate clauses and non-finite clauses

Definitions

Main clause: the most important clause in a sentence to which other clauses may be linked.

Subordinate clause: a clause that adds detail to or develops the main clause, linked with a **subordinating conjunction** such as *because, if, although*, etc.

Non-finite clause: a clause beginning with a non-finite verb, for example:

- **a present participle:** a verb form ending in *–ing*, e.g. *running, building, forming, falling*, etc.
- **a past participle:** a verb form often ending in *–ed*, e.g. *formed, happened*, etc., although there are several exceptions, e.g. *known, built, fallen*, etc.

How can I link and develop my ideas?

Look at this exam-style question:

> Assess the following statement: 'Climate change presents a greater threat to tropical rainforests than it does to deciduous rainforests.'
> **(8 marks + 4 SPAG)**

Now look at a sentence from one student's response to it:

> *Climate change could have increasing effects on the temperature, rainfall and soil in both of these biomes because it may alter the structure and biodiversity of their ecosystems.*

This is the main clause in this sentence. This subordinate clause develops the writer's argument by adding an explanation to provide supporting evidence. This subordinating conjunction links the subordinate clause to the main clause and signals an explanation.

Now look at these three sentences taken from the same student's response:

> *In the Amazon rainforest there was a longer than normal period of drought between 2005 and 2010. There was an unusual northerly shift in rain-bearing winds. River levels dropped and certain species of light-wooded trees grew more.*

1. How could you express the connection between these three pieces of information more clearly? Experiment with different ways of linking them in one or two sentences.

Conjunctions bank

when	because	whereas	if	although	even though	as	until	unless

2. Look closely at your answer to question 1, and compare it with the original version above. Which do you prefer, your version or the original? Write a sentence or two explaining your choice.

How can I link and develop my ideas in different ways?

You can also connect two related pieces of information in one sentence using a non-finite clause.

Compare these two extracts:

> **Extract A** *Similar changes to temperature and rainfall in the UK could happen. This would threaten some species of trees in areas that have well-drained, highly permeable soils. These are found in places like the chalk Chiltern Hills and sandy soils in Norfolk.*

> **Extract B** *Similar changes to temperature and rainfall in the UK could happen, threatening some species of trees in areas that have well-drained, highly permeable soils, found in places like the chalk Chiltern Hills and sandy soils in Norfolk.*

In Extract A, three pieces of related information are expressed in three separate sentences.

In Extract B, the writer clearly expresses how they are linked using this present participle to form a non-finite clause and this past participle to form a second non-finite clause.

3. Link these **four** pieces of information in just one sentence using non-finite clauses:

> *(1) Climate change could have increasing effects on temperature, rainfall and soil in both tropical and deciduous rainforests. (2) This could alter the structure and biodiversity of these ecosystems. (3) It could lead to an upset in the balance of the ecosystem. (4) This is known as a dynamic equilibrium.*

Did you notice?

The sentence you wrote in question 3 is much longer than the sentences in the original answer. Very long sentences can be difficult to read.

4. Try rewriting the sentences you wrote in question 3 as two or three sentences. Which version expresses the information most clearly?

Improving an answer

Look at these six sentences taken from a student's response to the exam-style question on page 150:

> *Climate change could have increasing effects on the temperature, rainfall and soil in both tropical rainforests and temperate deciduous forests.*
>
> *This could reduce their organic productivity.*
>
> *Tropical rainforests produce nearly 50% more organic matter than temperate deciduous forests.*

> *This could suggest that climate change is a greater threat to tropical rainforests.*
>
> *Climate change is likely to create more extreme weather in both biomes.*
>
> *A change in balance could have significant impact on both biomes.*

5. Rewrite the sentences above to link and develop each point as clearly as possible. You could:

- use subordinating conjunctions and/or non-finite verbs to link ideas

- link the points into one, two, three or more sentences.

6. Rewrite the sentences again, experimenting with different ways of linking them. Which version is the most clearly expressed? Write a sentence or two explaining your choice.

Component 2
The Human Environment

Content overview

In this component you will learn about human geography and issues about people and the environment.

- Topic 4 starts with an overview of how and why cities around the world change, before focusing on case studies of a major UK city (Birmingham) and a major city in an emerging country (Mexico City).

- Topic 5 investigates why global development is uneven, before focusing on a case study of an emerging country (India).

- Topic 6 investigates the global and UK distribution of food, energy and water resources, before you choose to study energy or water resource management in more depth.

Your assessment

You will sit a 1 hour and 30 minute exam, with three sections.

- **Section A** has questions about changing cities: you must answer **all** the questions in this section.

- **Section B** has questions about global development: you must answer **all** the questions in this section.

- **Section C** has questions about resource management: you must answer Question 3, and then choose **one** question from Question 4 (energy) **or** Question 5 (water).

- You may be assessed on geographical skills in any section, and can use a calculator.

- Each section is worth 30 marks; in addition, up to four marks will be awarded for spelling, punctuation, grammar and use of geographical language (SPAG).

- There will be a variety of different question types, including multiple-choice, calculations and open questions.

- Open questions are where you write a longer answer, from one or two sentences to extended writing worth up to eight marks. In the eight-mark questions, four additional marks will be awarded for SPAG.

4 | Changing Cities

As more of the world's population live in cities then the way cities change is also becoming more important. Urbanisation is a global process that has gathered speed over the last 20 years and its effects are becoming more complex. The search is on to find a way to make living in cities sustainable. Different countries have tried a range of strategies to make their cities more sustainable and environmentally friendly. Some progress has been made in terms of recycling in cities and attempts to reduce air pollution but so far no city can claim to be truly sustainable. This section will look at major world patterns in urbanisation and at two contrasted major cities, Birmingham and Mexico City, to see what progress they have made towards becoming sustainable.

Your learning

In this section you will investigate key learning points:

- the nature of urbanisation in emerging, developing and developed countries
- the reasons why urbanisation has occurred at different times and speeds
- the reasons for UK population distribution and location of its cities
- what affects the rate and degree of UK urbanisation
- the site and connectivity of Birmingham, a major UK city
- the structure of Birmingham's centre, suburbs and urban-rural fringe
- the processes of urbanisation, suburbanisation, counter-urbanisation and re-urbanisation in Birmingham
- the causes and impact of national and international migration there
- the causes and impact of de-industrialisation and de-centralisation and increasing inequality in Birmingham
- changes in retailing in Birmingham
- how Birmingham is trying to be more sustainable and to improve the quality of life for the people who live there
- the site and connectivity of Mexico City, a major city in an emerging country
- the growth of Mexico City and the structure of its centre, suburbs and urban-rural fringe
- the causes and impact of national and international migration in Mexico City
- inequality and quality of life in Mexico City and issues arising from its rapid growth, such as air pollution, housing and employment
- the advantages and disadvantages of bottom-up and top-down approaches to solving Mexico City's problems.

Urbanisation is a global process

Developing an urban world

The majority of people in the world now live in cities, and between 2015 and 2030 the number of people living in cities will increase from 3.8 billion to 5.1 billion. Nearly all this growth will take place in cities in the emerging or developing world. In 2014, there were 2.9 billion people living in cities in emerging or developing countries and by 2020 this figure will reach 4.1 billion. By contrast the urban population of developed countries will only grow from 1 billion to 1.05 billion. Figure 1 shows how the population living in urban areas is expected to increase from 1950 to 2030.

The process of urbanisation in developed countries

Most of the growth in towns and cities in the developed world took place in the 19th century at the same time as the Agricultural and Industrial Revolutions. In the countryside new machinery on farms meant fewer workers were needed, while in the towns there were new job opportunities in the new factories. In the UK, towns grew rapidly by 10% per year between 1830 and 1890, and have continued to grow ever since. Now 82% of the UK population lives in urban areas. There have been some recent changes, such as **counter-urbanisation**, where people leave towns to live in the countryside, and **re-urbanisation**, where some, often young, people choose to move to live close to city centres.

The process of urbanisation in emerging and developing countries

In developing and emerging countries, such as Mexico, growth of towns and cities has been more recent than in developed countries. Most growth has taken place in the last 50 years, and has happened much faster than in developed countries. This results in important

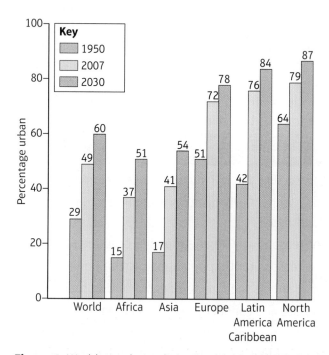

Figure 1 World population living in cities in 1950, 2007 and 2030

differences between urban areas in developed, emerging and developing countries. For example, because of rapid growth in emerging and developing countries there is not enough time to build sufficient houses for those moving into cities. Some people have to rent or build their own homes in slums or **shanty towns**.

Did you know?

The world's fastest growing cities from 2006 to 2014 were:

1 Beihai in China
2 Ghaziabad in India
3 Sana'a in Yemen
4 Surat in India.

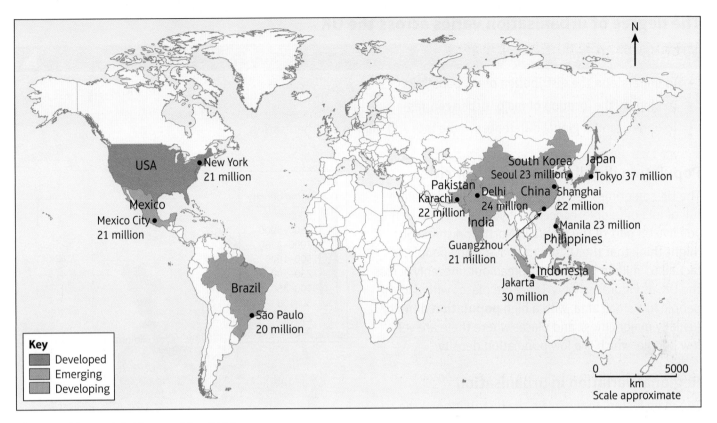

Figure 2 The world's biggest cities, 2014

Why are cities in emerging and developing countries growing so fast?

There are two main reasons cities are growing so rapidly.

1 **Natural increase**: birth rates are higher than death rates. Migrants tend to be young and death rates are low, so cities are dominated by young children.

2 **Migration** from the countryside, which is a result of push factors (such as mechanisation of farming, lack of farm jobs, crop failures and harsh conditions of rural life) and pull factors (such as better jobs and higher wages, and better services such as piped water, electricity, healthcare and education).

This growth has resulted in the formation of very large cities known as **megacities**.

Activity

Study Figure 1.

1 What percentage of people were living in cities in Europe in 1950 and in 2007?

2 By how much is the percentage of people living in cities in Asia expected to increase between 1950 and 2030?

3 In which continent is the percentage of people living in cities predicted to double between 1950 and 2030?

4 Study Figure 2. Write two short paragraphs to describe and explain the pattern of cities shown on the map.

Exam-style question

Explain the very rapid growth of megacities in developing or emerging countries. **(4 marks)**

Exam tip

The growth of megacities is often due to a range of factors so do not just write about one factor; make sure you give four or five factors.

The degree of urbanisation varies across the UK

Learning objectives

- To understand the distribution of UK population
- To identify the location of major urban centres
- To understand regional differences in the rate and degree of urbanisation

Population distribution and major cities

The UK sometimes seems to be an overcrowded place full of lots of people, especially if you live in a town. If you live on part of the moors in North Yorkshire you might think that the UK did not have many people. In fact all 63 million people are spread out unevenly across the UK, as Figure 3 shows. There are places with a lot of people in a small area, with a high **population density** (usually major cities), and places where there are very few people, which is a low population density.

Regional variation in urbanisation

The main factors that explain the distribution of the UK population are physical, historical, economic and political.

Physical factors

The UK can be roughly divided into two main parts by a line drawn from the River Tees in the north-east to the River Exe in Devon. To the north and west of this line the land is mostly higher, with mountains and steep slopes in Wales, Scotland and the Pennines. To the south and east of this line the land is lower and flatter.

These physical factors affect population density. In the north and west the land is higher, slopes are steep, soils are thin and farming is difficult and hard work; as a result, fewer people live here. The rich soils to the south and east (Herefordshire and East Anglia) also result in lower population density as these areas are mostly farming communities generally far from large towns.

Historical factors

In the 19th century, the Industrial Revolution had a big impact on population distribution. This led to rapid growth of factory towns on the coalfields of central Scotland, north and north-east England and south Wales. Industrial cities, such as Birmingham, Manchester,

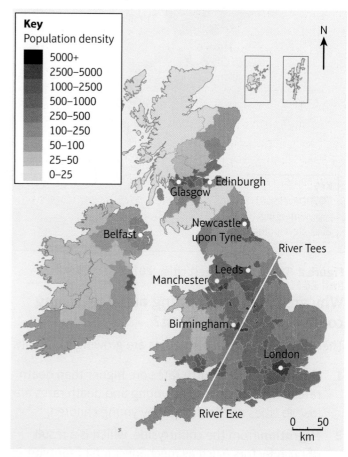

Figure 3 Population distribution in the British Isles, 2010

Glasgow, Bradford, Swansea and Newcastle, grew rapidly. In 1801, London was the only city in the UK with over 100,000 people; by 1901 there were 33 cities with over 100,000 people (home to 56% of the total population). Similarly, in 1801, only 17% of the 10 million population of the UK lived in towns of over 10,000. By 1891, 54% of the 33 million population lived in these towns and cities, which became important industrial centres with large populations. Although some of these centres have declined since then, these cities remain large important **conurbations**.

London stood out from the other towns of the UK in 1801 and continues to do so today because of its size and its importance. London had been the capital city and an important port for so long that it attracted industries and in-migration of people in search of work.

Recent economic factors

From the 1950s onwards, UK economic growth focused on **tertiary industries**, such as transport, health and education, and **quaternary industries**, such as research and development. These need space and access to good transport and communications, plus access to the growing markets of the European Union. They are strongest in different parts of the UK, especially southern and south-east England. Places such as Swindon, Basildon, Harlow and Basingstoke all grew rapidly. In particular London has continued to grow rapidly and it is the centre of UK road, rail and air communications, has a large market, a large labour force and is a world centre of banking, culture and the creative industries.

Table 1 Growth of UK towns and cities, 1981, 2001 and 2011

Rate of population growth for the decades ending 1981, 2001, 2011	1981 (%)	2001 (%)	2011 (%)
Major cities	−1.9	2.0	8.0
Large cities	1.0	1.7	6.1
Small cities	1.5	2.1	6.3
Large towns	1.4	3.0	6.0
Small towns	5.6	5.8	6.8

Political factors (London)

London is the centre of UK government and decision making. This has been an important factor in encouraging firms and people to move to live in or near the capital. This is reinforced by the UK's relationship with the European Union: the UK buys and sells many goods and services there. London's importance as a world-class financial centre is another reason for its continued growth.

Activity

Study Table 1.

1 Which group of towns grew most rapidly in the ten years after 1981?

2 When did major cities experience their fastest growth?

3 Overall what have been the main changes in the growth of cities between 1981 and 2011?

4 Why do more people live in the south-eastern part of the UK than in the north-western part of the UK?

Checkpoint

Now it is time to review your understanding of urbanisation.

Strengthen

S1 Which two continents had the fastest growing cities between 2006 and 2014?

S2 Where are areas of low population density in the UK, and why?

S3 How did the Industrial Revolution change population distribution in the UK?

Challenge

C1 Why are cities in emerging and developing countries growing so quickly?

C2 Why were towns on the coalfields so important in the 19th century?

C3 Explain how political factors affect the distribution of population in the UK.

Case Study – Birmingham: a major UK city

Learning objectives

- To understand the site and context of a major UK city
- To recognise the importance of its connectivity in regional and global contexts
- To know the structure of the city in terms of its functions and building age

The site and situation of Birmingham

The city of Birmingham grew up on a dry point **site** on a south-facing, sandstone ridge overlooking a crossing point of the River Rea. Before the 19th century, Birmingham was a small market town on the Birmingham plateau overshadowed by the surrounding county towns of Stafford, Worcester and Warwick. The original main road to London from the north-west crossed the Midlands via Lichfield and Coventry, not Birmingham.

Birmingham developed its own industries of jewellery, gun making and the brass trade. To create high quality goods, these industries needed skilled labour but only small amounts of raw materials in the time before canals were built to carry bulky goods.

From the 1830s, Birmingham began to spread rapidly outwards. This was when its **situation** in the centre of the Birmingham plateau and the middle of the country became so important. First canals and then railways connected Birmingham with other Midlands towns and the rest of the UK, enabling manufacturing to easily source raw materials and reach markets.

Activity

Study Figure 4 and use an atlas.

1. Which motorways meet at Birmingham?
2. Use your atlas to describe how Birmingham is connected to the rest of the UK by motorway. Include details of distances to well-connected cities, and any areas which are poorly connected.
3. Explain why Birmingham's good communications network is useful for industry, business and leisure.

Today Birmingham is still at the heart of the UK road and rail network (Figure 4). Birmingham is also a major global centre, based on its airport and its reputation as a conference centre.

The structure of Birmingham

Figure 5 shows the centre of Birmingham, and the **central business district** (CBD). This is one of the oldest areas of the city, dominated by department

Figure 4 The motorway network around Birmingham

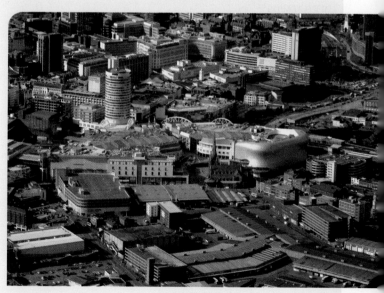

Figure 5 Part of Birmingham city centre

stores, specialist and variety goods shops, offices, theatres and hotels. This is the heart of the city and the centre of local government. Many buildings in the CBD are quite new following redevelopment projects, such as the new Bullring shopping centre. The quality of the environment in the CBD is quite high with some open green space. Because land here is expensive the building density is high, with buildings both close together and taller than in the rest of the city.

Beyond the CBD are the 19th-century inner-city areas, which were redeveloped in the 1970s into **comprehensive development areas** (CDAs). Here the buildings are tower blocks of flats or high density terraces. There are few shops, even fewer factories and a few churches with limited open green space.

The suburbs extend beyond the inner zone and occupy a large part of the city's area. Some of the suburbs were built in Victorian times, while others were built in the 1930s, 1950s and 1960s. Some are centres of council housing (many of which have been purchased) and others were built as private estates. Here the density of buildings is low, and the land use is mainly housing with a few shops and some good quality green space.

The industrial zones of the city stand out clearly, radiating outwards from the city centre, with two important ones radiating in an easterly and north-easterly direction. Suburban industrial areas are also significant in the geography of the city, and are usually located close to a main road.

On the outskirts of the city is the urban–rural fringe. This is where town meets country. There is a mixture of land uses here, such as some housing, golf courses, business parks and airports.

Exam-style question

Explain why there are differences in the age of buildings and functions in a cross section from the centre of a major UK city to the outskirts. **(4 marks)**

Exam tip

Make sure you name the UK city and give reasons for both parts of the question.

Activity

1   Make a copy of the table below, then add details to show the differences between different parts of Birmingham.

	CBD	Inner city	Suburbs
Age of buildings			
Density of buildings			
Functions			
Land uses			
Environmental quality			

2   Study Figure 5, which shows the CBD and the area just outside it, the CBD Frame. Discuss where these two areas are in the photograph and how you can tell.

Checkpoint

Now it is time to review your understanding of the site, context and connectivity of Birmingham.

Strengthen

S1 What is the site of a place?

S2 Describe the situation of Birmingham, and why it was important in the city's growth.

S3 What were Birmingham's 19th-century industries?

Challenge

C1 Which towns were important in the area before Birmingham?

C2 Explain why inner-city parts of Birmingham were redeveloped.

C3 Why are building densities high in the CBD?

The changing city

Urbanisation (18th and 19th centuries)

Urbanisation in Birmingham was based on the manufacture of jewellery, guns, buttons and brass before factory production in the 19th century led to rapid urbanisation. New estates were built in a hurry in places like Small Heath, Selly Oak and Saltley for people and their children arriving from the countryside.

Suburbanisation (1920s and 1930s)

Birmingham had to expand and in the 1920s suburbanisation saw large estates of both council houses and private houses built: mostly semi-detached houses, on large areas of land. These estates often lacked shops and clinics. However, they were laid out with wide tree-lined roads and grass verges in an attempt to maintain the quality of the environment.

Counter-urbanisation (1970s onwards)

Counter-urbanisation involves people abandoning cities in favour of areas which are more rural. In the case of Birmingham this movement was boosted by the redevelopment of the city's inner-city areas. Here five new CDAs were created by demolishing all the old 19th-century terraces and courts. The redevelopment forced people to move out either to estates on the edge of the urban area or to new towns like Redditch.

Re-urbanisation (after 1990)

More people now want to live close to the amenities the city centre offers. New apartments have been built near the canals and in converted factories across the city centre. Birmingham is in the process of giving itself a facelift by actively redeveloping parts of its CBD and inner areas. Older tower blocks have been refurbished, and new centres developed like the Mailbox (Figure 6): a mixture of shopping, leisure, offices and apartments.

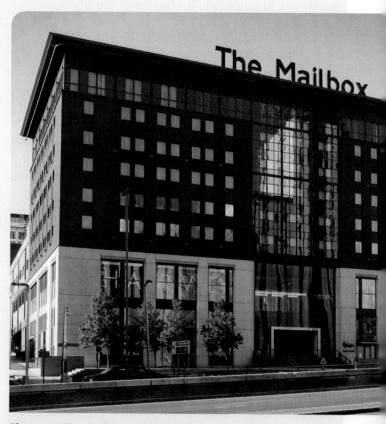

Figure 6 The Mailbox, Birmingham

Activity

1 Explain what is meant by counter-urbanisation.

2 What is meant by the re-urbanisation of cities?

3 Make lists of reasons people may wish to leave big cities, or move into city centres. Which age groups may be involved?

4 Look again at the headings on these two pages. Use them to draw a graphic of Birmingham which summarises how movements of people have changed the city. Add details such as locations and dates.

Migration

The population geography of cities like Birmingham has changed a lot over the last 50 years as a result of national and international migration.

National migration

- Migration to retire. This involves people who decide to retire to a different part of the UK such as the south-west of England.

- Search for better job prospects. This is rural-to-urban or urban-to-urban migration when people (often young) seek better job opportunities in cities like Birmingham. Of course some Birmingham people also seek jobs in London and other UK cities or abroad.

- Study. This type of migration mainly involves young people and is often temporary. Birmingham is the UK's second biggest student city, with five universities and 78,000 students aged over 18 in 2011, an increase of 63% in ten years; 10% of students are from overseas (see Topic 8, page 283).

International migration

- In the 1950s, responding to a shortage of workers the UK government encouraged immigration from former colonies in the Caribbean, India, Pakistan and Bangladesh to fill jobs that UK people no longer wanted to do in transport and industries like textiles and steel.

- Since 2000, many migrants have come from eastern Europe, especially Poland, Latvia and Estonia, seeking better jobs and living standards. The majority of the immigrants are young; 80% are aged 18–34 (Table 2).

- Flight from conflict. In the 2012–15 period, many people fled from fighting in Syria and Afghanistan and migrated to Birmingham and other UK cities.

Table 2 Top ten non-UK countries of birth, 2011

Country of birth	% of total population
Pakistan	5.2
India	2.5
Ireland	1.5
Jamaica	1.4
Bangladesh	1.3
Poland	0.9
Somalia	0.7
China	0.6
Kenya	0.4
Nigeria	0.3

The impact of migration on parts of Birmingham

The arrival of migrants in Birmingham has affected different parts of the city.

The immigrants from the 1970s sought cheap housing and found this in the older, inner-city parts of Birmingham such as Sparkhill, Sparkbrook and Aston. Here they found terrace houses which were cheap to rent and later to buy, and since then communities of people from Pakistan, India and Bangladesh have developed in these areas. There are now many shops and services, including places of worship, in these parts of the city.

Many of the more recent immigrants have often located towards the eastern side of the city quite close to the centre in areas around Bordesley. Here too there were houses which were relatively cheap to either rent or buy. Most are terrace houses with some blocks of flats and here too community centres have been built to cater for existing and new communities.

Population characteristics and de-industrialisation

Learning objectives

- To identify Birmingham's key population characteristics
- To understand the reasons for population change
- To recognise the cause of de-industrialisation

The following are some key facts about Birmingham from the 2011 census.

- Just over 1.1 million people live in the city.
- Since 2004, the population has increased by almost 100,000 (this is an average of 0.9% per year).
- This growth is caused by a rising birth rate and falling death rate, combined with migration from the UK and internationally.
- Birmingham is one of the UK's most diverse cities with 42% of its inhabitants from ethnic groups other than white.
- In the same vein, 46.1% of Birmingham residents said they were Christian, 21.8% said they were Muslim and 19.3% said they had no religion; 22% of the residents of Birmingham were born outside the UK compared with a national average of 14% for England.

Birmingham's population pyramid (Figure 7) shows age groups with more people than the national average (shaded grey) and age groups with fewer people than the national average (shaded red).

Activity

Study Table 3. Sparkbrook is an area of mainly Victorian terraced housing 2 km south east of Birmingham city centre.

a   How does Sparkbrook compare with the rest of Birmingham in terms of the percentage of young and old people?

b   Draw three pie graphs to show the ethnicity of Sparkbrook, Birmingham and England. Describe the differences you can see.

Table 3 Comparison of inner-city Sparkbrook with the rest of Birmingham, 2011

	Sparkbrook (inner city) (%)	Rest of Birmingham (%)	England (%)
Persons aged 0–15	30.8	22.8	18.9
Persons aged 16–64	61.0	64.3	64.8
Persons aged 65 and over	8.2	12.9	16.3
Persons born overseas	42.5	22.2	13.8
White ethnicity	12.4	57.9	85.4
Asian or Asian British ethnicity	61.4	26.6	7.8
Black or black British ethnicity	10.8	9.0	3.5
Other or multiple ethnicity	15.4	6.5	3.3

De-industrialisation in Birmingham

De-industrialisation is the decline of industries in a city. The main causes are the following.

- **Globalisation** This is the process by which cities become part of a world market. In Birmingham this meant that its industries of car and motorcycle manufacture suffered badly in the 1970s from imported vehicles from Japan and western Europe.

- **De-centralisation** The 1970s were also a time of **de-centralisation** in Birmingham when many inner-city areas were redeveloped. Factories were either closed and demolished, or they moved out of the city.

- **Technological advances** The development of new technologies associated with metal manufacture were slow to be applied to the older factories in Birmingham. As a result some firms went out of business because they did not have the new technology which often made the goods cheaper.

- **Transport developments** Part of the redevelopment of central Birmingham in the 1970s was the construction of an inner ring road. In order to build the new road, older factories, warehouses and houses had to be demolished. Some of these factories never reopened and others moved away from Birmingham.

Impacts of de-industrialisation on Birmingham
- Factories closed.
- Workers were made redundant.
- Some factories relocated to the suburbs or to new towns like Redditch.
- There was large-scale unemployment and the need to retrain many workers.
- It left many brownfield sites, with empty factories and warehouses.
- There was some large-scale **pollution** of the land where former industries such as metal smelting had taken place.

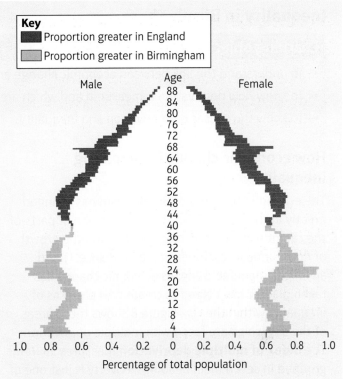

Figure 7 Birmingham's population compared with the average for England, 2011

Activity

1 Study Figure 7. In which age groups does Birmingham have more and fewer people than the national average?

2 What are the implications of the population pyramid for (a) schools and (b) the health services in Birmingham in the future?

3 Classify the causes and effects of Birmingham's de-industrialisation into local and global.

Did you know?

Birmingham's 78,000 students have an impact on the city's geography and population structure. In two areas of Selly Oak over 80% of residents are students. Students make up most of the bulge around age 20 on Birmingham's population pyramid (Figure 7).

Inequality in Birmingham

How economic change is increasing inequality

The economic structure of Birmingham has changed greatly in the last 50 years, with the decline of parts of the car industry, high unemployment and the growth of newer industries, for example in finance, IT and advanced manufacturing. As economic change has taken place it has helped to create new patterns of inequality within the city. Figure 8 shows those areas of the city which are faced with multiple deprivation. The **index of multiple deprivation** measures 38 items grouped in seven main headings. Poverty is just one of these indices, and it is important to remember that not all deprived people live in deprived areas.

Activity

Study Figures 8 and 9.

1 Describe the location of the most deprived areas in Birmingham.
2 Describe the location of the areas with least deprivation.
3 To what extent are the most deprived areas also areas with many unemployed people?

Deprivation in Birmingham

The maps show clearly some of the issues facing the different parts of the city. The inner-city areas are: very disadvantaged in terms of deprivation; areas with people who are often poor; areas with high unemployment; areas with some poorer schools; and areas with poorer health provision.

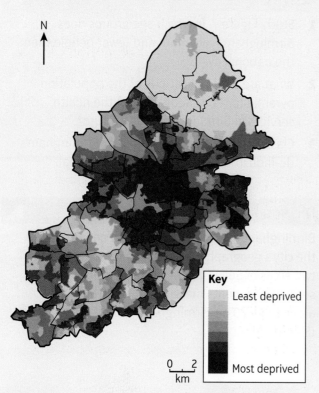

Figure 8 Birmingham wards showing areas of multiple deprivation, 2011

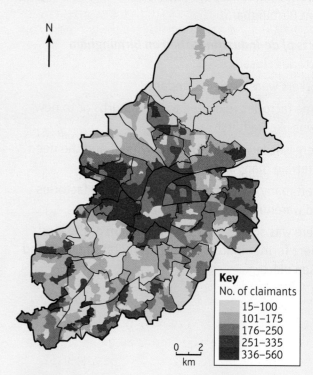

Figure 9 Out-of-work benefits claimants in Birmingham, 2014

164

However, it would be wrong to think that deprivation is confined to the inner-city areas of Birmingham. Some of the suburban areas, particularly towards the south and west, also have issues such as: high levels of deprivation; high unemployment; areas with people who are poor; poor living conditions; and poor schools.

Much of the deprivation is the result of the decline in manufacturing industries and the flight of industry away from both inner-city and suburban sites in Birmingham. It is often combined with older housing and obsolete buildings which are no longer suitable for newer industry. This in turn leads to a lack of investment and hence a spiral of decline.

Why is there inequality in Birmingham?

- There are few factories, providing few local jobs, with the result that people have to travel to find work and this adds to the expense.
- Many of the new jobs are only part-time or temporary and do not pay well.
- There may be some discrimination against newcomers and some racial discrimination, though this is being actively tackled and overcome.
- The large number of people arriving in a short time makes it hard to provide what is needed quickly, for example schools and health services.
- Older houses in these areas can be damp and hard to heat and this can lead to health issues.
- Many migrants are well qualified, for example as doctors, dentists and lecturers; but in the 21st century people with few qualifications find it harder to find good quality jobs.
- Economic change is so rapid that cities find it hard to keep pace, and cities like Birmingham have not had the money to do all they would wish to in order to reduce the inequality of areas.

Quality of life in Birmingham

The **quality of life** in Birmingham varies in the same way that the levels of deprivation vary. Some suburban areas of the city, such as Sutton Coldfield, remain prosperous as they have been for a long time and here the quality of life is seen as good with relatively low crime rates, high purchasing power, a wide range of shops, and low air and water pollution. Dissatisfaction

> ### Exam-style question
> Explain why economic change in a major UK city has increased inequality. **(4 marks)**

> ### Exam tip
> Make sure you define terms such as 'inequality' used in a question at the start of your answer.

with rubbish collection is moderate, as are complaints about light and noise pollution, but there are many areas of green space.

In inner-city Sparkbrook there is some deprivation but people are generally not unhappy with the quality of their lives. There is a wide range of shops selling produce from all over the world, including specialist vegetable and other shops. There are concerns over crime, or more accurately the way the media dubbed the city the gun capital of the UK. There is some concern over air pollution and rubbish collection, and there is less green space than in areas further from the city centre, but the quality of life is still seen by most people as good.

Checkpoint

Now it is time to review your understanding of changes in Birmingham, together with migration, inequality and the causes of deprivation.

Strengthen

S1 What are the differences between counter-urbanisation and re-urbanisation?

S2 Why has the economic structure of Birmingham changed recently?

S3 How does the index of multiple deprivation measure deprivation?

Challenge

C1 Migrants are often young people. How does this help explain the shape of Birmingham's population pyramid?

C2 What are the links between de-industrialisation and deprivation?

C3 Explain why a good education system is important to a city like Birmingham.

Changes in retailing in Birmingham

Learning objectives

- To know about recent changes in retailing
- To understand the impact of these changes on the city
- To identify specific trends, such as out-of-town shopping areas and the growth of internet shopping

There have been changes to retailing in Birmingham over the last 40 years which have had a significant impact on different parts of the city. The CBD consists of an inner and outer **core** (Figure 10) and wider **frame**.

The inner core consists of department stores, specialist shops and office blocks. The outer core consists of smaller shops, theatres and public administration buildings such as the town hall, located there because they cannot afford to pay such high rents as the inner core shops. The frame is an area of wholesale markets which includes road and rail stations.

The CBD is constantly changing, some parts are expanding into nearby areas (this is called the **zone of assimilation**) where, for example, houses may be converted to offices. In other places the CBD is retreating where firms are closing because property is too old or cramped; this is called the **zone of discard**.

Activity

Study Figure 10.

1   What types of shop are found in the inner core?

2   Why are the functions in the outer core located away from the inner core?

3   Explain why the CBD is expanding in some areas and contracting in others.

Why has Birmingham's CBD changed?

In the early 1990s, the CBD changed as a result of de-centralisation in the city. The first wave of de-centralisation was the 19th-century movement of people away from the high-cost, noisy, polluted city centre to the suburbs. The second wave of de-centralisation saw the movement of manufacturing industry away from the city centre to the suburbs, such as Bournville in 1879.

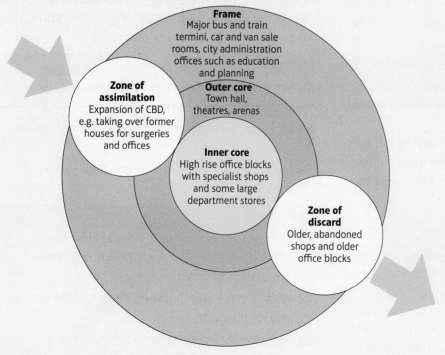

Figure 10 The core and frame of the CBD

In the 1970s, the third wave of de-centralisation was the movement of retail shops out of the city centre. New shopping centres opened in suburbs and then out-of-town shopping centres began to be developed in the 1980s, such as Merry Hill in Dudley. This was the site of a former steel works but then it became a massive new shopping centre in 1985. This created real competition for central Birmingham and between 1990 and 1995 trade in the centre declined by 12%.

The advantages of Merry Hill for retailing are:

- ability to park for free
- under-cover shops out of the weather
- pedestrianised area
- large retail shops like Debenhams and Marks and Spencer.

The fourth wave of de-centralisation saw the growth of internet shopping. More people own computers and have discovered the ease of online shopping. However, Birmingham has been able to avoid a drop in trade by further redevelopment of the city centre.

The CBD fights back

In the 1980s, Birmingham city centre realised it needed to fight back against the out-of-town developments. This was achieved through:

- a series of flagship projects which included the building of the International Convention Centre (ICC) in 1991 and the National Indoor Arena (now the Barclaycard Arena) in 1992
- pedestrianising the city centre to make a more pleasant shopping environment
- encouraging stores to have late-night opening.

As a result, trade in Birmingham city centre grew by 5% between 1995 and 1997. However, retailing in the city continued to change and develop in response to changing local and national conditions.

In 1998, the Mailbox opened in Birmingham. This former Royal Mail sorting office was converted into high-end retail shops (Harvey Nichols), restaurants and offices.

In 2003, the Bullring shopping centre (Figure 11) was reopened after a major makeover. This created a modern shopping centre with parking in an enclosed centrally heated mall.

The next phase was the redevelopment of the New Street station area which has become the new Grand Central shopping centre.

Activity

What were the main methods used by Birmingham to redevelop its central area?

Did you know?

The Bullring in Birmingham has been a centre for markets for 800 years.

Figure 11 The Bullring shopping centre, Birmingham

Checkpoint

Now it is time to review your understanding of retailing in Birmingham.

Strengthen

S1 What are the two parts of the CBD?

S2 What types of land use are found in the frame?

S3 What is the zone of assimilation?

Challenge

C1 What was the second wave of de-centralisation and how did it affect Birmingham?

C2 Why is internet shopping so popular?

C3 How has Birmingham fought back against internet shopping?

Making urban living more sustainable and improving the quality of life

Learning objectives

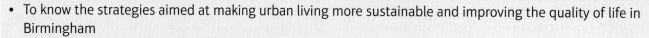

- To know the strategies aimed at making urban living more sustainable and improving the quality of life in Birmingham
- To understand the challenges to making urban living more sustainable
- To understand how to calculate an eco-footprint

The challenge for people in Birmingham is to make their city more sustainable. **Sustainable development** meets present needs but crucially limits consumption of resources today for the benefit of people in the future.

Recycling

UK households produce over 30 million tonnes of waste each year and much of this still goes to landfill sites. More can be recycled.

One glass bottle recycled saves enough energy to power a computer for 30 minutes.

Up to 60% of the rubbish in a dustbin could be recycled; as could 80% of most cars.

On average 16% of the money we spend on a product is packaging and that ends up as rubbish.

The recycling rate for England was 43.5% in 2013; Birmingham achieved 30.1% so clearly still has a way to go in its recycling programme.

Green transport

Birmingham has a range of buses (some powered by gas) used to reduce car transport and pollution in the city. The city has a network of bus lanes which also help to persuade more people to use them for their journeys to work. Electric vehicles were used as part of the CABLED project (Coventry and Birmingham Low Emission Demonstrators 2009–2012).

Birmingham has 571 parks covering 3500 hectares (ha, 35 km^2); more than any other European city.

Activity

Study Figure 12.

1 Write some key points for a social media site which identifies how much more paper and organic matter could be recycled.

2 Write a second set of points for social media to say what actions each home could take to reduce all waste.

3 Identify which of the actions to recycle more could be carried out by individuals and which would need to be led by governments.

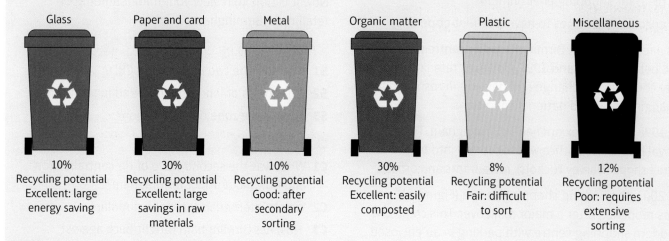

Glass	Paper and card	Metal	Organic matter	Plastic	Miscellaneous
10%	30%	10%	30%	8%	12%
Recycling potential Excellent: large energy saving	Recycling potential Excellent: large savings in raw materials	Recycling potential Good: after secondary sorting	Recycling potential Excellent: easily composted	Recycling potential Fair: difficult to sort	Recycling potential Poor: requires extensive sorting

Figure 12 Recycling household waste

Sustainability in Birmingham

In 2010, Birmingham ranked 15th in the list of sustainable cities in the UK (Table 4).

Birmingham reduced carbon emissions in 2009/10 by 12%, that is by 745 tonnes.

Birmingham created 1000 new jobs in the Grand Central development in 2016 and each new development adds to the jobs total.

Birmingham is working hard to build new schools for its children and to improve the quality of the education offered.

There is continued investment in energy-efficient measures for housing, such as the new homes in Balsall Heath.

Table 4 Birmingham growing greener – how Birmingham has ranked against other cities in the UK (the greenest city ranked 1)

	2007	2008	2009	2010
Overall rank in sustainability	19	19	17	15
Environmental quality	19	17	5	10
Quality of life	15	14	17	19
Futureproofing	19	18	18	9

Community centre, Sparkbrook

Sustainability means thinking about the future for the community and economy, as well as the environment. In 2012, a new community centre was opened in Sparkbrook. Housing three GP practices it serves around 15,000 people, also offering local council services, a library, and providing rooms for community use and offices for start-up local enterprises. The centre has environmentally friendly features and achieved a sustainable building 'excellent' rating.

Did you know?

Birmingham has won 14 consecutive gold medals from the Chelsea Flower Show.

Activity

Study Table 4.

1 Suggest **three** reasons why Birmingham has improved its position in the list of the sustainable cities.

2 Why might the environmental quality have declined between 2009 and 2010?

3 What does futureproofing mean?

Measuring the environmental impact of Birmingham – its eco-footprint

One of the ways that we have of measuring the impact that cities have on the environment is through their ecological footprint (**eco-footprint**). The eco-footprint looks at how much land is needed to provide something with all the energy, water and materials it uses. It also calculates how much pollution is created by burning oil, coal and gas and how much land is needed to absorb the waste created by the people of the city.

Eco-footprints are expressed in terms of how much land is needed to support the lifestyle of the people. The UK average is 5.3 ha per person. The success that Birmingham has had in reducing its eco-footprint can be shown by the fact that its eco-footprint is only 4.15 ha per person.

Checkpoint

Now it is time to review your understanding of the ways in which Birmingham's sustainability and eco-footprint can be improved by different strategies.

Strengthen

S1 How does Birmingham's recycling rate compare with the UK average?

S2 By how much did Birmingham reduce its carbon emissions between 2009 and 2010?

S3 How many parks does the city have?

Challenge

C1 What is the CABLED project?

C2 What does an eco-footprint measure?

C3 How sustainable do you think Birmingham is? Why do you think that?

Case Study – Mexico City: a major city in an emerging country

Learning objectives

- To understand the site and context of a major city in an emerging country
- To recognise the importance of its connectivity in regional and global contexts
- To know the structure of the city in terms of its functions and building age

The location and context of Mexico City influences its growth, function and structure.

Site of Mexico City

Mexico City began life as Tenochtitlan, the capital of the Aztecs. It was founded in 1325 on an island in Lake Texcoco. The Aztecs built causeways to link the island to the western shore of the lake. These could easily be defended in the event of an attack. The lake also provided drinking water for the city and a ready source of fish to supplement people's diet of maize and beans.

Situation and connectivity

The Central Plateau on which Mexico City stands is a relatively flat area surrounded by mountains. Movement of people and goods from earliest times was along this plateau, and Mexico City is at the focal point of all these routes. Later railways and roads followed these north–south routes (Figure 13). The city is also central to the main routes which connect North and South America. All land routes between the two Americas have to pass through Mexico City.

Cultural, economic and global importance

- Mexico City's culture is a mixture of indigenous (pre-Spanish) and Spanish traditions of foods, music, religion and architecture. It is the most important cultural centre in Mexico. The city is home to national opera and theatre as well as TV and radio stations which operate across both Mexico and the neighbouring countries.

- With a population of over 21 million it is the largest metropolitan area in the western hemisphere. It is also the largest Spanish-speaking city in the world.

- It is one of the most important financial centres in the Americas. In 2011, the city had a gross domestic product of US $411 billion making it one of the richest urban areas in the world.

- However, there is great inequality in income, lifestyle, housing, employment and access to services.

Activity

1   Study Figure 13 and a map of Central America in an atlas.

   a   Draw a sketch map showing Mexico's coastlines and borders, and add symbols to show the Sierra Madre mountains.

   b   Add the location of Mexico City and annotate details of its site and situation from the text.

2   Why has movement in the Central Plateau of Mexico always focused on Mexico City?

3   Why is it important for Mexico City to be situated between North America and South America?

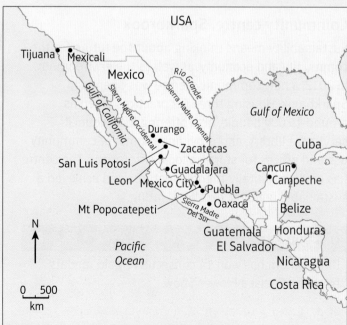

Figure 13 The situation of Mexico City

The structure of Mexico City

Mexico City, like many very large cities, has an important central business district (CBD) which houses banks, insurance and other financial offices. There are also government offices and headquarters of private companies (both Mexican and international).

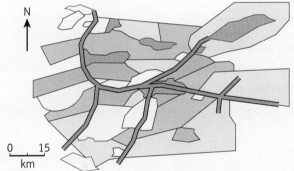

Figure 14 Land use in Mexico City

Beyond the CBD are the inner city areas with middle-class zones of ageing apartment blocks together with some high quality modern apartment complexes. Further out, the pattern is rather complex: a mixture of industrial areas, high luxury areas (mostly gated communities) and crowded areas, some of which are older tenements and others are **squatter settlements**.

Population growth, housing segregation, income level, industrialisation and transportation developments created this pattern. Figure 15 shows a model of land use in Latin American cities. Beyond the CBD it shows a spine of shops connected to the major shopping centre. The market is a traditional area for selling food and

goods. Around the spine are the elite homes of the rich. There are middle-class homes in the zone of maturity and the middle-class tract. The zone of in situ accretion is where new blocks of flats are built amongst existing blocks of flats and houses. The **disamenity** zones are the poorest areas often run by drug lords. The homes on the urban–rural fringe are the 'periférico', usually slums and shanty towns.

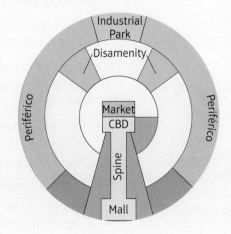

- CBD has both traditional and modern elements
- High class homes surround CBD, Spine and Mall
- Common to find massive peripheries

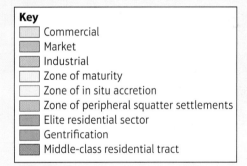

Figure 15 A model of Latin American cities

Mexico City's character is influenced by its fast growth

Learning objectives

- To recognise the reasons for past and present trends in population growth
- To identify the causes of national and international migration
- To understand the impact of migration on different parts of the city

Reasons for the variable population growth of Mexico City

The rate of population growth in Mexico City changed from 1900 to 2000 and the city's share of the country's total population changed.

- **Rural-to-urban migration** People left the countryside in search of jobs, better housing, schooling and modern healthcare and wanting to escape the hardship and poverty of parts of the countryside.
- **Rates of natural increase** A significant part of the growth came from the rise in rates of natural increase especially in the period 1950–1980. The main cause of rising natural increase was a fall in the death rate.
- **Economic investment and growth** One reason for the attraction of Mexico City to migrants from the countryside was the growth in job opportunities in factories and offices as economic investment was channelled into the city.

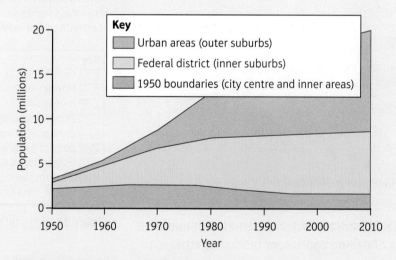

Figure 16 Population growth in Mexico City

Exam-style question

Define the term 'squatter settlement'. **(2 marks)**

Command word

When you are asked to **define** something you state what the term means.

Exam tip

If you are asked to define a term, it is important to include a description of what that term involves, as well as saying where it can be found and if possible giving an example.

Activity

Study Figure 16.

a Estimate the population of Mexico City in 2010.

b Compare the population size and growth in the city centre, inner and outer suburbs between 1950 and 2010.

c Look again at the information about the structure of Mexico City on page 171. Give **one** reason for the population increase in the outer suburbs, and **one** reason for the population decline in the inner areas.

Causes and impact of national and international migration to Mexico City

National migration

Puebla is a poor region to the east of Mexico City. Here life is hard, and there are few alternatives to farming. The literacy rate is only 65%, two-thirds of people lack proper housing and over 60% have no clean water. As a result, many people have left the area and moved to Mexico City. In contrast, over 82% of people in Mexico City have access to both clean water and healthcare.

International migration

People are moving to Mexico City from Europe, Japan and the USA because of the growth of jobs in new factories and offices in the city. Mexico City accounts for 45% of all the country's industrial production and firms such as Renault and banks such as Santander have opened new branches there recently. The cultural life of the city and its domination of services in the country are other attractions.

What has been the impact of these changes on parts of Mexico City?

- Despite the fact that fewer people are now migrating to the USA, the numbers arriving in Mexico City from the countryside continue to remain high. The pressure on housing remains high; even more poor people are having to build their homes in shanty settlements on the edge of the city.
- There have been arrivals of people from other countries such as the USA, France and Germany choosing to live in Mexico City. Most of these people live in the richer homes close to the city centre with its shops, banks, entertainments and other amenities.
- The slum areas beyond the city centre are badly overcrowded. As property is demolished people are having to seek new homes in the shanty towns even further from the city centre.
- The government has begun a programme of home building, mostly in the suburbs towards the eastern and southern edges of the city, which have concentrations of middle-income people.

Activity

1. Where are squatter settlements located in Mexico City?
2. Why are the homes of richer people close to the city centre?
3. What has been the impact of people moving from other countries to live in Mexico City?
4. Study pages 172–173. Make lists of the push factors and pull factors which explain why people migrate to Mexico City.
5. Describe the impact on the suburbs and the edges of the city of the changes in Mexico City in the last 30 years.

Did you know?

In 2015, the population of Greater Mexico City was over 21 million, making it one of the biggest megacities in the world. The population of Guadalajara, Mexico's next biggest city, was a mere 4.8 million.

Exam-style question

Explain why squatter settlements are found in major cities in developing or emerging countries. **(4 marks)**

Exam tip

Check the question carefully – here you need to show you know what a squatter settlement is (the feature), link it to the process (why squatter settlements develop), and give an example.

Inequality and quality of life in Mexico City

City growth and growing inequality

As Mexico City has grown so fast, the inequality within the city has also become worse. The problem is that many of the thousands of people arriving in the city are very poor and have no job. So there is a lot of competition for the jobs that are available, and this means low wages can be paid. Many get work in the **informal economy**. As a result it is hard for the poor to save or to become wealthier. So there are more and more poor people as the city grows and this increases the inequality.

The pattern of residential areas in Mexico City

Anna Gonzales lives in a poor part of Mexico City called Netzahualcoyotl. She and her family of five share a simple two-room home made from scraps of wood and some concrete blocks scavenged from the waste dump. There is no toilet, no glass in the windows and no running water. The family have to share a water tap five minutes walk away. For six days a week Anna walks to her job as a maid for the Romero family.

The Romero family live in a beautiful 14-room house with a large garden and a swimming pool. To Anna their home is like a castle. The Romeros pay Anna US$7 for a 12-hour day, which consists of cooking, cleaning and doing the laundry. By 7 pm Anna heads for home and the Romero family sit down to a big meal of chicken, fish or meat. Anna cooks rice and beans for her family; they can only afford meat once a week.

The families live only a mile apart in the same city but they live in different worlds. The contrast in their lives is an example of spatial inequality. This can be seen very clearly in Figure 17. Anna does not earn enough to be able to qualify for the government housing schemes that are being built on the edge of the city.

Figure 17 Part of Mexico City – rich and poor

Activity

1 Describe the main differences between the two types of housing in Figure 17.

2 Write 100 words for a leaflet to go to rich families in Mexico City urging them to pay their servants more money. Make it very fierce in its tone, saying what might happen if pay does not improve and why paying more will be a good thing for everyone in the long run.

3 Explain what 'spatial inequality' in Mexico City means.

Reasons for difference in quality of life in Mexico City

Income

Some people are very poor and exist on a bare minimum. They live in shanty towns and slums; others have to live on rubbish dumps. The average disposable household income per person in 2013 was US $13,085, lower than the Organisation for Economic Co-operation and Development (OECD) average of US $25,908. But this average conceals the fact that the top 20% of people in Mexico City earn 13 times as much as the bottom 20%. Mexico is developing rapidly, but this vast gap between rich and poor explains much about the wealthier areas and the poorer areas of the city.

Arrival from the countryside

People who have recently arrived in Mexico City from the rural areas are usually poor and have to live in slums or shanty towns.

Political power

The wealthier people are also those with political power. They are able to get homes in the better parts of the city.

Working hours

Poorer people also have to work longer hours in Mexico City; 29% of employees work very long hours compared with an average of 13% working long hours in other developing and emerging countries.

Mexico City has the best living standards in Mexico, but it is also one of the most unequal cities in the Americas. Benito Juarez, right in the centre of Mexico City, is the richest borough. Milpa Alta, a semi-rural borough on the hills to the south, is the poorest. Average incomes in Benito Juarez are four times greater than Milpa Alta.

Table 5 Differences in quality of life in Mexico City, 2010

	Benito Juarez	Milpa Alta
Annual population growth rate	−0.27%	3.2%
Infant mortality rate per 1000 births	11.6	20.3
Food poverty	0.5–3%	10%
Houses with inside piped water	98%	53%
Houses with unstable roof	3%	24%

Activity

1 Why do poorer people live in slums and shanty towns?

2 What is the income gap between rich and poor people in Mexico City?

3 What are the political reasons why some parts of the city are wealthier than others?

Exam-style question

Explain why the quality of life can vary so much between people living in a major city in a developing or emerging country.   **(4 marks)**

Exam tip

If the question asks you to explain do not waste time describing.

Checkpoint

Now it is time to review your understanding of the situation and growth of Mexico City and inequality and quality of life in the city.

Strengthen

S1 Describe Mexico City's situation within Mexico and the Americas.

S2 Describe three reasons for the growth of population in Mexico City.

S3 Compare the diet of the Gonzales family and the Romero family.

Challenge

C1 Use data from the text to summarise the main differences between poorer and wealthier people in work, housing and access to services like education and water.

C2 Explain how population growth and inequality affect different parts of Mexico City.

C3 What is likely to be the impact of the gap between rich and poor in Mexico City on local politics?

Effects of rapid growth in Mexico City

People living in Mexico City face a series of challenges.

Water supply

Providing water for the city has always been a problem, the Aztecs had to build aqueducts to bring water into their capital. The demand for water means that it has to be pumped from reservoirs 96 km to the west. The remaining 70% of the city's water supply comes from 4280 wells sunk deep into the underground **aquifers**, which are running dry. As water is extracted so the land sinks and buildings, power lines and sewage pipes are broken.

Housing

Mexico City cannot provide enough housing for all its people.

- The poorest members of the city tend to be the most recent arrivals from the countryside. As a result some are forced to live on garbage dumps, sorting rubbish to find things they can recycle for cash. They may even build their homes in squatter settlements on the edge of the rubbish.
- Other recent arrivals from rural areas live in slums on the edge of town. Most houses are one-room shacks made of waste materials. Many lack electricity and running water, and streets are seldom paved. Sewage often pollutes the water supply so diseases such as typhoid and cholera are often an issue.
- Migrants who have a job and have been in the city longer live in run-down blocks of flats closer to the city centre.
- The richer areas are increasingly becoming gated communities with security forces as a result of the fear of crime, kidnapping and drug wars.
- The government is trying to provide some housing by building lower income housing developments on the edge of the city. These houses are subsidised but still the cost leaves little for food, clothing, utility bills, commuting and healthcare.

Activity

1 Where do the latest arrivals from the countryside live in Mexico City?

2 Design a poster to advertise your new security offering (for example: cameras, dogs, gadgets to trap burglars in the home) which would appeal to residents of gated communities.

3 How is the government trying to provide housing for the poor?

Informal employment and under-employment

Mexico City is a dynamic centre of manufacturing and finance. It has 18% of Mexico's population and produces 24% of national wealth, but the city has grown faster than the number of 'proper' jobs. So an estimated 60% of jobs in Mexico City are in the informal economy. For example, 60% of house-building and 25% of taxis are unofficial. In the historic area of the city centre there are around 25,000 street sellers of things like sweets, cigarettes and food, and services such as car cleaning. The informal economy occupies every part of the city.

For workers in the informal economy, employment can be insecure and they are open to exploitation, while collecting taxes from the informal economy is a challenge for government.

Miguel Gonzales is a skilled plumber but he does not get enough plumbing work; he often has to resort to shining shoes to keep himself, his wife and his four children. Miguel is under-employed, one of a large group in the city. He lives in a two-storey middle-class home. Others under-employed include street musicians, water sellers, and thousands more smallscale workers, who work for very low pay just to survive. So for Mexico City, although there is unemployment, the big issues are under-employment and informal employment.

Table 6 The main advantages and disadvantages of Mexico City's air pollution measures

Measure	Advantages	Disadvantages
Prohibiting drivers from using their cars one day per week	Less traffic so less pollution	Drivers get round it by buying two cars
Metrobus programme replaced old polluting buses with new ones	New buses have reduced carbon monoxide and particulates by 50% since 2005	New buses are expensive, so fares rise
Building a new US $2 billion underground train line	Reduces the number of cars Cuts average commuting times from 150 to 78 minutes	Very expensive to build

Pollution

Air pollution

In the 1970s, Mexico City was recognised as having a major air pollution problem. The city is surrounded by mountains on three sides preventing the dispersal of pollutants such as ozone, carbon monoxide and **microparticulates**. The high altitude and strong sun mean warm days and cold nights, perfect conditions for the formation of ozone. Added to this are dried-up lake beds which contribute tonnes of fine dust in the dry season.

People living in the city suffered from runny eyes, sore throats and respiratory diseases. A main source of pollution was transport exhaust fumes. Table 6 summarises the government's actions to overcome these issues.

Waste pollution

Every day Mexico City produces 13,000 tonnes of rubbish; unfortunately the waste disposal system can only remove 9000 tonnes each day. The rest is dumped in any bit of open ground, streets, waterways and drains where it clogs the system. From time to time rubbish dumps have been closed and a rubbish mountain results. Worse still, 70 million tonnes of rubbish have been buried beneath waste dumps and these are now polluting water supplies. Of Mexico City's 13,000 tonnes of rubbish, 3600 tonnes go to landfill each day, 3000 tonnes make compost and 800 tonnes make plastic bottles. The rest has no designated destination.

Activity

1 What causes air pollution in Mexico City?

2 What has the city done to reduce its air pollution? Do the advantages of Mexico City's air pollution control measures outweigh the disadvantages?

3 Produce a graphic showing what happens to Mexico City's 13,000 tonnes of rubbish each day.

Exam-style question

Examine the main effects of rapid urbanisation on quality of life in a major city in a developing or emerging country. **(8 marks + 4 SPAG)**

Command word

Examine questions ask you to break something down into its different parts, the impacts, and show how they are linked together in affecting quality of life.

Solving the city's problems and improving quality of life

Learning objectives

- To identify the characteristics of bottom-up and top-down strategies
- To understand the advantages and disadvantages of these approaches
- To evaluate the role of government policies in improving the quality of life within Mexico City

Bottom-up strategies for making the city more sustainable

Community-based initiatives in Mexico City can be seen in the area of Neza in the south-eastern outskirts of the city. Here a small group of migrants formed a group and created a plan to develop the area in an organised way.

In time they were able to raise small amounts of money through savings, built schools and later improved the area through voluntary work. The next step was to open a health centre and to start a programme of supported self-build for people arriving from the countryside. As a result, this part of Mexico City has less crime than other parts of the city and has emerged as a leader in community development.

Advantages of small-scale community development

- Small scale so people feel involved and are likely to go on supporting them after the initial interest has faded.
- Do not take long to get going.
- Do not need a lot of money.
- Do not need a lot of people initially – can set up as an example to others.

Disadvantages of small-scale community development

- Do not have a lot of money, so may not be able to scale up.
- Cannot easily deal with big problems like air pollution.
- May not have political support.

Did you know?

Traffic can be so bad in Mexico City that the super-rich have taken to using helicopters to get from one place to another.

Activity

1 Why do you think that the community development in south-east Mexico City wanted to build a school as soon as possible?
2 How did the people raise money for community developments?
3 How do you think a large-scale government scheme would be different?

Government-led top-down initiatives

The mayor and managers of Mexico City have been active in recent years to address some of the challenges that the city faces.

Air pollution

In terms of air pollution and environment, the city's monitoring programme works extremely well. In 2007, Mexico City implemented a green management initiative and drew up and published a 15-year cross-disciplinary Green Plan (Plan Verde). The plan focuses on areas such as public spaces, waste handling, land use and sanitation. In terms of transport, the Metrobus is a bus rapid transit system (using eco-friendly vehicles) of 16 routes which has reduced air pollution in

Figure 18 The Metrobus in Mexico City

the city. Overall air pollution is down by 35% from the levels in 2000.

Dealing with waste

After the closure of one of its massive rubbish tips, the city set up a massive farmers' market (the 'Mercado de Trueque' or 'barter market') in a large park west of the capital. Under a canopy of big trees, families brought their paper, metals and other recyclable waste to exchange for 'green point' vouchers based on weight. Residents then redeemed their points for seasonal produce from local farmers. Over 3000 families lined up with bags of rubbish on the market's opening day. The city estimates the market brought in nearly 11 tonnes of recyclables in its first day. Since then it has been held the first Sunday of every month. However, this is still a small dent in a very big problem.

The main advantages of government strategies are as follows.

- There is political power to make sure it happens.
- The city government can make sure there is enough money for the project.
- It creates work for people in the city.
- It is possible to deal with large-scale issues such as flooding and air pollution, which smaller community-led strategies cannot do.

The main disadvantages of government strategies are as follows.

- They can take a long time to put into action.
- They may suffer from budget cuts or corruption and so never happen.
- They do not involve local people who may feel alienated.

Activity

1 How successfully do you think Mexico City has tackled its air pollution problem?
2 Are the markets described above likely to solve Mexico City's rubbish problem?
3 What are the main disadvantages of large-scale city-wide government schemes?

Exam-style question

Evaluate how successful one major city in a developing or emerging country has been in improving the quality of life for its people?
(8 marks + 4 SPAG)

Exam tip

When answering a question which asks 'How far…' or 'How successful…' it is important to include both things that have gone well and things that have not gone so well and then to come to a conclusion.

Command word

Evaluate questions ask you to make a judgement about the value or success of something. You need to review the evidence, discuss the strengths and weaknesses, and write a conclusion justifying your judgement.

Checkpoint

Now it is time to review your understanding of the impacts of Mexico City's rapid urbanisation and ways to improve the quality of life there.

Strengthen

S1 How many wells does Mexico City need to provide its water supply?
S2 What are the main causes of air pollution in Mexico City?
S3 Draw a diagram to illustrate where a poor migrant family might live when they first arrive in the city and then where they might live later when they get a job.
S4 Why do you think 'under-employment is the main problem, not unemployment'?

Challenge

C1 What do you think is the biggest problem arising from Mexico City's rapid urbanisation, and why?
C2 In which sort of projects are community groups most successful?
C3 What sort of projects are best suited to action by city governments?

Investigating Changing Urban Environments

Activity

Re-read the ideas about the variations in the quality of life from pages 158 to 169 and then create another two or three key questions which will help you to answer the main task question.

Tip Think about other factors affecting accidents such as weather and types of road junction to form your key questions.

(F) The enquiry question

The important thing when setting out on a geographical enquiry is to be clear on the purpose. One good way to do this is to ask a question. For this enquiry on urban areas the task question is:

Why are there more accidents at some points around a junction in Birmingham city centre than at others?

To help answer the task question, geographers next devise some key questions. These help to provide a focus for the enquiry.

For this task one of the key questions is:

Where are the main concentrations of accidents?

(F) Locating the study

It is important to provide maps showing where the investigation is located. You should include maps at a local and national scale, plus detailed maps showing your survey or data collection sites. You can then use your location and survey site maps to give a detailed overview of the place in which your investigation will take place. This part of your enquiry helps set the scene.

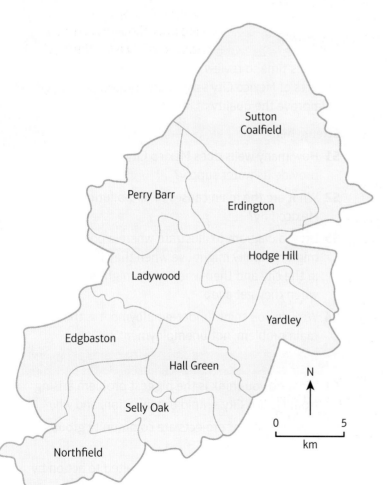

Figure 19 Map of named city areas of Birmingham

Ⓕ Background

Road accidents, especially those involving children, are an important consideration in both rural and urban environments. In recent years the number of road accidents has been declining but their severity has been increasing. Roads are being designed to help reduce accidents but more needs to be done.

In the UK every year about 400 people die from violent crime. By contrast every year over 3000 children die on our roads – nearly nine a day. Although the number killed and injured is falling, it is still too many.

Ⓕ Methodology

Once you have decided on your three key questions and located your study, the next step is to select the methods you will use to collect the data. Geographers use both **primary data** (which is collected first hand) and **secondary data** (which has already been published). In your investigation you should choose at least one **quantitative** method (using numbers), for example a traffic census, and one **qualitative** (descriptive) method, for example photographs or field sketches. It is also important to think about the scale of the fieldwork you will undertake. It would be very difficult to survey all the key roads in a place like the centre of Birmingham. One method is to use a sample, for instance, of the road junctions.

Sampling

Sometimes the most accurate way to investigate an issue is to take a sample; in this case, of roads in Birmingham. There are three main types of sampling.

- **Random sampling** – is used where the area is the same throughout; for example, a field of crops. It does not matter where in the field you take the samples. Random sampling is achieved by generating random numbers and using them as co-ordinates, such as co-ordinates to generate Ordnance Survey grid references.
- **Systematic sampling** – is used in places with an environmental gradient: where things change in a regular fashion, such as traffic along a road. You could sample at ten equally spaced points along a road to investigate changes in traffic density and flow. Every point should be evenly spaced or distributed.
- **Stratified sampling** – is used in places with a lot of different parts. You need to make sure that the number of samples taken is representative of the total area. So in an area with two types of geology, split 40% to 60% over the area, you take in total ten samples, four on one type of rock and six on the other.

Exam-style question

Some students collected traffic data at a systematic sample of major road junctions in the city centre. Explain **one** reason for using systematic sampling to collect this data. **(3 marks)**

Exam tip

Make sure you say what systematic sampling means, before explaining why it would be useful here.

Exam tip

You need to investigate two secondary sources:
- Census data, such as Neighbourhood Statistics from the Office for National Statistics
- one other secondary source.

For each method you select it is important that you decide where, when and how you will collect the data, the size of the sample and why it helps to gather data for the overall investigation. An example of how to present your methodology is shown in Table 7.

Table 7 Counting traffic for one hour on the A38 at the Smallbrook Queensway junction, Birmingham

Method	Outline of method	Purpose of method	Recording
Carry out a traffic census on both sides of the A38 and on the adjoining Smallbrook Queensway and Holloway Head roads in Birmingham.	I chose these sites based on my analysis of the secondary data showing high levels of accidents in this area. I collected data on weather conditions, quality of light and type of vehicle and recorded numbers in each case.	The reason for using this method was to identify what factors affect the possibility of accidents along a busy stretch of main road.	For both northbound and southbound carriageways, record the number of cars, vans and lorries, buses, and motorcycles and cycles passing in one hour.

Risk assessment

Now that you have decided on the methods you will use to collect your data, you will need to produce a risk assessment. In your risk assessment you should consider the following: the potential risks, the severity of each risk – on a scale of 0 (low) to 10 (high) – and how the risk can be managed. An example is shown in Table 8.

Table 8 Risk assessment

Risk	Severity rating	Management
Being injured by traffic	8/10	Choose a place for the survey back from the curb and take care when crossing the road. Wear a high visibility vest.

Activity

1   Copy the table below.

Method	Outline of method	Purpose of method	Recording

Using, first, the method of a field sketch of a danger point and, second, the method of repeating a traffic survey in different weather conditions, describe each method and explain how and why you would conduct them. Use a highlighter to identify where in your descriptions you have explained how you carried out the methods. You should also suggest why the methods will help with answering the main task question.

2   For secondary research investigate local sources of information (police, district or city council) for details of the number, type, frequency and location of accidents in your chosen area.

(F) Data presentation

Having collected your data, you will next need to think about how to present it. Geographers use a range of simple and more sophisticated graphical techniques to present their findings. For your enquiry you should aim to produce a number of both simple and sophisticated techniques. A sophisticated technique is one that uses at least two variables to represent the data: divided bar graphs located either side of the chosen road would be an example of a sophisticated technique using the two elements of location and traffic type. Techniques that could be used to present information for the chosen road or area are:

- annotated photographs/field sketches
- located divided bar graphs for the same area under different weather conditions
- a map of the main danger areas of the site.

When presenting your techniques you should aim to create hand drawn and digitally produced forms of presentation.

Activity

Study Figure 20 and Table 9.

1 At what time of year do most serious accidents happen at this junction?

2 Are there patterns in the weather associated with serious accidents?

3 Why are cyclists at high risk in this type of environment?

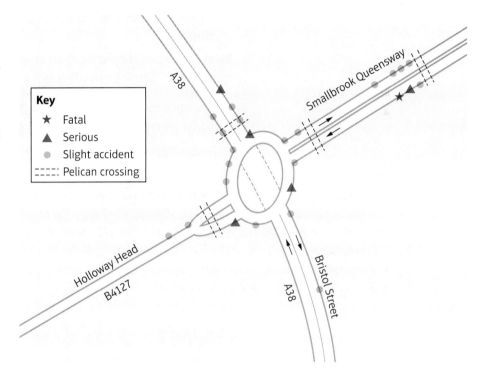

Key
★ Fatal
▲ Serious
● Slight accident
- - - - Pelican crossing

Figure 20 Map showing the location of accidents at the Smallbrook Queensway junction, Birmingham (2012–14)

Table 9 Accidents at the Smallbrook Queensway junction, Birmingham (2012–14)

Accident	1	2	3	4	5	6
Severity	Serious	Serious	Serious	Serious	Serious	Fatal
Month	July	December	November	January	February	March
Time of day	1750	0650	0721	0802	1658	0100
Weather	Dry, windy	Wet, rain and drizzle	Dry	Wet, rain	Dry	Dark, wet, rain
Type	Pedal cycle and taxi	Pedal cycle and van	Pedestrian and car	Pedestrian and car	Two cars	Taxi and pedestrian
Injured party	Cyclist	Cyclist	Pedestrian	Pedestrian	Car driver	Pedestrian

(F) Analysis and conclusions

The next stage of the enquiry is to analyse the data collected and to see how far it addresses your key questions and if these are going to help address the task question. When you are analysing your data it is important to:

- **describe** the general trends from the data – for example, 'There were more accidents during the winter months than the summer months'
- **make comparisons** between the two sets of data for the two occasions of the surveys – for example, 'The flow of traffic was not reduced in wet weather'
- **explain** the reasons linked to geographical theory – for example, 'The flow does not seem reduced or slower in poorer weather conditions and this links to theories that accidents are more likely to happen in poor weather conditions'.

Read the extract below from an analysis a student wrote about data collection in Birmingham. This is a structured response by the student with:

- reference to the data and figure (red)
- use of geographical terminology (green)
- explanation of data and links to theory (yellow).

The flow of traffic along the Smallbrook Queensway was roughly the same (Occasion 1 northbound 237 vehicles per hour, southbound, 198 vehicles per hour, Occasion 2 northbound 218 vehicles per hour, southbound 174 vehicles per hour) on the two occasions of the survey as Figure 20 suggested. However, on the second survey it was raining heavily. This made conditions more slippery and therefore more dangerous. I recorded two cars skidding in the wet at the entry to the tunnel, which suggests the drivers had not changed their speed for the conditions.

Activity

Study Figure 20 and Table 9.

Identify the key elements of this location that make it a particularly dangerous location for accidents.

Once you have analysed your data using the structure above, you need to write a conclusion for the key questions as well as for the overall task question. When writing your conclusion for the key questions you should summarise the findings from the presentation techniques you used. Then state whether your data has proved your key question to be correct or partly correct or incorrect.

The following is an extract from a conclusion written by a student.

The purpose of my investigation was to find out why some points at the Smallbrook Queensway junction are particularly dangerous for road accidents. I can conclude that the road junction I selected is generally a danger point and more dangerous in wet weather. My data supports the theory that weather conditions have an impact on the frequency of road accidents at dangerous points along a road.

F Evaluation

The final part of the enquiry is to evaluate the success of your study. You should review the data collection methods and data presentation techniques, as well as the validity of the overall study.

When writing your evaluation you should follow the structure below for reviewing the data collection methods and data presentation techniques.

- A description of how successful the method/technique was overall.
- The value of the method/technique in providing/presenting appropriate data.
- How the method/technique could have been improved.
- How the method/technique has impacted on the study as a whole.

Below are a student's reflections on their geographical investigation of accidents at the Smallbrook Queensway junction.

> I think overall the methods I used to investigate the traffic flow and danger points worked well. The traffic flow census showed just how much traffic uses this road, but also how it varies with the weather (not much in volume). Presenting the data as divided bar graphs showed the importance of cars, buses and taxis at this junction on the road. The annotated sketches helped to identify the main danger points. I could have improved the study by taking a census at different times of day to see the impact of rush hour, and by suggesting how the junction could be improved.

Activity

1 Suggest how the data collection methods and data presentation techniques could be improved if another student repeated the study.

2 Analyse the conclusion to the study. What is good about it and how might it be improved?

Checkpoint

Now it is time to review your understanding of how to plan and conduct an investigation into changing urban environments.

Strengthen

S1 With a partner produce a flow diagram of planning an enquiry, starting from the choice of enquiry questions and ending with analysis and evaluation.

S2 Explain the difference between at least three methods of sampling and explain how they could each be used in a city.

S3 Make a list of the types of qualitative data you might collect on an investigation into traffic in either an urban or rural area.

Challenge

C1 Explain where and why hand-drawn sketch maps may be very useful in urban areas.

C2 Why is the evaluation part of the study so important?

C3 If you were going to do this study again what three things would you change?

Exam-style question

Some students used figures from the 2011 census for Birmingham in their investigation. What type of data is this?

☐ A Qualitative and primary

☐ B Qualitative and secondary

☐ C Quantitative and primary

☐ D Quantitative and secondary

(1 mark)

F Investigating Changing Rural Environments

Learning objectives

- To understand how to conduct a geographical investigation of change in rural settlements
- To know how to choose enquiry questions, fieldwork methods and data sources for a rural settlement investigation
- To know how to present, analyse and evaluate data collected from a rural settlement investigation

Activity

1 What challenges do you think Ambleside faces in managing the large numbers of tourists that visit during the summer months? Suggest **three**.

2 Why do you think that one of the key questions for this enquiry is about where there are most pedestrians in Ambleside and which way pedestrians are moving?

3 Suggest **two** more key questions that would help answer this task question.

F The enquiry question

When conducting a geographical enquiry, it is important to have a purpose. One way to do this is to ask a task question.

For this enquiry on rural settlements, the task question is:

What impact does tourism have on Ambleside, a settlement in the Lake District National Park?

To help answer the task question, geographers next devise some key questions. These help to provide a focus for the enquiry.

For this task, one of the key questions is:

Does pedestrian density and movement vary within Ambleside?

Every year, 16.5 million people visit the Lake District, most of them travelling by car. Ambleside is a 'honeypot' location for tourism – it is a place that most tourists want to visit. Ambleside is a small town (2600 people live there).

F Locating the study

It is important to provide maps showing where the investigation is located. You should include maps at a local and a national scale, plus detailed maps showing your survey or data collection sites. You can then use your location and survey site maps to give a detailed overview of the place in which your investigation will take place. This part of your enquiry helps set out the scene.

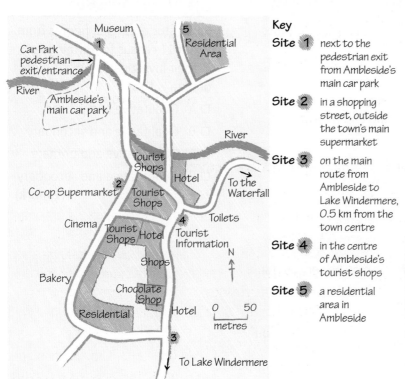

Figure 21 A student's sketch map of Ambleside, with the five survey sites marked on it

Key

Site 1 next to the pedestrian exit from Ambleside's main car park

Site 2 in a shopping street, outside the town's main supermarket

Site 3 on the main route from Ambleside to Lake Windermere, 0.5 km from the town centre

Site 4 in the centre of Ambleside's tourist shops

Site 5 a residential area in Ambleside

Figure 22 Ambleside and mountains

Ambleside is located 0.5 km north of Lake Windermere, on a small area of flat land between three large mountain groups and at the confluence of two tributaries of the River Rothay.

(F) Methodology

Once you have decided on some suitable key questions and located your investigation, the next stage is to choose the methods you will use to collect your data. Geographers use both primary data (data which you collect yourself) and secondary data (data that has already been published). In your investigation, you should choose at least three quantitative (using numbers) methods, for example counting pedestrians, and one qualitative (descriptive) method, for example a questionnaire of visitor experiences.

For each method, it is important that you decide where and how you will collect the data, and why the data collected will help to answer the overall task question. You cannot collect data from every part of the settlement, or count every pedestrian all through the day, so you need to sample.

- **Random sampling** – data is collected by chance. An example might be writing all the street names in Ambleside onto bits of paper, putting them in a bag and selecting the first ten names pulled out. That way every location has the same chance of being selected.
- **Systematic sampling** – the locations of the sites are found at equal intervals from each other. An example might be to measure pedestrian numbers every 100 metres along one road.
- **Stratified sampling** – is used when the study area has significantly different parts. An example might be identifying different areas of land use within the settlement (such as residential or tourism-centred) and making sure each area is surveyed.

An example of how to present your methodology is shown in Table 10.

Table 10 Measuring the density and direction of pedestrians (quantitative method)

Method	Outline of method	Purpose of method	Recording
Measuring the number of pedestrians and their direction. Sample measurements collected at Sites 1 to 5. Stratified sampling method used for site selection.	Five different groups carried out the investigation. Each group counted the number of pedestrians at each of the five survey sites for 15 minutes. We counted pedestrians going up the road and those going down the road as two separate counts. Then each group moved onto the next site and repeated the survey.	We used this method to see if some areas of Ambleside experienced higher pedestrian densities than other areas, and to see if there was evidence of a flow of pedestrians around Ambleside.	Each group had two clickers. One person recorded pedestrian numbers in one direction up the road and another recorded pedestrian numbers in the opposite direction. Then we recorded the total numbers for each direction after 15 minutes onto a table on our clipboards.

Investigations on changing rural settlements often involve a questionnaire – for example, a questionnaire to survey people's opinions about congestion in Ambleside. When deciding on a questionnaire, you should consider:

- what questions will allow you to collect the information that you need for your investigation
- whether the questions should be open (allowing people to offer opinions) or closed (for example, yes or no).

Activity

1   What do you think are the advantages and disadvantages of recording pedestrian numbers using a clicker (each time you click it, it records the next number) rather than making a tally on a sheet of paper?

2   Make a blank copy of Table 10.

   a   Choose **two** investigations from the following: traffic congestion, use of car parks, visitors' experiences of Ambleside and pedestrians' experiences of Ambleside. Discuss what you could find out about them, how you could do so, and why they will help with answering the main task question.

   b   Then complete the table. For each investigation, describe the methods and explain how and why you would conduct and record them. Use a highlighter to identify where you have explained how you would carry out the methods.

3   You have been asked the following key question, 'How do visitor numbers affect people living in Ambleside?' Create a questionnaire that would enable you to gather the information you need to answer this key question.

Exam-style question

Some students took photos of a village and annotated them to show visitor attractions. State whether an annotated photo is a qualitative or quantitative technique.   **(1 mark)**

Exam tip

Remember the difference by thinking of quantity (something you can measure in numbers) for quantitative and quality (about your experience of things) for qualitative.

Now that you have decided on the methods you will use to collect your data, you need to produce a risk assessment with your teacher's guidance before you collect and record your data. In your risk assessment, you should consider: the potential risks, the severity of each risk – on a scale of 0 (low) to 10 (high) – and how the risk can be managed. An example is shown in Table 11.

Table 11 Risk assessment

Risk	Severity rating	Management
Traffic accidents	8/10	Take care crossing roads and stand well back from the road when at each survey point. Wear a high visibility vest so vehicles can see you.

Table 12 Ambleside pedestrian data (collated data from all five student groups)

Times	Site 1		Site 2		Site 3		Site 4		Site 5	
	North	South	North	South	North	South	North	South	North	South
9.30am–9.45am	6	11	5	7	3	4	8	8	0	1
10.00am–10.15am	4	18	6	15	4	7	22	18	1	1
10.30am–10.45am	4	21	9	16	10	12	31	28	2	0
11.00am–11.15am	8	15	21	20	14	18	38	32	0	3
11.30am–11.45am	3	47	8	32	18	8	51	39	4	7
Totals	25	112	49	90	49	49	150	125	7	12

(F) Data presentation

Once you have collected your data, you then need to decide how to present it. Geographers use a range of graphical techniques to present their findings. For your investigation, you should aim to produce a number of simple and sophisticated techniques. A sophisticated technique is one that uses at least two variables to represent the data. An example of this would be a pedestrian flow line map for the different sites. Techniques that could be used to present information for Ambleside include:

- a flow line map showing direction and size of pedestrian flow at each site
- an isoline map, where lines join up places on a map of equal value
- a dispersion graph, plotting the range of data collected from each site
- located proportional circles of pedestrian numbers for each site
- a GIS map with a base map of Ambleside (physical features), with a layer for roads, a layer for shops and tourist attractions and a layer containing the survey information.

Presenting data on pedestrian density and movement

The students measured pedestrian numbers for 15 minutes at each site at five different time slots during one morning. Figure 23 shows an example of how the students presented their data using located bars. A located bar map is a sophisticated data presentation technique because it records two variables: pedestrian numbers and location.

- First a base map is required: remember to mark the precise point where each survey took place.
- A suitable scale needs to be used that will cope with the highest and lowest figures from the data.
- The base of the bar needs to be located at the point where the data was collected.

The students created five located bar maps: one for each survey time slot and one for the totals for each site (all five time slots put together). This allowed them to compare pedestrian numbers through the morning. However, it was also a very time-consuming task.

Exam-style question

Study Table 12. Calculate the median value and the range for the Totals row. **(2 marks)**

Exam tip

When you put a series of numbers in order the median is the middle one (or the mean of the middle two). The range is the difference between the highest and lowest number in the series.

Command word

When asked to **calculate** you work with numbers to answer a problem. Show your working and include the correct unit if one is required.

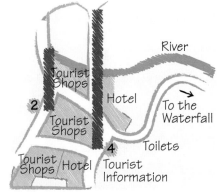

Figure 23 The students' located bar map for 11.30am–11.45am at Sites 2 and 4

(F) Analysis and conclusions

The next stage of the enquiry is to analyse the data collected to begin answering your key questions. When analysing the data, it is important to:

- **describe** the general trends from your data – for example, 'The number of pedestrians increased through the morning'
- **make comparisons** using data – for example, 'Pedestrian densities were highest at Site 4 (with a range of 74 throughout the morning) and lowest at Site 5 (with a range of 10)'
- **explain** the patterns of your data with links to geographical theory – for example, 'The flows of pedestrians at Site 1 are consistent with Ambleside being a honeypot location, with large flows from the car park into the town but very small flows northwards up Rydal Road out of town'.

Read the extract below from an analysis a student wrote about data collected in Ambleside. The student gave a structured response with:

- reference to the figure and data (red)
- use of geographical terminology and theory (green)
- an explanation of their data and links to geographical theory (yellow).

Pedestrian density was highest (275 people) in the main tourist area of Ambleside (Site 4) and at Site 1, leading from the town's main car park into town. Density increased through the morning as more visitors arrived (by 11.45 the cumulative total travelling south from Site 1 was 112 people. Density and flow patterns support Ambleside's honeypot status, in which tourist numbers overwhelm residential pedestrian movements.

Once you have analysed your data using the structure above, you need to write a conclusion for each key question as well as the overall task question. When writing your conclusion, it is important to:

- focus on your task question and key questions: what did your investigation find out?
- summarise your findings from the data you collected and presented and link each finding to the evidence
- point out any anomalies in your data – these are results that are very different from what you expected: you might try to explain them
- refer back to any theory that related to your investigation (like the concept of honeypots).

You then need to write your overall conclusion to the task question, in this case: 'What impact does tourism have on Ambleside?'

Read the extract below from a conclusion written by a student.

The purpose of my investigation was to investigate the impacts of tourism in Ambleside. From looking at pedestrian density and flows, I can conclude that visitors to Ambleside (arriving by car) dominate the numbers of pedestrians, the direction of flows and the locations in which pedestrian density is highest. This is consistent with Ambleside acting as a tourism honeypot.

Activity

1   Discuss the two paragraphs with the student's analysis and conclusion. For **each** paragraph decide: what is good about it, how it might be improved or developed, anything that you think should be added. Justify your decisions.

2   Rewrite the **second** student paragraph with your suggested improvements.

(F) Evaluation

The final part of the enquiry is to evaluate your investigation. Here you think about how well you answered the task question or theory, and how you could improve or develop the process. The key questions below will help you review your data collection methods, results and conclusions.

- How successful and useful were your methods for sampling and collecting data? Could they be improved?

- How accurate were your results? Did your data collection methods affect the results?

- Did missing or inaccurate data make the study unreliable or affect your conclusions?

Pedestrian direction counts at Site 4 were most difficult because people came from three directions and doubled back to visit other shops. The location of Site 4 could have been improved.

It would have been interesting to have extended the survey to Waterhead (Lake Windermere) to compare pedestrian densities there, but it was too far for us all to walk there in 15 minutes.

I found Site 5 the most interesting because very few tourists went there. It helped me think about the impacts of tourism.

Drawing five maps took ages! It was also a shame that we didn't find a way to show the different directions pedestrians were moving in, north and south.

Figure 24 Students' reflections on their geographical investigation in Ambleside

Checkpoint

Now it is time to review your understanding of how to plan and conduct an investigation into changing rural settlements.

Strengthen

S1 Students considered ways in which they could have improved the way they presented data. In which part of the investigation would they record their thoughts on this?

S2 Explain one way in which the physical geography of a rural settlement can affect the impact tourists can have on that settlement.

Challenge

C1 Note down examples of how random, systematic and stratified sampling could be used in a rural settlement investigation.

C2 Write out example(s) of the methods below, deciding if they are qualitative or quantitative, primary or secondary, and the strengths and limitations of information gained from each of them:

   a method(s) to measure pedestrian densities

   b method(s) to record numbers of tourist facilities

   c method(s) to investigate reasons why people have come to the rural settlement

   d method(s) to investigate changes in resident population numbers over time.

Changing Cities

Urbanisation is taking place across the world and the process is gathering speed. Cities are struggling to cope with the effects of this rapid growth and at the same time to become more sustainable. Different countries have tried a range of strategies to make their cities more sustainable and small starts have been made in terms of recycling in cities and attempts to cut down air pollution. However, much remains to be done.

Checklist

You should know:

- ☐ the causes of urbanisation in emerging, developing and developed cities
- ☐ the factors behind the UK distribution of population
- ☐ the site, situation and connectivity of Birmingham
- ☐ the key processes of urbanisation, suburbanisation, counter-urbanisation and re-urbanisation in Birmingham
- ☐ how national and international migration has impacted on parts of Birmingham
- ☐ the impact of de-industrialisation and de-centralisation on Birmingham
- ☐ how economic change is increasing inequality in Birmingham
- ☐ why and how retailing is changing in Birmingham
- ☐ how Birmingham is trying to be more sustainable and to improve the quality of life
- ☐ the main influences on the growth and structure of Mexico City
- ☐ how the character of Mexico City is influenced by its fast rate of growth
- ☐ the causes and impacts of national and international migration in Mexico City
- ☐ the issue of inequality and quality of life in Mexico City
- ☐ the issues arising from the rapid growth of the city, such as housing and employment
- ☐ the advantages and disadvantages of bottom-up and top-down approaches to solving Mexico City's problems.

Which key terms match the following definitions?

a   The central area of the city, dominated by department stores, specialist and variety goods shops, offices and cinemas.

b   The increase in the percentage of people living in towns and cities, causing them to grow.

c   Development which meets the needs of the present without compromising (limiting) the ability of future generations to meet their own needs.

d   The movement of people and employment from major cities to smaller settlements and rural areas located beyond the city, or to more distant towns and cities.

e   The movement of people back towards city centres away from rural areas and from suburbs.

f   The decline of industrial activity in a region or in an economy.

g   The movement of people, factories, offices and shops away from city centres to suburban and edge of city locations.

h   The process of people changing their place of residence, either within or between countries.

To check your answers, look at the Glossary on pages 296–301.

Changing Cities

Question 1   Compare the process of urbanisation in developing or emerging countries with that in developed countries.
(4 marks)

Student answer

Cities in the developing world are growing very fast. This is because death rates are falling due to better medicine and birth rates are high. In developed countries the death rate also fell and birth rates fell, so cities like Birmingham also grew, but not as fast as in developing countries.

6th

Verdict

The first part on developing countries is correct, but there are two problems with this answer. One is that the question asks for a comparison and there is hardly any comparison except in the last sentence. Secondly there is no mention of the key fact that the process took far longer in developed countries. This answer shows some level of understanding but does not provide a complete answer.

Exam tip

Make sure that you check the key command words in the title so that you answer the question that was set. If the command word is 'compare' you should make plenty of comparisons.

Question 2   Evaluate the view that economic change has increased inequality in a named major UK city.
(8 marks + 4 SPAG)

Student answer

One reason that there is inequality in parts of Birmingham is because many people have no jobs or badly paid jobs. This is in places like Sparkbrook and Bordesley Green. A lot of factories have closed in Birmingham recently so there is less work for people. The jobs that people can get are often low paid or part-time. There is also discrimination in some parts of Birmingham. Large numbers of immigrants have arrived in parts of inner Birmingham in the last ten years and that has led to problems finding work for some of them. Many of the immigrants have young children and this is putting a strain on schools and hospitals so adding to inequality. The immigrants have come to Birmingham to find a better life and good jobs.

8th

Verdict

The answer implies economic change in terms of factory closures but does not explain why factories have closed or put the changes in the context of outdated factories and urban regeneration. It talks about the impacts of immigration to Birmingham and some reasons migrants move to the city, but the point needs to be made that this is partly due to economic factors. The information is accurate but lacks detail. More information about the nature and impact of the economic changes is needed.

Exam tip

Make sure when you answer a question that as far as possible you use the key terms that are in the question. This question specifically mentions economic change so there should be explanation of what that economic change consisted of, and then detail of how it increased the inequality in the city. There is a lot of useful information in the answer above but it needs shaping to answer the question that was asked. This is an important part of exam technique.

Pearson Education Ltd accepts no responsibility whatsoever for the accuracy or method of working in the answers given.

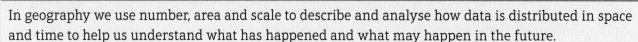

Number, area and scale

What you need to know

In geography we use number, area and scale to describe and analyse how data is distributed in space and time to help us understand what has happened and what may happen in the future.

- **Number** is used to describe how much of a measured value there is, e.g. the population of a city.

- **Area** is how much space something occupies and is always written as a unit squared, e.g. the relationship between the number of people in a given area can be described as population density.

- **Scale** is the appropriate system within which we analyse relationships meaningfully, e.g. the speed or rate change in a population is the difference in size on a time scale

Sample question

Students had collected data on population growth after the 2011 census (Table 1) and wanted to investigate the values of different ways of describing demographic trends in London (area: 1583 km²).

Table 1 Population growth

Year	Population	Population density
2012	8,300,000	5243
2013	8,400,000	
2014	8,500,000	
2015	8,600,000	

How many more people lived in London in 2015 than in 2012?

Population difference

$= $ Population in 2015 (p_2) − Population in 2012 (p_1)

$= 8,600,000 - 8,300,000$

$= 300,000$.

In 2012, London's population density was 5243 people per km². What was it in 2015?

Population density

$= $ Population ÷ Area

$= 8,600,000 ÷ 1583$ km²

$= 5433$/km² (to nearest whole figure).

How much bigger was London's population in 2015 compared with 2012?

The population of London has increased by a scale factor of $p_2 ÷ p_1$

$= 8,600,000 ÷ 8,300,000$

$= 1.04$ (to 2 decimal places).

Therefore the approximate percentage increase is:

$(1.04 × 100) - 100 = 4\%$.

Calculate how quickly London's population was growing between 2012 and 2015, in terms of the annual percentage growth rate.

Annual percentage growth rate

$$= ([(p_2 - p_1) \div p_1] \div [\text{Difference in time, } t_2 - t_1]) \times 100$$

$$= ([300{,}000 \div 8{,}300{,}000] \div [2015 - 2012]) \times 100$$

$$= 1.2\%.$$

Apply your knowledge

Students wanting to compare the growth of megacities at a global scale have collected data about the populations of Mumbai in India and London in the UK (Table 2).

Table 2 Comparison of population growth in Mumbai and London

Year	Mumbai	London
1971	6,540,000	7,450,000
1981	9,685,000	6,610,000
1991	12,792,000	6,890,000
2001	16,665,000	7,170,000
2011	18,695,000	8,170.000

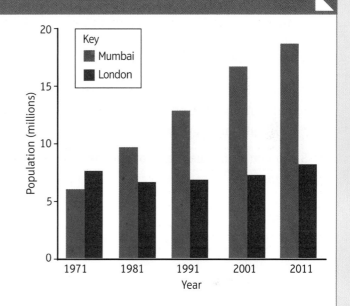

Figure 1 Population growth in Mumbai and London

1. How many more people are there in Mumbai and London in 2011 compared with 1971?

2. Use the following formula to work out the scale of this growth for Mumbai from 1971 to 2011:

   $p_2 \div p_1 = $ Scale factor.

3. If London had grown by the same scale factor as Mumbai over the 40 years from 1971, what would its population have been in 2011?

4. London's population fell between some census dates so the growth rate was not constant. Calculate the average annual percentage population growth rates for Mumbai and London, 2001–2011. Which city had a faster growth rate during this ten-year period? Suggest reasons for this.

Students have been studying patterns of population distribution within Greater London using a sample transect from the City of London to Havering borough.

1. They decided to describe the relationship between a borough's population density (the number of people in an area) and its distance from the City of London. Why couldn't they just use the number of people?

Table 3 Comparison of relation between population density and distance from City of London for several London boroughs

	City of London	Tower Hamlets	Newham	Barking and Dagenham	Havering
Distance from the City of London (km)	0	7.6	10.6	15	25.4
Population in 2011	7400	254,100	308,000	185,900	237,200
Area (km²)	2.9	19.8	36.2	36.1	112.3
Population density				5150	2112

Using the formula 'Population density = Population ÷ Area', copy and complete Table 3. Using the table, construct a line graph to show the relationship between the number of people living in an area and the distance from the city of London.

2. The students decided a choropleth map might help them understand the distribution of population more easily. Copy the map they started (Figure 2) and use shading to illustrate your calculations about population density along the transect. Describe what this shows.

3. Do you think the graph or the map gives the best representation of this data? Explain your choice.

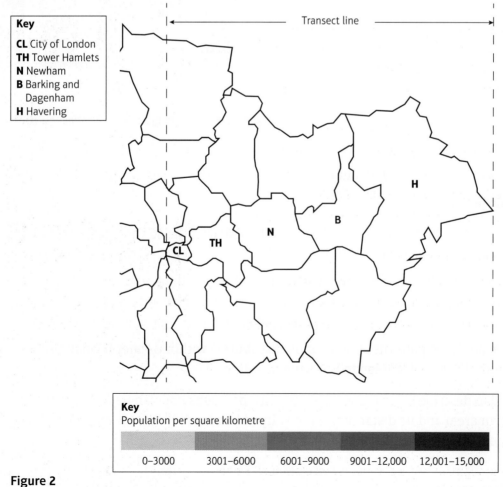

Key
CL City of London
TH Tower Hamlets
N Newham
B Barking and Dagenham
H Havering

Transect line

Key
Population per square kilometre

0–3000   3001–6000   6001–9000   9001–12,000   12,001–15,000

Figure 2

5 | Global Development

The development gap, both between and within countries, can be very wide. How can development be measured? What are the relative merits of individual indicators such as gross national product compared with a composite measure such as the human development index? A range of factors have led to spatial variations in the level of development globally and within the UK. What have been the consequences of uneven development? A number of strategies have been used to try to address the development problem including international aid and inter-governmental agreements, such as the Sustainable Development Goals. Development strategies are often classed as either top-down or bottom-up. What are the advantages and limitations of these different types of approach?

Your learning

In this section you will investigate key learning points:

- how to define development using economic, social and political measures
- the different factors that contribute to human development
- the human development index and measures of inequality and corruption
- how development varies globally and within the UK
- why development varies to such an extent between and within countries
- the impact of uneven development
- the importance of food and water security to development
- the range of strategies used to help a country develop
- the differences between top-down and bottom-up development strategies
- how the level of development in an emerging country, India, is shaped by location and context with the world
- how the interaction of factors (economic, social and demographic) influences India's development
- the effect of geopolitics and technology on development in India
- what the positive and negative impacts of rapid development are for the people and environment in India.

5 | Global Development

Contrasting ways of defining development

Learning objectives

- To appreciate there are different ways of defining development
- To know a range of economic, social and political measures of development
- To understand food and water security

Human development

Development is a broad idea linked to improving the quality of people's lives. One aspect involves money and wealth, which is an economic measure. Other aspects consider social factors such as good health care, or political factors such as freedom of speech. Many people consider good health to be more important than wealth, and people in countries that are not democracies may envy those who live in democratic countries. The sustainability of the natural environment is also an important factor for long-term development. Figure 1 shows one view of the factors that comprise the quality of life.

Development occurs when there are improvements to individual factors making up the quality of life. For example, development occurs in a low-income country when:

- the local food supply improves because of investment in machinery and fertilisers
- the electricity grid extends outwards from the main urban areas to rural areas
- a new road or railway improves the accessibility of a remote region
- levels of literacy or gender equality improve throughout the country.

A recent UN Human Development Report (HDR) stated: 'Human development is about putting people at the centre of development. It is about people realising their potential, increasing their choices and enjoying the freedom to lead lives they value'. Since 1990, HDRs have explored challenges including poverty, gender, democracy, human rights, cultural liberty, globalisation, water scarcity and climate change.

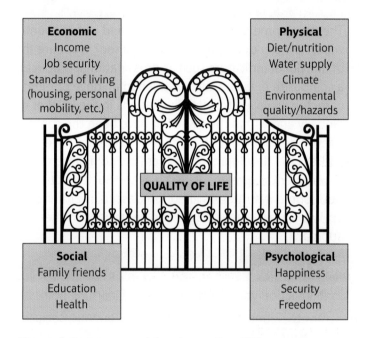

Figure 1 Factors comprising the quality of life

Factors affecting development

It can be useful to group the factors that affect human development. However, some factors may fall into more than one group.

Economic factors – average wealth or income, the growth rate of an economy, trade surplus/deficit, the unemployment rate and the cost of living.

Social factors – health, education, housing, equity, and opportunities for leisure and recreation.

Technological factors – electrification, internet access, and efficiency gains in farming and industry.

Cultural factors – how happy people are with their place in the world shaped by, among other things, democratisation, the balances between traditional and imported cultures, and the work–life balance.

Food and water security

Food

There is a huge geographical imbalance between food production and food consumption. This has resulted in a lack of **food security** in many countries. In 2015, almost 800 million people in the world did not have enough food to lead a healthy, active life. The three main strands of food security are:

- **availability** – sufficient amounts of food being available on a consistent basis
- **access** – having sufficient resources to obtain appropriate foods for a nutritious diet
- **consumption** – making appropriate use based on knowledge of basic nutrition and care, as well as adequate water and sanitation.

Water

For about 80 countries, home to 40% of the world's population, lack of water is a constant threat (Figure 2, see also Topics 2 and 6). The situation is getting worse, with demand for water doubling every 20 years. Where there is enough water, it is being wasted and polluted on a large scale. **Water security**, especially access to clean water, has become a major issue in an increasing number of countries. Securing access to clean water is a vital aspect of development.

- More than 840,000 people die each year from a water-related disease. In developing countries most deaths still result from water-borne disease.
- At any one time, half of the world's hospital beds are occupied by patients suffering from water-borne diseases.
- 750 million people around the world lack access to safe water – approximately one in nine people. The majority live in rural areas.
- Women and children spend 140 million hours a day collecting water.

Figure 2 Water distribution in the Gobi desert, Mongolia

Exam-style question

Define the term 'water security'. **(1 mark)**

Exam tip

Knowing key terms is important, not just for questions like this. You can use the Glossary to revise key terms.

Command word

When asked to **define** something you should state what the term means.

Activity

1. Which factor in each of the boxes in Figure 1 do you think is the most important? Justify your choices.
2. What is meant by water security?
3. Describe the scene in Figure 2. What problems do you think this creates for people in the region?
4. Choose **one** set of factors (economic, social, technological or cultural). Describe how improvement in these factors would affect development.

How development is measured

- To use gross domestic product per capita
- To understand the human development index
- To know measures of inequality and political corruption

Did you know?

In 2014, the United Nations stated that more than 1.2 billion people around the world were living on less than US$1.25 a day (£0.88 at the time of writing) and 2.4 billion were living on less than US$2 a day. What could you buy with US$1.25? Action to meet the Millennium Development Goals is reducing the number of people affected.

Gross domestic product

A major economic indicator of development is **gross domestic product (GDP)**. GDP is the total value of goods and services produced within a country in a year. To take account of the way in which countries vary in population size, the GDP per capita (per person) is often used. This is calculated by dividing the GDP of a country by its population. There are many other individual measures of development which include the infant mortality rate, the number of people per doctor, the internet penetration rate and electricity consumption per capita.

The human development index

No single measure can provide a complete picture of the differences in development between countries. This is why the United Nations combines four measures in the human development index (HDI). This index was introduced in 1990 and is updated annually. It is a key part of the HDR. The measures included in the current index are:

- life expectancy at birth
- mean years of schooling for adults aged 25 years
- expected years of schooling for children of school-entering age
- gross national income (GNI) per capita (US$PPP).

GNI per capita is broadly similar to GDP per capita (but includes overseas income). PPP means 'purchasing power parity'. This takes into account the way in which the cost of living can vary between countries. The HDI ranges from 0 to 1 (1 being the most developed) and it divides the countries of the world into four groups, often equated as: very high = developed; high = emerging; medium = emerging; low = developing.

Table 1 compares the top and bottom ranking for three measures: GDP, GDP per capita and HDI.

Figure 3 A poor fishing village in Papua New Guinea – a developing country

Table 1 Top five and bottom five rankings by various measures

Rank	GDP (US$ million)	GDP per capita (US$)	HDI
1	USA (17,348,071)	Monaco (187,650)	Norway (0.944)
2	China (10,430,589)	Liechtenstein (157,040)	Australia (0.935)
3	Japan (4,602,419)	Luxembourg (116,650)	Switzerland (0.930)
4	Germany (3,868,291)	Qatar (97,519)	Denmark (0.923)
5	UK (2,988,893)	Norway (97,226)	Netherlands (0.922)
5	Palau (240)	Niger (427)	Burundi (0.400)
4	Marshall Islands (189)	Central African Rep. (383)	Chad (0.392)
3	Kiribati (175)	Malawi (343)	Eritrea (0.391)
2	Nauru (153)	Burundi (279)	Central African Rep. (0.350)
1	Tuvalu (38)	Somalia (131)	Niger (0.348)

It is not surprising that the rank position of countries varies when using a composite index such as the HDI compared with a single indicator of development such as GDP. For example, countries investing heavily in the health and education of their populations will do better under the HDI compared with the GDP.

Activity

Study Table 1.

1 What do the five lowest ranked countries in terms of GDP have in common?

2 Why does a large rich country such as the USA not feature in two of the three top five lists?

3 Norway is ranked high in terms of GDP per capita and HDI, do you think the former supports the latter? Suggest some reasons why.

Political corruption

The quality of government is a big factor in development. Countries where the quality of government is poor often have a high level of corruption. The Corruption Perceptions Index, 2013, grades countries from 'highly corrupt' to 'very clean'. The Index was launched in 1995 by the non-governmental organisation Transparency International.

- The five least corrupt countries were: Denmark, New Zealand, Finland, Sweden and Norway.
- The five most corrupt countries were Somalia, North Korea, Afghanistan, Sudan and South Sudan.

Checkpoint

Now it is time to review your understanding of how development is defined and measured.

Strengthen

S1 Define GDP and GDP per capita.

S2 In which continent are the lowest ranked countries in terms of HDI?

S3 Why do you think life expectancy at birth is part of the HDI?

Challenge

C1 What is the advantage of using the HDI to examine global inequality compared with GDP per capita?

C2 The majority of the five most corrupt countries share a common factor (recent civil war). How does this increase the likelihood of corruption?

C3 Refer back to Table 1. Four of the top countries by GDP per capital generate their money from one of two sources. Suggest what these are and group the countries.

Uneven development globally and in the UK

Learning objectives

- To understand the extent of the global development gap
- To recognise that development is also unequal within countries
- To know the extent of regional inequality in the UK

Figure 4 shows how GDP per capita varies around the world at the scale of individual countries. It is clear where regions of high and low GDP per capita are located. The **development gap** between the world's wealthiest and poorest countries is huge (see Table 2).

- The highest GDP per capita (Figure 4) is found in North America, much of Europe, Australia, New Zealand, oil-rich states in the Middle East and advanced Asian economies such as Japan, South Korea, Hong Kong and Singapore.
- The lowest GDP per capita is concentrated in Africa and in poor Asian countries, such as Afghanistan, Burma and Cambodia.

Table 2 gives data for four measures of development at the continental scale. As countries and regions develop:

- the infant mortality rate falls
- the total fertility rate declines
- the life expectancy at birth rises
- the percentage of the population living in urban areas increases.

Although the development gap can be measured in different ways it is generally thought to be increasing.

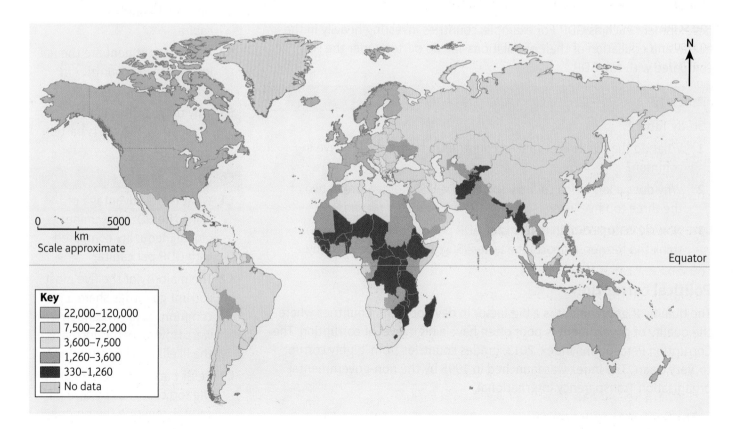

0 — 5000
km
Scale approximate

Equator

Key
- 22,000–120,000
- 7,500–22,000
- 3,600–7,500
- 1,260–3,600
- 330–1,260
- No data

Figure 4 World map showing GDP per capita in US$, 2014

Table 2 Four measures of development by continental region, 2014

Region	Infant mortality rate (per 1000)	Total fertility rate	Life expectancy at birth (years)	Population living in urban areas (%)
World	37	2.5	71	53
Africa	59	4.7	60	40
Northern America	6	1.8	79	81
Latin America and Caribbean	17	2.1	75	80
Asia	33	2.2	72	47
Europe	6	1.4	78	73
Oceania	22	2.5	77	70

Measuring inequality within countries

The scale of inequality *within* countries is often as much an issue as the inequality *between* countries. The **Gini coefficient** can be used to show the extent of income inequality. A low value indicates a more equal income distribution. A high value shows more unequal income distribution. In general, rich countries have a lower income gap than poorer countries. South Africa (63.4) and Brazil (52.9) are regions of high income inequality. Europe has the lowest income inequality, for example Norway (25.9) and Slovenia (25.6).

Uneven development in the UK

Figure 5 shows regional differences in **gross disposable household income (GDHI)** per head in the UK for 2012.

- London had the highest GDHI per person in the UK at £21,446 – 27.7% above the UK average.
- The South East, the East of England and the South West were the only other regions with GDHI per person above the UK average.
- Northern Ireland had a GDHI per person of £13,902 – 17.2% below the UK average.

Figure 5 shows the GDHI in the 12 'Standard Regions' in the UK. These are large regions and there are big variations within each Standard Region.

Recent reports show that regional inequality in the UK is the highest in western Europe and that the UK is more regionally divided than it was 30 years ago. In general, people in London and the South East have more wealth than elsewhere in the country. However, London has the greatest wealth inequality because of the huge gap between the very rich and very poor. Similar regional contrasts are also apparent in other development factors.

Activity

Make a copy of Table 2.

a Rank the six continental regions for each of the four measures of development. Best = 1, Worst = 6.

b Total the rankings for each region to form a composite index of development, similar to the HDI.

Figure 5 Map of regional GDHI per head, 2012

Factors affecting development

Learning objectives

- To understand that a range of factors have led to a high level of global inequality
- To understand that uneven global development has a range of consequences
- To appreciate that access to housing, health, education, employment and technology, and food and water security are affected

Causes of global inequalities

A variety of factors have led to an unequal world.

The physical environment – (a) many landlocked countries have developed more slowly than coastal nations; (b) tropical countries have grown more slowly than those in temperate latitudes; (c) small island countries face considerable disadvantages; and (d) countries affected by natural hazards face particular difficulties.

Demography – demographic transition is a significant factor; the highest rates of economic growth are experienced by nations where the birth rate has declined the most.

Political and economic policies – open economies (e.g. the UK) that encourage foreign investment have developed faster than closed economies (e.g. Russia). Institutional quality in terms of good government, law and order and lack of corruption results in higher rates of growth.

History – through **colonialism** European powers, such as the UK and France, expanded their territories around the world and imposed unequal trading relationships on the colonies, which were exploited for their raw materials. The term '**neo-colonialism**' is used to describe how rich countries can still dominate poorer countries economically and politically.

Social investment – countries that have prioritised investment in education and health have generally developed at a faster rate than nations which have invested less. As countries develop, fertility declines. Education, especially female literacy, is the key to lower fertility. Female education increases knowledge of birth control, creates greater social awareness and opportunities for employment.

Reasons for inequality in the UK

The lowest living standards in the UK tend to be in the following areas:

- remote areas, where the physical geography is challenging, such as the highlands of Scotland, the Welsh mountains and the moorlands of south-west England. Opportunities for employment are limited, wages are low and many jobs are seasonal
- areas that were once important for traditional heavy industries, which declined sharply in the second half of the 20th century.

Emerging economies, such as South Korea, Brazil, China and India were able to produce goods more cheaply than the UK. As a result, heavy industry moved away (**de-industrialisation**) from countries such as the UK, the USA and France. Unemployment rose and average incomes declined in traditional industrial areas (such as shipbuilding in the north-east or coal mining and iron and steel in South Wales).

Many traditional industrial areas have struggled to replace lost jobs. Modern industries have preferred to locate in London and the South East in particular. As a result, the South East has higher per capita incomes, lower rates of unemployment, higher house prices, and better infrastructure.

The impact of uneven development

The development gap has big consequences. Billions of people do not have a standard of living which reaches that specified in the Universal Declaration of Human Rights: 'Everyone has the right to a standard of living adequate for the health and well-being of himself and of his family....'

Access to housing – people on low incomes have very limited access to adequate housing. Over 30% of the world's urban population live in **slums**, such as in Mexico

City. The **urbanisation of poverty** has moved the focus of global poverty from rural to urban areas.

Health – investment in health is crucial to development. Around 6.6 million children under the age of 5 die each year. The World Health Organisation (WHO) says that most could be saved if they had access to inexpensive vaccines, clean water and sanitation. About 70% of all HIV/AIDs deaths occur in sub-Saharan Africa – the world's poorest region.

Education – the UN sees education as vital for the future for sustainable development of the planet. However, more than 775 million people in poor countries cannot read or write. Those with the least education have the largest families. Large families are also common where child mortality is high. Maintaining a large family usually means that saving is impossible, **debt** and malnutrition are likely, and it may not be possible to educate all children in a family.

Employment – the opportunities for employment are much more limited in developing countries where large numbers of people work in labour-intensive agriculture and the **informal sector**. Typical jobs are shoe-shiners, street food stalls, messengers, repair shops and market traders, which are: generally low paid; often temporary and/or part-time in nature; lacking in fringe benefits and job security.

Technology – improvements in technology in developing countries can bring great benefits. However, reaching a certain level of technology in a country requires investment in the technology itself and people with the necessary skills to operate it efficiently. Many developing countries struggle on both counts. **Appropriate technology** can be better than more advanced alternatives as it is generally:

- low in energy consumption and cost – appropriate to the local financial and geographical conditions
- within the technical capacity of members of the community to operate and maintain themselves
- able to use locally sourced materials and spare parts that can be purchased and transported easily
- something that involves the local community at all stages of development.

Food and water security – poor countries frequently lack the ability to import food, innovate in agriculture or invest in rural development. The Food and Agriculture Organisation (FAO) has estimated that between 2012 and 2014, 805 million people around the world were affected by undernourishment. The FAO has stressed the need to produce food where the poor and hungry live, and to boost agricultural investment in these regions.

Water scarcity has been presented as the underlying factor for many of the world's environmental problems. It is threatening to put world food supplies in jeopardy, limit economic and social development, and create serious conflicts between neighbouring countries that share a drainage basin.

Checkpoint

Now it is time to review your understanding of uneven development and the factors affecting development.

Strengthen

S1 Define the total fertility rate.

S2 Explain two ways in which the physical environment can make development difficult.

S3 Why do so many children under the age of 5 die each year?

Challenge

C1 What are the main reasons for regional inequality in the UK?

C2 Suggest why appropriate technology is often better for developing countries than more advanced technology.

C3 a   What is the informal sector of an economy?

   b   Why do so many people work in the informal sector in many developing countries?

Figure 6 School in Indonesia

International strategies to reduce uneven development

Learning objectives

- To understand the importance of trade and investment in the development process
- To appreciate the value of different types of international aid
- To know that other factors such as remittances and debt relief are important in development

The roles of trade and investment in development

Investment in a country is the key to increasing trade. Some developing countries have increased their trade substantially in recent decades. Examples are China, India, Brazil and Mexico, attracting the bulk of **foreign direct investment (FDI)**. The emergence of newly industrialised countries has been the biggest success of globalisation.

However, about 2 billion people live in countries whose trade has fallen in relation to national income. For example, Africa's share of world trade has fallen in recent decades (especially sub-Saharan Africa: 2.7% in 1980; 1% in 2012). Non-governmental organisations (NGOs), such as Oxfam and CAFOD, argue strongly that trade is the key to real development, being worth much more than aid.

Fair trade

Poor countries argue that the way world trade operates is unfair. One answer to this is **fair trade**. Most large stores in developed countries stock some fair trade products. Most are food products, such as bananas, coffee and tea (Figure 7). Under the fair trade system small-scale producers group together to form a cooperative, which deals directly with retailers (cutting out 'middlemen') in developed countries, who pay more than the world market price for the products traded. Farmers in developing countries get a better standard of living and some money to reinvest.

Advocates of the fair trade system say that it is a model of how world trade can and should be organised to tackle global poverty. Currently fair trade is less than 1% of total world trade.

Figure 7 A Fairtrade tea product

Intergovernmental agreements: aid and debt relief

International **aid** provides a vital part of the income of many poor countries. Most developing countries have been keen to accept **foreign aid** because of the:

- **foreign exchange gap** – countries lack the money to pay for imports, such as machinery and oil, which are vital to development
- **savings gap** – population pressures and other factors prevent the accumulation of enough capital to invest in industry and infrastructure
- **technical gap** – a shortage of the skills needed for development.

Figure 8 shows the different types of international aid. The basic division is between official government aid and voluntary aid. Voluntary aid is organised by NGOs/charities such as ActionAid and Oxfam.

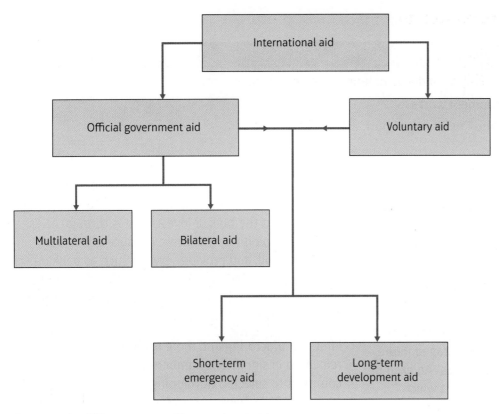

Figure 8 The different types of international aid

In 1970, at the United Nations, the developed countries promised to spend 0.7% of **gross national product (GNP)** on international aid. However, in 2013 only five countries (Norway, Sweden, Luxembourg, Denmark and the UK) passed this target. International aid is more of a priority in some countries than others (the USA only managed 0.19%). However, it is not just the total amount of aid that is important, but the way in which the money is spent. Critics of foreign aid say that often it can be wasteful and that it can create a culture of dependency.

Debt relief

Debt is a major problem for the world's poorer nations. Debts acquired from previous colonial rulers, and for post-war investment to develop manufacturing, were made worse by the 1973 oil crisis. Annual debt repayments can amount to a considerable part of a country's income. The Heavily Indebted Poor Countries (HIPC) Initiative was established in 1996 by the International Monetary Fund (IMF) and the World Bank to reduce or cancel debts.

By 2015, debt reduction under the HIPC Initiative had been approved for 36 countries, 30 of them in Africa, providing US$76 billion in debt-service relief over time. Examples of countries being helped include Afghanistan, Ethiopia, Niger and Haiti.

The importance of remittances

Many international migrants send money back to their families in their country of origin. These **remittances** are a very important source of income, exceeding aid, for many developing countries. They totalled more than US$400 billion in 2012.

> **Exam-style question**
>
> Describe **two** ways in which the scale of global inequality can be reduced. **(4 marks)**

> **Exam tip**
>
> Try to select two distinctly different factors to reduce the chance of repetition in your answer. Make at least two good points for each factor.

Top-down and bottom-up strategies

Learning objectives

- To understand the processes of top-down development
- To know how bottom-up development works
- To appreciate the advantages and limitations of both approaches

Top-down development

Top-down development occurs through the actions of governments and **transnational corporations (TNCs)**.

The traditional 'top-down' approach is when experts from developed countries, and the governments of developing and emerging countries, plan large-scale projects with very limited involvement of the people who are going to be directly affected. Sometimes they are poorly targeted towards the local people most in need. The poorest people can be disadvantaged in the process through 'unintended consequences'. An example might be a major dam and reservoir project which involves flooding people's lands without providing adequate compensation, such as the Mun River Basin, Thailand.

Development through FDI by TNCs might also be thought of as top-down development. TNCs aim to make large profits. The developing countries receiving this FDI may benefit from job creation and income from exports, but this is not the main objective of a TNC.

TNCs and national governments are two main elements of the global economy. The governments of countries individually and collectively set the rules for the global economy, but the bulk of investment is through TNCs. TNCs can exploit raw materials, produce goods such as cars and oil, and provide services such as banking. The 100 largest TNCs represent a significant proportion of total global production. Table 3 shows data for the world's ten largest TNCs in 2015.

First manufacturing and more recently service industries relocated in significant numbers from developed countries to selected developing and emerging countries. TNCs have taken advantage of lower labour rates to reduce costs, as well as growing markets there. This process has helped some countries, such as China, to develop since the 1960s.

TNCs generate huge revenues for the global economy in general and in the countries in which they choose to locate in particular. They play a major role in world trade in terms of what and where they buy and sell.

Table 3 The world's ten largest TNCs in 2015

Rank	Company	Revenue (US$ billion)	Industry	HQ country
1	Walmart	485.7	Retail	USA
2	Sinopec	446.8	Petroleum	China
3	Royal Dutch Shell	431.3	Petroleum	Netherlands/UK
4	China National Petroleum	428.6	Petroleum	China
5	BP	358.7	Petroleum	UK
6	ExxonMobil	382.6	Petroleum	USA
7	State Grid	339.4	Power	China
8	Volkswagen	268.6	Automobiles	Germany
9	Toyota	247.7	Automobiles	Japan
10	Glencore	221.0	Commodities	Switzerland/UK

Concerns have been raised about the power of large TNCs, particularly those operating in poor countries. Such concerns include the exploitation of cheap labour, non-payment of tax, provision of poor working conditions, and the potential political influence TNCs have (host countries do not want to lose investment and decisions may favour TNCs).

Bottom-up development projects

NGOs have often been much better at directing aid towards sustainable development and communities than government agencies. The selective nature of such aid has targeted the poorest communities using appropriate technology and involving local people in decision making. This is often referred to as the 'bottom-up' strategy. WaterAid is an NGO that has adopted a bottom-up approach to development, evident in their work in Ethiopia and Kenya. It stresses the local and small-scale, putting particular emphasis on sustainability. Figure 9 shows WaterAid's approach to development.

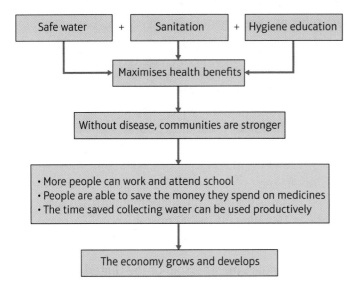

Figure 9 WaterAid's approach to development

The development of the Grameen Bank in Bangladesh is another example of bottom-up development. It shows the power of **microcredit** in the battle against poverty. Microcredit is the granting of small long-term loans on easy terms to poor people, mainly for small business ventures (e.g. buying a cow to supply milk). The average loan is about US$100. Over 95% of loans have gone to women or groups of women. Experience has shown that this approach:

- ensured the best security for the bank
- provided the greatest benefit for the borrowers' families.

The founder of the Grameen Bank sees **social business** as the next phase in the battle against poverty. This new business model combines the free market with the quest for a more humane world.

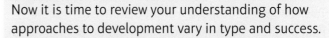

Checkpoint

Now it is time to review your understanding of how approaches to development vary in type and success.

Strengthen

S1 Give two advantages and two disadvantages of TNCs.

S2 What is the difference between top-down and bottom-up approaches to development?

S3 Suggest why debt relief is so important to low-income countries.

Challenge

C1 Refer to Table 3. What industry sectors do these companies represent?

C2 Explain the role of technological advances in the process of globalisation.

C3 Why is trade generally viewed as more important than aid in the development process?

Case Study – How India, an emerging country, is developing

Learning objectives

- To be aware of India's strategic location
- To understand India's size and population in relation to other large nations
- To know India's membership of major international organisations

India's location and context in the world

In terms of land area, India is the seventh largest country in the world, covering almost 3.3 million km² (Table 4). The country is part of continental Asia. Much of India forms a peninsula which narrows to the south and which divides the Indian Ocean into the Bay of Bengal and the Arabian Sea (Figure 10). There are two major island groups: the Andaman and Nicobar Islands far to the south-east, and the nearer Lakshadweep Islands to the south-west.

India shares international borders with six countries: Pakistan, Nepal, China, Bhutan, Bangladesh and Burma. To the south-southeast, a short distance across the Palk Strait, is Sri Lanka. India has land borders of about 15,200 km and a coastline over 7500 km long.

Table 4 Largest countries in the world by land area

Country	Land area (million km²)	Population (million)
Russia	17.1	142,905,208
Canada	10.0	33,740,000
USA	9.8	321,020,000
China	9.6	1,376,130,000
Brazil	8.5	203,054,835
Australia	7.7	22,839,595
India	3.3	1,277,401,883

India is the largest country in the Indian subcontinent (an area of 4.4 million km² – about the size of Europe). The subcontinent is generally taken to include India, Pakistan, Bangladesh, Nepal, Bhutan, Sri Lanka and the Maldives. This region is increasingly referred to as South Asia.

An important aspect of India's context in the world is its huge population, estimated to be 1.27 billion in 2015; close behind China's 1.37 billion (the USA is third with 321 million). In less than ten years' time India will have overtaken China as the most populous country in the world. India's annual population growth accounts for about 19 million of the 89 million annual increase in global population. This is more than any other country.

Apart from India's membership of the United Nations, the country is also a member of the World Trade Organisation, the Commonwealth of Nations (the **Commonwealth**), the Indian Ocean Rim Association, the Non-Aligned Movement, and the South Asian Association for Regional Cooperation.

India's location in Asia has undoubtedly been a factor in its economic development. India has been motivated by the more rapid development of other emerging

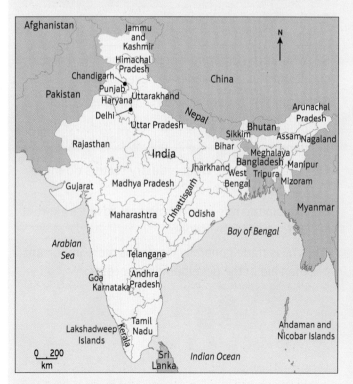

Figure 10 Map of India showing states and boundaries with neighbouring countries

nations in the region such as Malaysia, Indonesia and China. What happened in these countries provided an example of how India could become more globalised.

Environmental contrasts

In view of the large size of the country, it is not surprising that India has a variety of contrasting physical environments. Its climate varies from tropical in the south to temperate and alpine in the north. India experiences the most prominent **monsoon** systems in the world. The monsoon blows from the north-east during the cooler months and reverses during the warmer months. The monsoon rain is vital for water supply and farming, but also results in flooding.

Social and religious composition

Indian society is divided into social ranks known as 'castes'. A person's caste is determined at birth by their parent's status. At the bottom of these social groupings are the so-called Untouchables. These people have no caste and do the most menial jobs. The caste system is understandably controversial and an increasing number of Indians would like it to fade away. This was certainly the view of Mahatma Gandhi, who is regarded as the 'father of the nation'. Gandhi was the leader of the Independence movement in British-ruled India (1858–1947) (Figure 11).

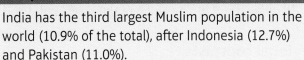

Gandhi Smriti

This national memorial honours the virtues of truth, non-violence, unity and equality.

The hallowed house, which treasures many cherished memories of the last days of Mahatma Gandhi now forms a part of our national heritage. The walls of the building reverberate with his message, "All men are brothers".

Gandhi's life and teaching have left an indelible mark on human history and the purpose of preserving this memorial is to foster and propagate his ideals.

On the morning of September 9, 1947, Gandhi arrived in Delhi from Calcutta to purge the city of the communal virus and to "do or die". He planted himself alone, amidst the raging torrent and listened to the tales of woe of the embittered and the uprooted. He had stayed here several times in the past but the last 144 days of his life spent here are more important in the nation's history. He has left a rich legacy of speeches and writings.

The epic life of the father of the nation ended here on friday, January 30, 1948. He fell a martyr to the bullets of the assassin on the prayer ground with Rama's name on his lips at 5.17 pm.

He was the victorious one in death as in life.

Figure 11 Plaque to Mahatma Gandhi, New Delhi

Although India has no official religion, over 80% of the population are Hindu. Of the remainder, 13% are Muslim. Other religions include Buddhism, Sikhism and Jainism which all have their origins in India.

Did you know?

India has the third largest Muslim population in the world (10.9% of the total), after Indonesia (12.7%) and Pakistan (11.0%).

Internal boundaries

Politically, India is divided into 29 states (Figure 10) and seven union territories. The largest state is Rajasthan. The smallest is Goa. Over 50% of India's population lives in the six states of Uttar Pradesh, Maharashtra, Bihar, West Bengal, Andhra Pradesh and Madhya Pradesh. The country's population is heavily concentrated in the broad fertile northern plains.

The Indian diaspora

An interesting aspect of globalisation is the spread of the Indian population abroad. The 20 million people who make up the Indian **diaspora** are scattered over more than 100 countries. In 2015 they sent back to India US$72 billion – a source of foreign exchange that exceeds revenues generated by India's software industry.

Activity

1 Which countries comprise the Indian sub-continent (South Asia)?

2 Using the information in Table 4, draw two bar graphs: (a) to show the size (land area) of the seven largest countries in the world and (b) to show their population density (you will need to calculate this from columns 2 and 3).

3 What is the Indian diaspora and why is it important?

Exam-style question

Describe the geographical location of an emerging country you have studied.   **(4 marks)**

Exam tip

A detailed answer should refer to (a) the continent in which the country is located, (b) the countries the case study borders, (c) adjacent seas/oceans, and (d) latitude/longitude.

Uneven development

- To understand the extent of the development gap within India
- To know the main reasons why development does not take place evenly across all regions
- To understand the meaning of the terms 'core' and 'periphery'

Regional contrasts

There are huge variations in socio-economic development within India, which has widened the development gap between the more advanced regions and those with slow progress. Rising inequality has become an important issue in India.

Table 5 shows the wide variation in GDP per capita by state for 2014. The average (mean) for the country is US$1627. Bihar, the lowest ranking state is US$945 below the mean. Goa, the highest ranking state is US$3276 above the mean.

Table 5 GDP per capita by state, top and bottom four states, 2014

Rank	State	US$
1	Goa	4903
2	Delhi	4642
3	Sikkim	3861
4	Chandigarh	3433
30	Assam	968
31	Manipur	909
32	Uttar Pradesh	793
33	Bihar	682

There is also considerable variation in all other socio-economic indicators.

- In 2011, literacy was highest in Kerala at 94% and lowest in Bihar at 64%. For females the highest literacy was also in Kerala, the lowest in Rajasthan at 53%.
- Life expectancy at birth ranges from 63 years in Assam to 75 years in Kerala, reflecting the gap in education and access to health services.

In general, the most advanced states are (a) a group of four states and territories in the north-west – Chandigarh, Delhi, Haryana and the Punjab, and (b) a line of states in the west and south – Gujarat, Maharashtra, Goa, Karnataka, Kerala and Tamil Nadu. These two regions can be broadly viewed as the **economic core regions** of the country.

Indian economic journals often refer to the 'progressive western side' of India.

- Gujarat and Maharashtra have a range of dynamic industries generating a high volume of exports. Mumbai is the state capital of Maharashtra.
- Karnataka's high rate of growth has focused on finance and ICT for the international market. The high-tech city of Bangalore, the third largest in India, is the focal point of economic activity in the state.

Some states in the south have witnessed recent prosperity. Growth in Tamil Nadu has been based mainly on manufacturing, particularly shipbuilding.

There are lower levels of development in the northern and eastern states – the **periphery**. States in the periphery often suffer from more difficult physical environments, for example Rajasthan (far west, desert), Uttar Pradesh (north, mountainous) and Madhya Pradesh (centre, arid plateau).

The contributions to national GDP of these three states are very small. Kolkata is the largest city in India's eastern periphery. In contrast to the dynamism of Mumbai, Kolkata is characterised by ageing, heavy and labour-intensive industries such as textiles.

Mumbai: economic giant of India

Mumbai (formerly Bombay) is India's largest city and the wealthiest in the country. It is the commercial, financial and entertainment capital of India. The city accounts for 7% of India's GDP, 25% of industrial output and 40% of maritime trade (2013). It hosts the Reserve Bank of India and the two largest regional stock exchanges. Bollywood is the world's largest film industry, producing around 1000 films a year, double that of Hollywood. As such, it is South Asia's biggest cultural industry and export.

Long the centre of India's cotton textile industry, Mumbai has attracted a range of economic activities in recent decades. These include chemicals, motor vehicle, electronics, ICT and metal industries; printing and publishing; and food processing. Mumbai is the main destination for FDI in India. Its TNCs include Bank of America, Bayer, GlaxoSmithKline, Volkswagen, Walt Disney and Citigroup.

The city has attracted migrants from all over India. This has resulted in a very high population density and intense pressure on living conditions. Around 40% of the city's households are in slums.

Work is in progress on the biggest infrastructure project in India's history – the Delhi–Mumbai Industrial Corridor (DMIC). This is a partnership project between India and Japan. The core of the US$100 billion project is a Dedicated Freight Corridor between the country's political and financial capitals.

Bihar: a state in the periphery

With a population of over 100 million, Bihar is the most densely populated state in India. The 2011 census recorded a population density of 1106 km². The state's population grew by 25% between 2001 and 2011. A high fertility rate has resulted in a large young dependent population.

Bihar has lagged behind the country in overall socio-economic development. Many live below the poverty level. Over 80% of the population is rural and employed in agriculture. Manufacturing is limited. Most workers in this sector are employed in household industries, steel and other metal industries, and food-processing. The state sector dominates employment – the private sector is extremely limited in Bihar. FDI has been minimal.

Patna is the state capital and is the only real centre of economic activity. The lack of job opportunities has resulted in high out-migration. In 2011, Biharis made up 30.7% of the people migrating to Delhi.

There are a number of reasons for Bihar's low level of development, which include:

- the state's economy was very underdeveloped in the colonial period
- it has generally experienced poor governance since independence
- there has been poor development of infrastructure such as power and irrigation
- there is lack of investment in education and health
- there is a lack of FDI.

Activity

Look at Table 5.

1 Calculate the difference from the mean GDP per capita for India for each named state.
   a What is the range (difference) between the first and last ranking states?
   b From the internet, copy an outline map of India showing the states. Shade the states above the mean one colour and those below another.

Checkpoint

Now it is time to review your understanding of India's location and context in the world, and the unevenness of its internal development.

Strengthen

S1 How does India's population compare with those of China and the USA?

S2 Comment on the social and religious composition of India.

S3 Describe the locations of the economic core and periphery in India.

Challenge

C1 What is the monsoon and why is it so important to India?

C2 What are the reasons for Bihar's low level of socio-economic development?

C3 How do the regions receiving the majority of FDI differ from the others in terms of industry?

Changing economic sectors, trade and aid

India has experienced a rapid economic advance in recent decades, resulting in it now being considered an emerging country rather than a developing country.

Sectoral changes

As a country develops the proportion of people working in different economic sectors usually changes as people move from less productive to more productive employment. Thus, the contribution of each sector to a country's GDP also changes. The main trends are (1980/1981–2010/2011):

- the large reduction in the contribution of agriculture to total GDP – from 37.2% to 14.5%
- the rapid increase in the contribution of services – from 45.8% to 67.1%
- a small increase in the contribution of manufacturing industry – from 16.9% to 18.4%.
- the rise of the **quaternary** sector from close to 0% to an estimated 6.1%. These figures are included in the services sector.

In 2012, agriculture accounted for 49% of India's workforce, with 20% in manufacturing and 31% in the service sector, including quarternary jobs in ICT and research and development.

The overall trends in employment are similar to what has happened with GDP. As farming has become more mechanised in the advanced states, the demand for farm labour has fallen.

The growth of manufacturing and services and the increase in employment in these sectors has mainly been in cities, so encouraging rural-to-urban migration and urbanisation.

The importance of the service and quaternary sectors

India has achieved economic growth in a different way from countries such as South Korea, Taiwan and China. In India, the service sector has been more prominent in the country's advance. India's software and ICT services sector has been at the forefront of the country's economic growth. The exports of this sector were worth about US$100 billion in 2014/2015.

India has become the global leader in **outsourcing**. India's low-cost labour has been used to provide ICT and other services to companies in developed countries. For example, many British and US companies have call centres in Bangalore and other Indian cities. Medical transcription and expert knowledge services are other aspects of the back-office functions that India supplies to large companies elsewhere in the world.

The tourism sector is growing rapidly. In 2012 it accounted for 6.6% of GDP. Over 39 million people are employed in tourism. India recorded over 22 million tourist arrivals in 2014.

GDP

The considerable sectoral change in the economy has increased GDP. GDP grew slowly from the 1950s, the rate of increase became much greater in the 1990s and has reached an even higher rate in the present century. India's economy has grown by an average of 7% for the last two decades. It became the world's fastest growing major economy from the end of 2014. It is now the world's seventh largest economy by nominal GDP.

Activity

Study the data about sectoral changes. Draw pie or divided bar graphs to show the changes to India's economy between 1980 and 2010, then annotate details from the text or write a summary to describe the changes.

Did you know?

India is a member of the global 'space club'. India's first satellite was launched in 1975. In 2014 it successfully put a satellite – *Mangalayaan* (Hindi for 'Mars vehicle') – in orbit around Mars.

Trade, aid and investment

Trade

Until the early 1990s India was a relatively closed economy. There were very high tariffs on imports along with other restrictions. Reducing the **barriers to trade** was an important part of the economic reforms India made at the time. As India has become more integrated into the global economy, the volumes of both its exports and its imports rose sharply (Figure 12).

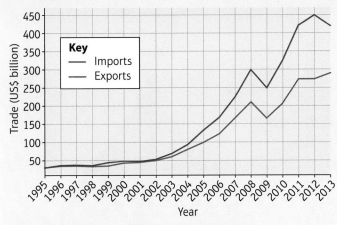

Figure 12 India's trade balance, 1995–2013

Aid

Historically, India is the biggest recipient of foreign aid. However, such aid has declined rapidly in recent years as the country has developed. India itself now sends aid to other countries, such as Bhutan, Nepal, the Maldives, Sri Lanka and Afghanistan. In 2014/2015 it was anticipated that Indian foreign aid expenditure at US$1.3 billion would be more than double its foreign aid receipts. Advocates of international aid say this shows how successful aid can be in the development process.

Foreign direct investment

Recent economic development owes much to an increasing level of FDI, a vital source of investment. FDI rose from US$17,800 million in 2005/7 to US$34,400 million in 2014. The Indian government is keen to encourage FDI into developing the country's infrastructure. In 2014/2015, the two major sources of FDI into India were investors based in Mauritius and Singapore. FDI is dominated by large investments from TNCs, but some smaller businesses are involved, especially in smaller start-ups, for example in India's technology sector.

Public investment

Every country's economy includes the public and private sectors. Public investment in education, health, transport and housing is essential to social and economic development. For example, India's well-educated workforce is vital to its ICT sector. Since the 1990s, India has been gradually selling off public companies through **privatisation**, which has also attracted more FDI. However, the public sector remains much larger than in the UK or the USA, and it employs many people.

Checkpoint

Now it is time to review your understanding of the impact of changing economic sectors on development; and the importance of trade, aid and investment.

Strengthen

S1 What is the difference between inward and outward FDI?

S2 Describe the process of privatisation. How will it change the economy?

Challenge

C1 How has the Indian government influenced India's economic development?

C2 Explain why India has changed from being a net recipient of foreign aid to being an aid donor.

Demographic and social change

Demographic change

India's demographic characteristics have changed at the same time as its economy. Fertility rates have declined rapidly from 5.2 in 1971 to 2.3 in 2015. This is not far above **replacement level fertility**, which is 2.1. However, there is considerable regional variation from this national average. In 1952, India became the first developing country to introduce a policy designed to reduce fertility and aid development, with a government-backed family planning programme. The birth rate fell from 45/1000 in 1951–1961 to 21/1000 today.

Mortality has also fallen considerably.

- The infant mortality rate, which was about 135/1000 in the early 1970s, fell to 42/1000 in 2015. The rate of improvement has been particularly high in recent years.
- The maternal mortality rate, which was 560 in 1990, dropped steadily to 190 by 2013. This is a very significant fall in a fairly short time period.
- Life expectancy at birth has improved from 50 years in 1970–1975 to 68 years today (Figure 13).

The considerable changes in fertility and mortality over the last 30 years or so have had a big impact on India's population structure. Figure 14 shows population pyramids for India in 1990 and 2010, and the UN projection for 2030.

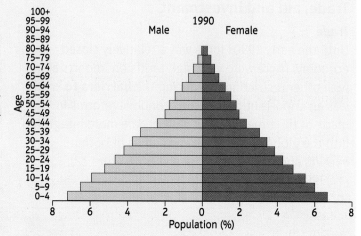

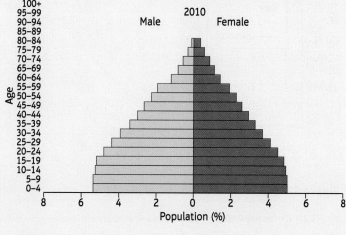

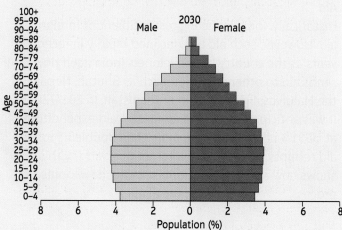

Figure 14 Population pyramids for 1990, 2010 and 2030

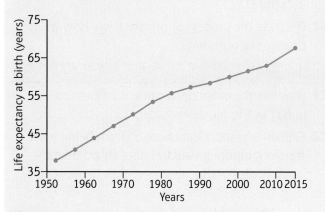

Figure 13 Changes in life expectancy 1950–2015

The large increase in the economically active population has helped to spur economic growth. This phenomenon has been called India's 'demographic dividend'.

- the proportion of the population under 15 (young dependents) declined
- the economically active population (15–64) increased
- the proportion of the population 65 and over (elderly dependents) increased.

The population pyramid for 2030 shows that these trends will continue with India experiencing **demographic ageing**.

Changing social factors

Urbanisation and the growing middle class
Economic development is the major cause of urbanisation because most of the jobs are in urban areas. Thus, it is not surprising that an increasing proportion of India's population are living in urban areas. Towns and cities are growing because of a combination of rural–urban migration and natural increase. However, the level of urbanisation in India remains a long way behind the global average (Table 6).

Table 6 Urbanisation in India

	2000 (% urban)	2015 (% urban)
India	30.9	32.7
China	49.2	55.6
World	51.6	54.0

Most of India's better paid jobs are in urban areas where most of the country's growing middle class live. Thus, there is increasing inequality between urban and rural areas, and between the middle class and the poor.

Education
Education has been a high priority for the Indian government. It is free and compulsory for all children between the ages of 6 and 14. India has more than 1.4 million schools and 36,000 higher education facilities. Apart from state schools and colleges, there is a strong private sector under state regulation. Improvements in education (Table 7) have been important to economic and social development. The education sector has attracted a considerable amount of FDI.

Table 7 Improvements in literacy

Indicator	2001	2011
Literacy rate (%)	64.8	74.0
Male literacy rate (%)	75.3	82.1
Female literacy rate (%)	53.7	65.5

Inequality
As well as regional inequality, India has other inequalities including gender, age, social position and religion. Although it is changing, the generally low status of women in Indian society remains disappointing and a considerable hindrance to development. Gender inequality is particularly high among marginalised groups, such as tribal populations and low castes.

Many older people feel left out of the benefits of progress. This is mainly because they have not benefited from the recent improvements in education and health. They are also more likely to remain in rural areas rather than migrating to urban areas where living standards are generally higher. Although India's constitution would appear to protect religious minorities, there has always been concern about discrimination, particularly in the poorer, rural parts of the country.

Activity

1 Describe the decline in the total fertility rate since 1971.
2 Comment on the improvements in literacy shown in Table 7.
3 Consider Figure 14. Explain the change in shape between the 2010 and 2030 pyramids in terms of India's changing demographics.

Exam-style question

Explain why the population structure of an emerging country you have studied has changed. **(4 marks)**

Exam tip

Make sure you refer to the standard three elements of population structure – the young dependent population, the economically active population, the elderly dependent population.

Changing geopolitics and technology

Learning objectives

- To recognise the effects of geopolitical relationships on India's development
- To understand how technology and connectivity enable development

India and Pakistan

India is a former British colony. It gained its independence in 1947 with the partition of British India into India and Pakistan. The former was to be primarily a Hindu state and the latter a Muslim state. In the largest mass migration in history, Hindus fled Pakistan for India and Muslims fled India for Pakistan. These people were fearful of what might happen if they stayed as minority populations. The eastern part of the original Pakistan became the independent nation of Bangladesh in 1971.

Since partition, India and Pakistan have fought three wars (1947, 1965 and 1999) over the disputed territory of Kashmir. In addition there have been many border skirmishes. Kashmir has been the main cause of conflict between the two countries. India controls the southern part of Kashmir and Pakistan the northern part (Figure 15). There are areas to the north-east under Chinese control which are also claimed by India.

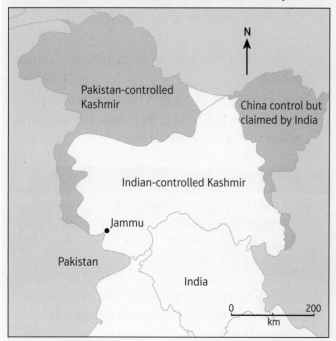

Figure 15 Map of the Kashmir region

Both India and Pakistan are nuclear powers. This is the main reason why other countries have been so concerned about the relationship between these two nations.

Figure 16 The Border Security Force along the India–Pakistan border

The Indian sub-continent

India sees the sub-continent as its 'backyard'. It has voiced recent concerns about Nepal and the Maldives and is anxious that both countries should be 'stable and inclusive' democracies. India also hopes for lasting peace in Sri Lanka following the fierce civil war there from 1983 to 2009.

China

Neighbouring China is also a nuclear power. India's relationship with China has had its difficult periods. The two countries fought a brief war in 1962 (Sino–Indian War). Current issues of concern between the two countries are (a) potential water resource conflicts in the Himalayan region and (b) increasing Chinese influence in the Indian Ocean.

India's central location in the Indian Ocean is a major factor in its strategic position. India is eager to strengthen its global image and sees the success of the Indian Ocean region as essential to achieving its national interests. For example, the east–west shipping routes that carry much of the oil from the Middle East to East Asia are not far to the south of India. India aims to become a hub of transport, communication and trade within its wider region. However, China has been extending its influence in the region, and there is competition between these two large nations.

Foreign policy and defence

Since independence India has followed a policy of **non-alignment** by not favouring either the USA and its Western allies or Russia and its allies. In recent years, relations with the West have become warmer, but not in terms of a formal military alliance. A recent ranking of countries according to their military might put India in fourth place after the USA, Russia and China. The UK and France were fifth and sixth.

The UK and India: the colonial legacy

Since independence, India's relations with the UK have gone through different phases, but have generally warmed in recent years. Opinions vary as to the impact of colonialism on the sub-continent. One legacy is that most of India's middle class speak English. This has been an important factor in India's integration into the global economy. In fact, more people speak English in India than in the UK. The UK is a popular destination for those emigrating.

The increasing economic power of India has not gone unnoticed in the UK. The UK is anxious to export more goods and services to India and to encourage more Indian investment in the UK.

India is a leading and influential member of the Commonwealth. The Commonwealth seeks to promote democracy, rule of law, human rights, good governance, and social and economic development.

Technology and connectivity

India has made major advances in terms of communications technology. India has not only benefited from increasing global connectivity, but has developed its own ICT industry to a high level. India now has the second largest wireless network in the world after China. High technology supports development in many areas.

However, there are clear digital divides in India between:

- economic core and periphery areas
- urban and rural areas
- high/middle income and low income groups
- young and old
- male and female.

In 2013, India had 61 million broadband connections. However, over 54% of these connections were in just five states – Maharashtra, Tamil Nadu, Delhi, Karnataka and Andhra Pradesh.

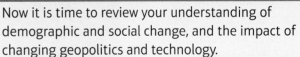

Checkpoint

Now it is time to review your understanding of demographic and social change, and the impact of changing geopolitics and technology.

Strengthen

S1 Does India have more or fewer people living in urban areas than China?

S2 When did India gain its independence, and from which European country?

S3 Describe the partition of Kashmir.

Challenge

C1 What does the policy of non-alignment involve?

C2 What effect does the digital divide have on regional and national development?

Positive and negative impacts of rapid development

- To recognise the positive and negative impacts of rapid development
- To identify how rapid development affects people
- To know how the government and people are managing these impacts

We have already looked at such issues as urbanisation, inequality and international relations. However, arguably the most important issue resulting from rapid development is the impact on the natural environment.

Unsustainable pressure on the natural environment

India has 2.4% of the world's land area, but is home to almost 18% of the world's population. In many parts of the country the limits of sustainability have either been reached or exceeded. Economic activity has polluted the nation's land, water and air, and contributed to global greenhouse gas emissions. The scale of pollution has had a big impact on the health of the population.

Air pollution

A 2014 study by the WHO found that 13 of the world's top 20 polluted cities are in India; Delhi is the most polluted in the world. India has very low standards of vehicle emissions. Air pollution reduces life expectancy by 3.2 years for the 660 million Indians who live in cities. In rural areas, indoor pollution inhaled from dung-fuelled fires, and paraffin stoves and lights, may kill more than 1 million people a year. Air pollution affects labour productivity, through illness. It is also damages agriculture – crop yields have been falling as plants struggle to grow in the presence of ozone, for example. There are concerns that tourism will be affected. The poor suffer disproportionately from air pollution.

Water pollution

India's water supply is under enormous pressure in terms of both quantity and quality. The number of rivers defined as 'polluted' in India rose from 121 to 275 between 2010 and 2015. Less than one-third of sewage generated in urban areas is treated, the rest flows directly into water bodies. The Ganges (Figure 17) and Yamuna are ranked among the world's ten most polluted rivers. The other causes of water pollution are industrial waste and agricultural runoff.

Figure 17 Major pollution in the Ganges

Deforestation and desertification

Deforestation has become a major problem. Causes include commercial logging, the conversion of forests to agriculture, urban and industrial expansion, mining, overgrazing, the construction of reservoirs behind dams and forest fires. Deforestation causes a range of serious problems which include flooding, loss of biodiversity, soil erosion and climate change. This is affecting the livelihood and food security of millions across the country. About 68% of India is prone to drought. The largest areas affected by desertification are in Rajasthan, Gujarat, Maharashtra, and Jammu and Kashmir.

Greenhouse gases

India is the world's third largest emitter of CO_2 (5164 million tonnes) after China (8320 million tonnes) and the USA (5610 million tonnes). The main reason is India's heavy reliance on coal as a source of energy (four-fifths of electricity is produced from coal).

India wants to reduce its emissions, but there are still about 400 million people without electricity. India needs to generate more power and plans to increase solar, wind and hydroelectric capacity. India, of course, emits considerable amounts of the other greenhouse gases as well. But, on a per capita basis, it is well behind developed countries such as the USA, Australia and the UK.

To meet its targets for lower emissions, India will also need to increase its forest cover to create an additional **carbon sink** of 2.5 to 3 billion tonnes of CO_2 equivalent.

Climate change

In 2015, a government minister stated that climate change was the biggest threat to India's economy. At the time, India was facing its driest monsoon since 2009. More than 60% of Indian farming relies on monsoon rain. The increasingly erratic monsoon rain patterns threaten the farming sector, which is worth almost US$370 billion and provides hundreds of millions of jobs.

Managing growth to improve India's quality of life and its global status

The government of India is very aware of the increasing inequality in the country brought about by rapid economic growth. There are growing social and regional divides.

Such trends are difficult to reverse quickly, but a number of plans are in place to help the poorest people and the regions in most need. The Smart

Cities Mission is a new initiative by the government to improve equality and the quality of life. The project will run between 2015 and 2020 and cover 100 cities across the country. Its core infrastructure elements include:

* adequate water supply
* assured electricity supply
* improved sanitation
* affordable housing, especially for the poor
* health and education
* efficient public transport.

India is aware of its growing economic strength and wants to play a more important role on the world stage. This is one reason why its relations with Western countries, the USA and the EU in particular, have improved in recent years. India is a member of the influential **G-20** and one of the **BRICS** nations. It is using its position within such groupings to push for a permanent seat in the United Nations Security Council, and more influence in big global organisations such as the World Bank, the International Monetary Fund and the World Trade Organisation.

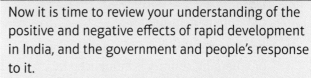

Checkpoint

Now it is time to review your understanding of the positive and negative effects of rapid development in India, and the government and people's response to it.

Strengthen

S1 Why has economic growth led to an increase in deforestation and desertification?

S2 State two facts to show how serious water pollution is in India.

S3 How do India's CO_2 emissions compare to those of China and the USA?

Challenge

C1 Why is India a major emittor of greenhouse gases?

C2 Describe and explain the extent of air pollution in India.

C3 How does membership of bodies such as the G-20 and BRICS raise India's global status?

Global Development

Definitions of development vary along with attempts to measure it. The level of development varies globally and within individual countries. Such unevenness of development has a range of consequences. Different strategies have been used to try to tackle the problems of uneven development. Emerging countries show that development can occur successfully, although the costs and benefits of change in such countries are unequally shared.

Checklist

You should know:

- [ ] how to define development using economic, social and political measures
- [ ] the extent of the development gap globally and within countries
- [ ] the causes and consequences of uneven development
- [ ] the range of international strategies used to try to reduce uneven development
- [ ] the advantages and limitations of top-down and bottom-up development strategies
- [ ] how the development of a developing or emerging country is influenced by its location and context in the world
- [ ] how the interactions of economic, social and demographic processes influence development in this country
- [ ] the ways in which changing geopolitics and technology have impacted on the country's development
- [ ] the positive and negative impacts of rapid development on people and the environment in this country.

Which key terms match the following definitions?

a The process where people, a place or a country change, or make economic or social progress.

b When all people at all times have access to sufficient, safe, nutritious food to maintain a healthy and active life.

c The total value of goods and services produced by a country in a year.

d Acquiring control over another country, occupying it with settlers, and exploiting it economically.

e The increase in the proportion of people in poverty in a country who live in urban areas.

f A movement that aims to create direct long-term trading links with producers in developing countries to ensure they receive a fair and guaranteed price for their products.

g Money owed by a country to another country, to private creditors (e.g. commercial banks) or to international agencies such as the World Bank or IMF.

h Money sent back by migrants to their family in the home community.

i A firm that owns or controls productive operations in more than one country through foreign direct investment.

j Tiny loans and financial services to help the poor – mostly women – start businesses and escape poverty.

k The most highly developed region(s) in a country.

To check your answers, look at the Glossary on pages 296–301.

Global Development

Question 1 Explain why the primary sector dominates employment in the poorest countries of the world?

(3 marks)

Student answer

The poorest countries of the world have more than 70% of their employment in the primary sector. Lack of investment in general means that agriculture and other areas of the primary sector are very labour intensive and jobs in the secondary and tertiary sectors are limited in number.

Verdict

The opening sentence includes a useful statistic showing the extent of the dominance of the primary sector in poor countries. The next sentence provides the necessary explanation in terms of both the primary sector and others sectors of the economy.

Exam tip

Your revision should always include learning some basic data that can back up statements you make.

Question 2 Suggest reasons for the changes in employment structure that have occurred in emerging countries.

(4 marks)

Student answer

In emerging countries such as India, China and Brazil, employment in the primary sector has fallen considerably in recent decades. At the same time, the secondary and tertiary sectors have become much more important. Emerging countries have attracted high levels of foreign direct investment from transnational corporations. This has not just been in manufacturing, but in the service sector in some countries such as India. The increasing wealth of emerging economies allows for greater investment in agriculture. This includes mechanisation, which results in falling demand for labour on the land. So, as employment in the secondary and tertiary sectors rises, employment in the primary sector falls.

Verdict

This answer shows clear knowledge and understanding of employment changes in the different sectors of emerging economies. Relevant use of examples adds to the depth of the answer.

Exam tip

The command word in this question is 'suggest', so you need to include some information to show your understanding of the changes.

Pearson Education Ltd accepts no responsibility whatsoever for the accuracy or method of working in the answers given.

Writing geographically: building information

When you are asked to write an explanation, discussion, assessment or evaluation, you need to provide as much detailed information as possible.

Learning objective

- To be able to use relative clauses and nouns in apposition to add detailed information to your writing, in a clear and fluent way

Definitions

Relative clause: a clause that adds information or **modifies** a noun, linked with a **relative pronoun**, e.g. *who, that, which, where, whose.*

Noun in apposition: two **noun phrases**, positioned side by side, the second adding information to the first, e.g. (1) *Bangalore,* (2) *the second fastest growing city in India, has benefited greatly from the technology industry.*

How can I add detail to my writing?

Look at this exam-style question:

> Assess the social and economic impacts of private investment by TNCs in a named developing/ emerging country. **(8 marks)**

Now look at a sentence from one student's response to it:

> *Many large companies that have chosen to locate their factories in India are attracted by cheaper labour and government incentives.*

main clause   relative pronoun   relative clause

In this sentence the noun phrase 'many large companies' is modified by the relative clause: it adds information to make clear which companies the student is writing about.

1. How could you restructure the sentence above using two separate sentences?

2. Why do you think the writer chose to structure this sentence using a main clause and a relative clause instead of writing it as two separate sentences?

Now look at these four sentences taken from the same student's response:

> *As a result of this investment, the people of Bangalore are provided with jobs and a more stable income. This means they have a higher disposable income. This encourages consumer spending and benefits local businesses. This creates a positive multiplier effect.*

3. How effectively is this information expressed? Look closely at the first word of each sentence.

4. How could you improve the written expression in the answer above, using relative pronouns?

   (a) Rewrite the sentences, using relative pronouns to link all the information in one sentence.

   (b) Now rewrite the sentence, using relative pronouns to link the information in two sentences.

224

5. Which version do you prefer? Is the information most clearly and fluently expressed in one, two or four sentences? Write a sentence or two explaining your choice.

How can I add detail to my writing in different ways?

You can also add detail to a sentence using a noun in apposition.

Compare these sentences:

> **Sentence A** *The training provided by companies such as Nokia,* which is a major mobile phone manufacturer, *has had a significant impact in India.*

> **Sentence B** *The training provided by companies such as Nokia,* a major mobile phone *manufacturer, has had a significant impact in India.*

In **Sentence A**, the writer has used a relative clause to add information clearly and succinctly. In **Sentence B**, the writer has used a noun phrase in apposition to add the same information clearly and succinctly.

How could you combine the information in the following pairs of sentences using a noun phrase in apposition?

> **Sentence C** *Many large companies have chosen to locate their factories in India. India is one of the fastest growing economies in the world.*

> **Sentence D** *Texas Instruments was one of the first technology companies to set up a base in Bangalore. Texas Instruments is a global, multinational manufacturer.*

Did you notice?

If you remove the relative clause or the noun phrase in apposition from the sentences above, they still make sense. They are separated from the rest of the sentence with commas.

6. Can you explain why? Write a sentence or two explaining your ideas.

Improving an answer

Look at an extract from another student's response to the exam-style question on page 224:

> *Private investment from TNCs has brought social and economic advantages to India. For example, it helps their employees. Their employees gain improved skills which make them more employable. It also helps smaller businesses. Smaller businesses can benefit from the TNC's employees' higher disposable income.*
>
> *However, it has also had some negative impacts. For example, the TNC's profits do not always benefit India because of leakage. Leakage is a concept that means the profits made by TNCs are taken out of the country. Furthermore, it could be argued that TNCs exploit their employees. Some employees may work long hours in poor conditions with low pay and little time for breaks.*

7. Rewrite the information in the answer above, making it as clear and succinct as possible. You could use (a) relative clauses and (b) noun phrases in apposition.

8. Look carefully at your response to question 7. Are all your sentences easy to read and understand, or are some of them too long and confusing? If so, try rewriting them to make their meaning as clear as possible.

Working with trend lines and scatter graphs

Trend lines

What you need to know about trend lines

Sometimes we want to predict or summarise what is happening with data or we have missing data. That is when we can use graphs to help us think about the overall trend in the data and estimate data we do not have.

- A **trend** is the general direction of change. On a graph you can draw a **trend line** to show the overall change in the data.

- You can also use graphs to estimate or **interpolate** missing values inside a dataset.

- You can also estimate or **extrapolate** extra values outside the range of a dataset.

Example

Some students drew a line graph to show changes in a country's exports over several years (Figure 1). Even though the results went up and down a lot, they were able to identify the trend. They drew a trend line through the middle of the points on the graph, with roughly an equal number of values on each side of the trend line.

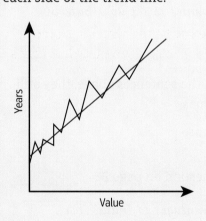

Figure 1 Trend line showing increasing trend

Figure 2 Pedestrian numbers in Compston Road, Ambleside

The students were investigating pedestrian movements in Ambleside, a small town in Cumbria. At five sites they counted the number of passing pedestrians in 15-minute time intervals. At one site they had to take a break at 10:00am but decided they could estimate the missing data. To do so they drew a graph (Figure 2) and interpolated the missing data.

Apply your knowledge

1. Describe the trend in pedestrian numbers on Compston Road that morning.

2. Use the graph to interpolate the missing figure for 10:00–10:15 and explain your working.

It started raining so the students stopped counting at 11:15. But they wanted a data set for two hours so they decided to estimate the figure for 11:15–11:30.

3. Use the graph to extrapolate the figure for 11:15–11:30 and explain your working.

4. Which do you think was most likely to be accurate – interpolating or extrapolating values?

Scatter graphs

What you need to know about scatter graphs

Scatter graphs are a way to plot data with two sets of values (or **variables**) on the same graph, to see if there is a relationship (or **correlation**) between them.

Example

- **Correlation** is when the two variables in the data are linked. In Figure 3 scatter graphs (a) and (b) show there is a link between the variables. In scatter graph (c) there is no link between the variables.

- You can draw a **line of best fit** through the middle of the data points, like a trend line. If most data points are close to the line, there is a strong correlation (Figure 3b). If the data points are far apart, the correlation is weak (Figure 3a)

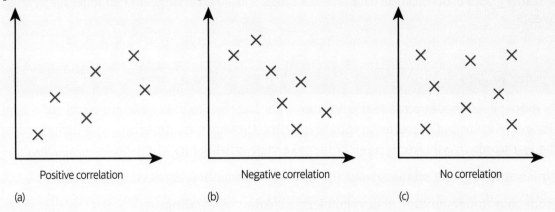

        Positive correlation   Negative correlation   No correlation

    (a)   (b)   (c)

Figure 3 Different types of correlation: (a) Positive correlation (b) Negative correlation (c) No correlation

Apply your knowledge

1. Use Figure 3 to draw sketches of the three types of scatter graph in your notes.

2. Draw and label lines of best fit through the middle of the data points on graphs (a) and (b).

3. Write this sentence under the correct graph, then write similar sentences under the other two: 'On this scatter graph, as one variable increases, the other variable decreases'.

Example

Some students were investigating data about development. They wanted to find out:

- if improving people's access to clean water would affect life expectancy

- if better access to clean water would lead to fewer child deaths.

They found data on 12 countries from the World Bank and plotted two scatter graphs (Figure 4).

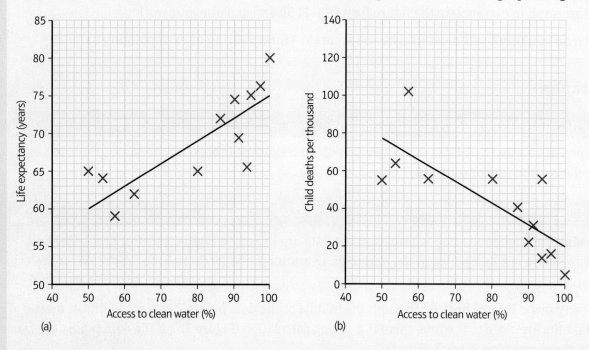

Figure 4 Scatter graphs of development data: (a) Water supply and life expectancy, 2013 (b) Water supply and child mortality, 2013

Apply your knowledge

1. As more people have access to clean water, what happens to life expectancy and child deaths? Use evidence from the scatter graphs to describe these two relationships and include some of the key words in bold from page 227 to make your writing more precise.

2. Which scatter graph seems to have the strongest correlation between the variables?

3. From your understanding of development, explain your findings.

Data with two sets of values (or variables) is called **bivariate data**. For example: in 2013, 93% of people in India had access to a safe water supply (value or variable 1) and life expectancy was 66 years (value or variable 2).

6 | Resource Management

In 2011, total world population reached 7 billion. There is growing concern about the ability of the Earth's natural resources to support this great increase in numbers of people. Continued global population growth increases the need for careful management of the Earth's natural resources in order to sustain human life.

Your learning

In this section you will investigate key learning points:

Resource management overview

- how natural resources can be defined and classified in different ways
- the ways in which people exploit environments to obtain water, food and energy, and how this can cause changes
- the global and UK distribution of natural resources and global patterns of usage and consumption of food, energy and water

Optional sub-topic 6A – energy resource management

- how non-renewable and renewable energy are being developed and how this can impact on people and the environment
- how and why global demands and supply of energy have changed in the last 100 years
- how attitudes to the exploitation, use and management of energy resources vary depending on the different stakeholders involved
- how countries at different levels of development have attempted to sustainably manage their use of energy resources

Optional sub-topic 6B – water resource management

- how the supply of fresh water varies globally
- how water consumption varies between countries and the reasons for these variations
- the different water supply problems faced by countries at different levels of development
- how the demands for water could be resolved and the strategies used by a developing or emerging country and a developed country.

Overview

Classifying and using resources

Exam-style question

Describe the differences between abiotic and biotic resources.

(3 marks)

Exam tip

You should provide key points relating to the difference between abiotic and biotic resources. When describing differences, you can use connectives such as 'whereas' in your answer.

Command word

Remember that for **describe** questions you do not need to provide an explanation.

Resources are any feature or part of the environment that can be useful to people. The term 'natural resources' refers to those resources that occur in the air, water or on the land. These natural resources can be defined and classified as follows.

- **Abiotic resources** – obtained from the **lithosphere**, atmosphere and **hydrosphere**. Examples of abiotic resources are minerals, soil, sunlight, precipitation and fresh water.
- **Biotic resources** – obtained from the **biosphere** and are capable of reproduction. Examples of biotic resources are animals, birds, plants, fungi and other similar organisms.
- **Non-renewable resources** – are those that cannot be 'remade', because it would take millions of years for them to form. Examples of non-renewable energy resources are coal, oil, uranium and natural gas.
- **Renewable resources** – those that are potentially inexhaustible and can be naturally replenished in a much shorter timescale. Examples of renewable energy resources are wind, solar and hydro-electric power (HEP).

Resources to meet our growing needs

Today we are extracting around 50% more natural resources than we did 30 years ago to obtain water, food and energy: approximately 60 billion tonnes of raw materials a year. Our natural environment provides us with life resources including cotton (clothing), energy (heat and electricity) and building materials (roads and houses). As global consumption demands continue to increase with the rapid industrialisation of countries such as India and China, these crucial life resources are being severely exploited.

How is exploitation changing environments?

Deforestation in Cameroon

Palm oil, often labelled with the umbrella term 'vegetable oil', is a resource that has grown in value with the rising demand for food. It is one of the primary ingredients used in a variety of foods, such as chocolate bars, ice cream and pizza. It is also used in other non-food products, such as lipstick and soap.

Figure 1 Deforestation in Cameroon

Rainforests cover about 48% of Cameroon. About 1% a year is cut down for timber and farming, including for palm oil **plantations**. Deforestation has a significant impact on this ancient forest, which is one of the Earth's **biodiversity** hotspots, home to 8000 species of plant and 250 species of mammals including chimpanzees, gorillas, forest elephants and leopards.

Deforestation results in soil erosion, particularly in tropical climates where heavy rainfall falls on cleared land. For example, scientists in Cote d'Ivoire found that each hectare of land covered by forest lost 0.03 tonnes of soil a year, increasing to 90 tonnes per hectare from farmland and 138 tonnes a year from bare soil. Madagascar loses 400 tonnes of soil per hectare each year.

This erosion costs developing and emerging countries billions of dollars a year in direct and indirect damages through the loss of valuable soil, the **pollution** of water supplies and impact on infrastructure and fishing. Careful management can reduce soil loss by 95%: without it erosion is a big problem for future food security.

Oil extraction in Ecuador

The Amazon rainforest is considered to be one of the most biodiverse places in the world. It is home to one in ten of Earth's known species and its dense forests cover 1.4 billion acres – one-half of the planet's remaining tropical forests.

During the 1960s, oil was discovered in the northern region of the Ecuadorian Amazon, known as the Oriente (the East). This remote area is home to **indigenous** tribes who live traditional lifestyles. The forests and rivers provide the physical and cultural **subsistence** base for their daily survival.

The operations involved in extracting oil can pose a threat to people and the environment. In some cases oil extraction has resulted in pipelines cracking and waste pits filled with crude oil waste and toxic sludge overflowing. This flows into the rivers of the Oriente, causing widespread pollution. This results in serious damage to local ecosystems and to the natural resources on which local people rely, particularly water for drinking, cooking, bathing and fishing, risking their health and long-term survival.

Overfishing in the North Sea

Millions of people rely on fish for a source of protein and a form of employment. For many years it was believed that our seas and oceans could provide a limitless supply of food to feed a growing world population. However, in the last 50 years unsustainable fishing practices have resulted in critical fish population levels – more are being caught than can be replaced through natural reproduction. Decades of overfishing in the North Sea have led to a severe decline in cod numbers. Catches of 300,000 tonnes in the 1970s fell to 20,000 tonnes in 2006, recovering to 70,000 tonnes in 2015.

Activity

Create an A4 fact file for each of the ways in which resources are being exploited. For each fact file include the following:

a   a location map

b   the reason why the resource is being extracted

c   the impact of the resource extraction on the environment.

Figure 2 Impact of oil extraction on the Ecuadorian rainforest

Did you know?

Air pollution is now the world's biggest environmental health risk, causing 7 million deaths in 2012. Just under half of deaths are caused by outdoor pollution, mostly in cities. It is mainly caused by emissions from power stations, industry and transport, especially burning fossil fuels. Just over half of deaths are from indoor pollution, mainly from cooking fires. Developing and emerging countries are worst affected.

How does the distribution of natural resources vary on a global and national scale?

Learning objectives

- To have an awareness of global patterns of natural resources
- To understand how natural resources are distributed in the UK
- To recognise patterns of distribution from maps and data

Global variety and distribution

When geographers look at distribution on a map they are investigating the spatial arrangement of features. In the case of the world's natural resources, these are not evenly distributed, as shown in Figures 3 and 4, and there are a number of reasons why the location of natural resources varies on a global scale, which we will now explore.

Minerals and fossil fuels

Some rare valuable minerals, such as gold and diamonds, are found in areas of volcanic activity. The existence of such minerals can have a significant influence on a country's economy. Other minerals, like iron, are far more common, with China, Brazil, India, Russia and Australia key producers. Fossil fuels are found in areas made of rocks formed by deposition (sedimentary rocks). The main oil reserves are found in the Middle East, with countries such as Saudi Arabia and Iran estimated to have reserves of more than 100 billion barrels.

Agriculture and forestry

The biosphere creates important resources for people, particularly through agriculture and forestry. Great variations in climate (see Topic 2) and the quality of soils from place to place mean that only some regions have forests or are suitable for farming. Today about 40% of the Earth's surface is made up of farmland and 30% is still covered by forests (see Topic 3). However, 80% of forests have already been exploited for timber and to create farmland.

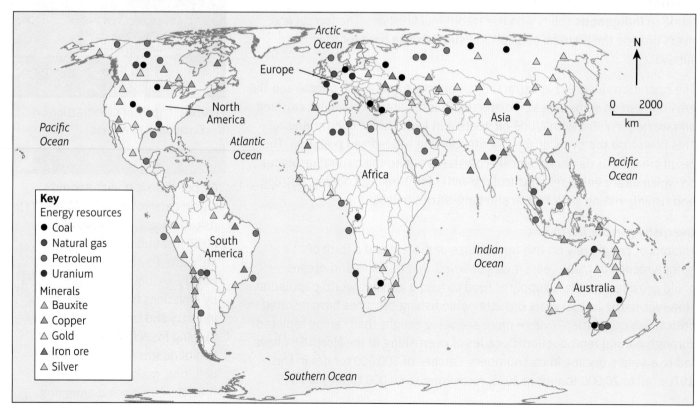

Figure 3 Global distribution of minerals and fossil fuels

Activity

Study Figure 3. Describe the global distribution of natural gas.

Tip Remember, when describing a distribution on a map, look for a general trend first then go on to give specific examples and describe any anomalies.

Natural resources in the UK

The geological history of the UK has shaped the distribution of minerals and fossil fuels (see Topic 1). Some of these resources, including iron and coal, helped fuel the industrial revolution, although far less is mined today. Oil and gas from the North Sea are important but declining sources of energy (see Topic 6A).

Much of the UK was once covered by broadleaved and coniferous forests, but today only 12% is woodland. About one third is ancient forest. Some of the largest areas of remaining ancient forests are part of the Caledonian Forest in Scotland.

About 75% of the UK is farmland. There is more pasture for grazing animals in the wetter and higher land of the north and west, and more arable farming in the drier south and east. One of the most productive arable areas is East Anglia, where potatoes, cereals and vegetables are grown in fertile soils, helped by warm summers and generally flat land.

Water resources are plentiful in some parts of the UK, particularly in the north and west, where annual rainfall is high and population density is lower (page 258). By contrast, in the south-east, population density is high, but rainfall is low. The combination of high population density and low levels of precipitation in the south-east creates serious water stress, and supply is not able to meet demand. The UK has implemented a number of strategies to find new water sources, reduce leaks and manage the demand for water. One possible solution is to redistribute the uneven supply and demand through water transfer schemes, for example the Ely Ouse transfer scheme in East Anglia, but these are too expensive to put in place for the UK as a whole.

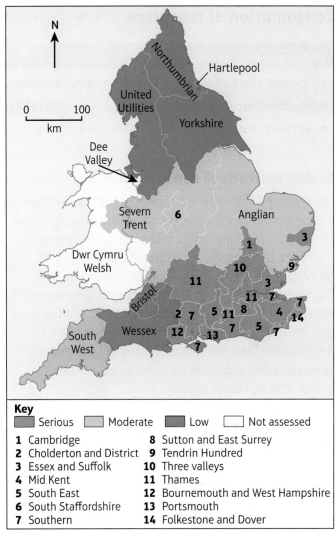

Key

Serious Moderate Low Not assessed

1 Cambridge	8 Sutton and East Surrey
2 Cholderton and District	9 Tendrin Hundred
3 Essex and Suffolk	10 Three valleys
4 Mid Kent	11 Thames
5 South East	12 Bournemouth and West Hampshire
6 South Staffordshire	13 Portsmouth
7 Southern	14 Folkestone and Dover

Figure 4 Levels of water stress in areas supplied by different water companies, 2007

Exam-style question

Study Figure 4.

- Describe the location of the areas with serious water stress. **(2 marks)**
- Explain why these areas of the UK experience serious water stress. **(3 marks)**

Exam tip

Remember to study the map carefully and pick out the specific areas using names.

Consumption of resources

Global patterns of consumption

Food, energy and water are essential for human life. People in developed countries are consuming up to ten times more natural resources than those in developing countries. On average, someone who lives in North America consumes around 90 kg of resources each day, whereas someone living in Africa consumes only around 10 kg per day. The combined factors of the rapid growth in the world's population, increased economic development and standards of living in countries such as China, India and Brazil have increased the rates of global resource consumption.

Global energy consumption

The global distribution of energy is influenced by a number of key factors, including the location of fossil fuel reserves and the ability to harness renewable energy resources such as solar and wind. Coal and oil reserves are located in places such as the Middle East where government instability can mean supply of energy is not always straightforward. The ability to harness renewable energy, such as solar and wind, will be dependent on the amount of sunlight and wind places receive.

It is estimated that global energy consumption will increase by 56% in the next 35 years, with Asia being one of the leading contributors to the increase. The economic development of China and India will be one of the key factors in the increase as standards of living improve. Asia's energy consumption has risen from 2931 **mtoe** in 2000 to 5545 mtoe in 2014.

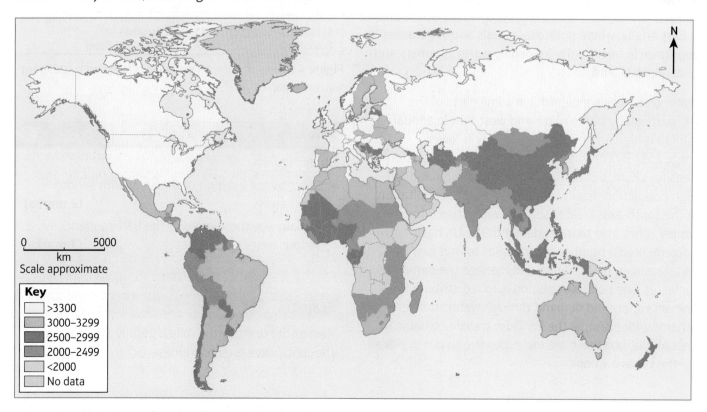

Key

- >3300
- 3000–3299
- 2500–2999
- 2000–2499
- <2000
- No data

0 — 5000
km
Scale approximate

N

Figure 5 Global food consumption in calories daily, 2010

Global food consumption

Figure 5 shows a clear pattern in the global consumption of food in calories: the richest countries such as America consume more calories per day than some of the poorest countries, such as Ghana. In some parts of Africa the average food consumption of less than 2000 calories per day is leading to under-**nourishment** and under-nutrition. The world has the ability to feed all of its inhabitants, but this does not happen because of greed, uneven **distribution** and poorer countries' inability to grow sufficient food. We have **obesity** in some countries while in others people suffer from hunger.

Activity

Study Figure 5.

a What is the average food consumption in calories for North America?

b Which continent has the lowest overall food consumption in calories?

Global fresh water

The amount of fresh water available globally is limited to 3% of the Earth's water (of which 2% is locked in ice caps and glaciers). The global supply of water is continuous, with the **hydrological cycle** replenishing the world's rivers, lakes and aquifers. However, this supply is unevenly distributed because of the amount of rainfall places receive and the rate at which water is lost through **evaporation** and **transpiration**. Many places have a rough balance between the two, but some parts of the world, such as rainforests and mountainous areas, receive more than they lose, resulting in a **water surplus**. Others, however, such as North Africa, receive little rainfall and have high rates of evaporation and transpiration, resulting in a **water deficit**.

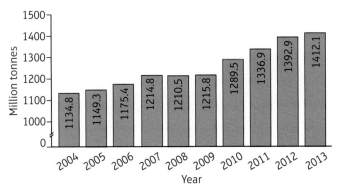

Figure 6 Total energy consumption in Asia, from 2004 to 2013

Exam-style question

Study Figure 6.

- What was Asia's energy consumption in 2007?
  (1 mark)

- Calculate the difference in energy consumption from 2004 to 2013. **(1 mark)**

Exam tip

If you are asked to calculate the difference on a graph you need to work out the figure for each year first. Then, using the two values, do a simple subtraction of the highest from the lowest. Make sure you include the correct units.

Command word

When you are asked to **calculate** you should use the numbers provided in the exam resource to work out the correct answer.

Checkpoint

Now it is time to review your understanding of how natural resources can be defined and classified; the ways in which people exploit resources in order to obtain water, food and energy; and how this has an impact on the environment. We will also revisit the global distribution and use of resources.

Strengthen

S1 Why is palm oil an important commodity to society?

S2 Summarise the reasons why oil exploitation in the Oriente region of Ecuador is damaging both the natural and human environment.

S3 Describe the difference between abiotic and biotic resources.

Challenge

C1 Using Gapminder, investigate the global patterns of usage and consumption of energy and water. Create an A3 annotated information display to represent the different patterns of usage and consumption.

C2 Explain two impacts of resource exploitation on environments.

C3 Study Figure 5. Suggest reasons for the differences in global food consumption in calories per day.

6A | Energy Resource Management

Classifying energy resources

The production of energy comes from different energy sources, which can be classified as renewable and non-renewable resources.

- Non-renewable energy sources are finite, meaning they will eventually run out – examples include **fossil fuels** such as coal, oil and natural gas.
- Renewable energy sources can be reused and therefore will not run out – examples include wind, hydro-electric power (HEP), solar, tidal and wave, **geothermal energy** and biofuels.

Some scientists classify nuclear energy as a renewable resource because it produces massive energy from small amounts of radioactive material, and little carbon dioxide (CO_2). However, unlike wind or solar power, it produces waste material and requires the mining of uranium, which is non-renewable.

The distribution of global energy consumption can be seen in Figure 1.

Did you know?

Fossil fuels really are fossils! Coal, for example, is formed from tropical plants that died millions of years ago. It is mostly carbon, so it turns into CO_2 when it burns.

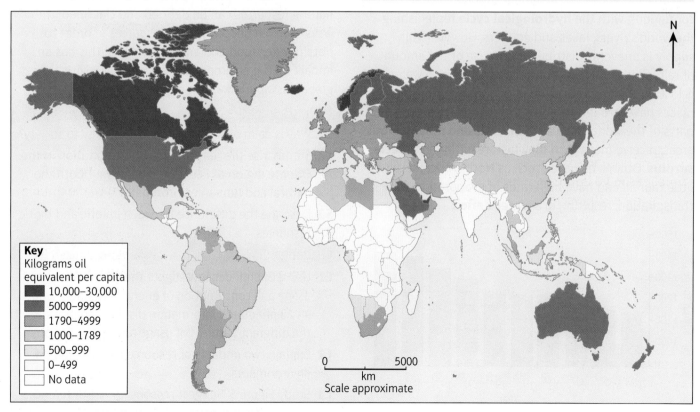

Key
Kilograms oil equivalent per capita
- 10,000–30,000
- 5000–9999
- 1790–4999
- 1000–1789
- 500–999
- 0–499
- No data

Figure 1 The world's energy consumption, 2009

Exam-style question

Study Figure 1. Describe the pattern of the world's energy consumption.   **(3 marks)**

Exam tip

When describing patterns on a map use the PQE technique: the general **P**attern, **Q**ualifications and **E**xceptions.

Did you know?

In 2015, the UK's last deep coal mine, at Kellingley Colliery in Yorkshire, closed. This ended over 2000 years of coal mining in the UK.

Production and development of one non-renewable energy source

Coal is an important world energy source, one which produces relatively cheap energy. In 2014, there was a 4% rise in consumption of coal but a 7% decline in production. The continued production of coal and development of coal as an energy source brings advantages and disadvantages, which are summarised in Table 1.

Table 1 Advantages and disadvantages of burning coal

Advantages	Disadvantages
There are still large quantities of coal available in 70 countries worldwide. World coal supplies should last for at least another 200 years.	Burning coal releases harmful greenhouse gases into the atmosphere, causing air pollution.
Mining coal is technically relatively easy and cheap.	Mining of coal is dangerous and has caused many deaths.
Coal is used in power stations in many countries around the world. It is an efficient resource for generating large amounts of electricity.	**Open-cast** mining of coal can have significant impacts on the surrounding environment and wildlife habitats.

Production and development of one renewable energy source

Wind energy has become one of the fastest growing renewable resources in the world, with a 16.5% increase in generating capacity in 2014, accounting for 3% of global energy production. China is the leading wind energy producer, generating 115 gigawatts (GW) per year. Wind energy is produced through wind turbines, which collect the **kinetic energy** produced by wind and convert it into electricity. In recent years, there has been considerable development in the efficiency and reliability of wind turbines, making them more efficient, more powerful and cheaper. There are many advantages and disadvantages to the continued use of wind energy, which are summarised in Table 2.

Exam-style question

Explain how using coal for energy has positive and negative effects on people and the environment.   **(4 marks)**

Exam tip

Here your response will need to give reasons for the impacts on both people and the environment.

Table 2 Advantages and disadvantages of wind energy

Advantages	Disadvantages
It is a clean fuel and does not pollute or emit greenhouse gases.	Many people feel that wind turbines spoil their view of the landscape.
It is one of the lowest priced renewable energy sources for the consumer.	Energy is only produced when it is sufficiently windy to turn the turbine blades.
Wind farms can be built on agricultural land, providing a source of income for the people who own the land.	It is not possible to store the power produced for use on calm days.
New technology means turbines are more efficient and make less noise.	Offshore wind farms are far from where the resource is needed, requiring expensive transmission lines.

Factors affecting energy mix

The UK's energy mix

The composition of the UK's **energy mix** for 2014 is shown in Figure 2. The reliance on the non-renewable resources of coal and oil is evident, accounting for 60% of the UK's total energy mix. While the reliance on non-renewable energy sources remained high in 2014, there was a decrease in the use of fossil fuels compared with previous years. The UK has made progress towards increasing the use of renewable energy sources, and has an overall target of 15% of energy generated by renewables by 2020 under the EU Renewable Energy Directive.

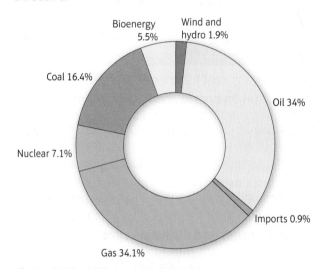

Figure 2 The UK's energy mix, 2014

Global variations in energy mix

The global energy mix continues to be dominated by non-renewable sources, with more than 80% of the total. It is predicted that the use of non-renewable resources could drop to approximately 76% by 2020. The current reliance on fossil fuels is a global concern for the future of our planet and human life.

Figure 3 The effect of burning fossil fuels

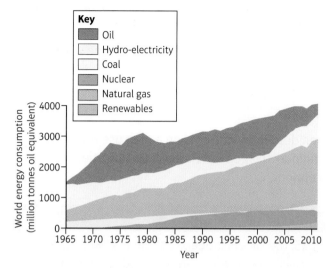

Figure 4 The world's energy consumption from 1965 to 2012

Activity

1 Using Figure 4, estimate:

   a the difference in total energy consumption between 1965 and 2010

   b the percentage of fossil fuels used in 2000.

2 Use the data in the table below to produce a divided bar chart for energy consumption in the USA by energy source in 2010.

Energy source	Percentage (%)
Petroleum	37
Coal	21
Renewable	8
Nuclear	9
Natural gas	25

3 Use your graph to describe the USA's energy mix. How does its reliance on fossil fuels compare with the UK's?

4 Suggest how the energy mix for the UK might change over the next 20 years.

The energy mix for individual countries varies with the country's level of development. This can be seen in the examples of India and Iceland in Figure 5.

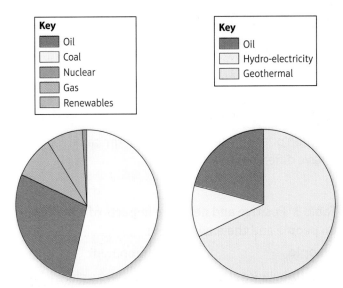

Key
- Oil
- Coal
- Nuclear
- Gas
- Renewables

Key
- Oil
- Hydro-electricity
- Geothermal

Figure 5 Energy mix for India (left) and Iceland (right), 2011

There are a number of reasons for the differences between India and Iceland.

- **Population** – India has higher energy demands to meet the needs of a population of more than 1.2 billion, whereas Iceland has to supply energy to only 320,000 people (2011). This means that India has to use whatever sources are available, whilst Iceland can use sources that may not be in such great supply.
- **Income and wealth** – Average incomes in India are low and the government lacks capital reserves, so people need to be provided with the cheapest available forms of energy. However, in Iceland, the people and the government can afford the high initial costs needed to produce energy from renewable sources.
- **Availability of energy supplies** – Iceland does not have any fossil fuels: it imports all the oil it uses. However, because it is a tectonically active area it has great geothermal energy potential from high-temperature rocks not far below the surface. It also has fast-flowing rivers in steep, deep valleys that provide great opportunities for the construction of dams and hydro-electric power stations. India, on the other hand, has huge coalfields and about 5.6 billion barrels of oil reserves, mainly in oilfields near the west coast. It makes economic sense for India to develop these reserves.

How and why has the demand for and supply of energy changed?

Over the past 100 years, population growth and rising income per person have been the key driving factors in the increased demand for energy resources. It is estimated that by 2035 the world's population will reach 8.7 billion, meaning an additional 1.6 billion people will require energy compared with today. Energy is vital for growing economies – powering **industry**, transport, **infrastructure**, information technology, the heating and cooling of buildings, agriculture, household uses and more. The relationship between income per person and energy demands is the most important factor, with developed countries consuming more than 14 times as much energy per capita as developing countries, and seven times as much as emerging countries.

Technological advances have increased demand for energy consumption (e.g. from electronic goods), while technology has also created new opportunities for energy supply from renewables (e.g. solar panels) but also for new technologies for mining fossil fuels, such as **fracking** (see pages 242 and 244–245).

Exam-style question
Explain why energy consumption per person has increased in the last 100 years. **(4 marks)**

Exam tip
For this question you will need to provide two clear reasons why energy consumption has increased. Try to include some statistics in your answer.

Checkpoint
Now it is time to review your understanding of non-renewable and renewable energy sources; the UK's energy mix and the reasons for variations in global energy mix; and changes in the demand for energy over the last 100 years.

Strengthen
S1 What is the difference between renewable and non-renewable energy sources?
S2 Describe two disadvantages of using coal.

Challenge
C1 Suggest how the energy mix for a country might be influenced by the following factors: resource availability, government policy, technology, environmental concerns, rising demand for energy.
C2 'Using renewable sources will benefit the people of today and our future generations.' Assess this statement.

How is increased demand for energy being met?

Learning objectives

- To understand how the development of renewable and non-renewable resources is affecting people and the environment
- To understand how technology can resolve energy resource shortages
- To appreciate that attitudes to the exploitation and consumption of energy resources are not the same for everyone: governments, organisations and individuals can have different views

Development of renewable energy resources

Wind energy – The London Array

The London Array, off the coast of Ramsgate, Kent, is the world's largest offshore wind farm, consisting of 172 wind turbines that rise out of the Thames Estuary. The project is owned by Denmark's Dong Energy, Germany's E.On and Masdar, of Abu Dhabi. The completion of the project in 2013 means the UK currently has approximately 3.6 GW of offshore wind power capacity. This is expected to rise to around 18 GW by 2020.

Figure 6 Part of the London Array

The development of wind farms such as the London Array brings both positive and negative impacts on people and the environment (Table 3).

Table 3 Positive and negative impacts of wind farms on people and the environment

People	Environment
The turbulence created by turbines can lead to temperature changes in the air around them – warming at night and cooling during the daytime.	Although the electricity generated by wind turbines does not produce any CO_2, the construction of the blades and pillars does.
Turbines produce noise – older designs typically produced 40–50 decibels. However, modern designs produce less and 40 decibels is only equivalent to the noise of a 15 km/h wind.	Turbine blades cause on average about four bird deaths per turbine per year. However, this is far fewer than the numbers killed by other energy sources.
The London Array will have a generating capacity of 630 MW of electricity, enough to power 470,000 homes.	It is predicted that the London Array wind farm will save 925,000 tonnes of CO_2 a year.

Activity

Identify the location of the London Array and mark it on an outline map of the UK. What are the advantages and disadvantages of its location?

Hydro-electric power (HEP) – Itaipú hydro-electric power plant in Brazil and Paraguay

The Itaipú hydro-electric power plant is located on the Parana River. It is jointly owned by Brazil and Paraguay. It provides 90% of Paraguay's and 18% of Brazil's electricity. The construction of the dam to harness hydro-electric power (HEP) has brought both positives and negatives to people and the environment. Some of these are shown in Table 4.

Solar power

Since 2009 there has been a significant increase in the generation of solar energy. In 2014 the total global solar power production was 178,391 MW. The top three leading solar energy producers are Germany, China and Italy, but the USA has the world's largest solar power plants, located in the Mojave Desert. The Solar Energy Generating Systems' solar farm produces a total of 354 MW, while the Ivanpah solar farm, currently the world's largest, can produce 392 MW.

Activity

Search for Ivanpah Solar Electric Generating System on an online map and look at a satellite view. What makes this location good for solar power? Name the nearby city that is a major consumer of electricity.

The development and production of solar energy brings with it a number of positive and negative impacts, as shown in Table 5.

Exam-style question

Describe the impacts of continued production and development of wind energy on people and the environment. **(3 marks)**

Exam tip

For this question you can explain both positive and negative impacts of production and development of wind energy. You need to talk about these impacts on both people and the environment.

Table 4 Positive and negative impacts of the Itaipú hydro-electric power plant on people and the environment

People	Environment
Families were forced to leave their homes and relocate to make way for the new dam.	The construction of the dam has destroyed a large area of forest on the Paraguayan side of the river.
The production of HEP means people from the two countries are less reliant on non-renewable energy resources.	HEP is a reliable, clean source of energy which contributes to the energy needs of Brazil's heavy industries, reducing carbon emissions.

Table 5 Positive and negative impacts of solar farms on people and the environment

People	Environment
Large solar farms can take up land that could be used for growing crops – although it is possible for farmers to grow crops alongside solar panels.	Manufacturing **photovoltaic cells** can be harmful to the environment because the panels are made of silicon and other toxic metals such as mercury, lead and cadmium.
Solar energy is a growing industry, creating many hundreds of thousands of jobs around the world.	Deserts are excellent locations for solar farms because of their clear skies and strong sunlight. However, desert habitats are fragile and easily damaged during farm construction.

Did you know?

Paraguay and Iceland generate 100% of their electricity from renewable sources.

Development of non-renewable energy sources

Oil reserves – the Athabasca tar sands, Canada

The area around the Athabasca River in Alberta, Canada, has significant oil resources in the form of tar sands. There are an estimated 180 billion barrels of bitumen in the loose sand deposits here, and this can be refined into petroleum. For many years, it was not thought to be economically viable to extract this resource, but dwindling oil supplies elsewhere, the rising cost of oil and the development of new extraction technology resulted in the commercial exploitation of these resources. However, their exploitation has led to concern about a number of impacts (Table 6).

Table 6 Positive and negative impacts of the extraction of oil from tar sands on people and the environment

People	Environment
Broken pipelines and leaks regularly cause spillages. These are extremely difficult to clean up, leaving humans exposed to harmful chemicals.	Large volumes of water are needed to extract the bitumen from the sands. As much as six barrels of water are needed for each barrel of oil produced.
The energy required to separate the oil from the sand is provided by natural gas – enough to heat 3 million Canadian homes.	Most tar sand extraction is carried out by surface mining, which means vegetation has to be cleared and surface soil and rock removed over a large area, meaning a loss of local habitats.
Extracting the resource and other jobs linked to the production process provide employment for 514,000 people across Canada. This is expected to increase to 800,000 jobs by 2028.	The refining of bitumen releases 5–15% more CO_2 into the air than does the refining of crude oil, thereby increasing greenhouse gas emissions.

Natural gas – fracking

The process of fracking involves drilling down into shale rock deposits, then injecting water, sand and chemicals into the rock at high pressure, which frees natural shale gas from the rocks and allows it to flow out to the head of the well where it is collected. The positive and negative impacts of fracking are shown in Table 7.

Table 7 Positive and negative impacts of fracking on people and the environment

People	Environment
Fracking has made fuel prices in the USA much cheaper for consumers because the USA has large shale deposits and so the country does not need to import energy from other countries.	Producing and using natural gas releases approximately half the carbon emissions of coal, so it is better for the environment to replace coal-fired power stations with gas-fired ones.
There is evidence that fracking can be linked with subsidence of homes, as rocks are disturbed deep underground. Fracking has also resulted in gas entering people's homes – flammable gas coming through taps, for example!	The chemicals used to release the shale gas may leak into and contaminate **groundwater** supplies. This could damage ecosystems that rely on the groundwater (and could affect humans who use the water, too).

Nuclear energy – uranium

Table 8 The top five producers of nuclear energy, 2014

Country	Electricity (MW) generated from nuclear power
USA	799,000
France	418,000
Russia	169,000
South Korea	149,000
China	124,000

Currently, 31 countries produce nuclear energy – there are 438 nuclear power plants worldwide. Together, these can generate approximately 379 GW of power. Nuclear plants are under construction in another 16 countries. The USA is the leading nuclear energy producer with 61 nuclear power plants in operation. The continued development and production of nuclear energy has led to global debates on the potential benefits versus the impacts on people and the environment (Table 9).

Did you know?

Electricity is measured in units called watts (W). 1000 watts make a kilowatt (KW), 1000 kilowatts make a megawatt (MW) and 1000 megawatts make a gigawatt (GW), which is 1 billion watts. A standard energy-saving lightbulb uses 11 watts.

Figure 7 A nuclear power plant

Table 9 Positive and negative impacts of nuclear energy on people and the environment

People	Environment
Nuclear power plants are expensive to build, but once they are operational they produce relatively cheap, reliable and plentiful electricity. They can produce energy when it is needed, day and night, all year round.	Nuclear power generation produces much less CO_2 than burning fossil fuels. This means it has a much lower contribution to global warming than energy produced from oil, gas or coal.
Nuclear power plants are very dangerous if they become damaged because of the potential for leaks of radioactive material into the atmosphere. Damage is rare but can happen as a result of human error, natural disasters or, potentially, terrorist attack.	The waste products of nuclear energy are highly radioactive and very difficult and expensive to manage safely. The risk of environmental pollution from stored waste products remains high for centuries.

Activity

Create a mind map to represent the impact of the development of coal, oil, natural gas, uranium, HEP, wind power and solar power on people and the environment. Include:

a a description of how renewable and non-renewable energy sources are being developed with named examples

b an explanation of how the development of each energy source is impacting on people and the environment.

You can find coverage of coal on page 237.

Disputes over energy resources

Fracking – a technological solution to energy shortages

The example of fracking shows how technology can play an important role in tackling energy problems. Although it was well known that shale rocks held oil and gas, it was not until fracking technology had been developed that it became possible to extract these energy resources. Further refinements and developments of the fracking process have made it increasingly effective and efficient.

Figure 8 This drill rig uses fracking technology to release trapped oil and gas from shale rock formations

In the USA, fracking has had a positive impact on the American economy. Fracking is supported by many Americans, business organisations and the American government.

- Over 2 million people have jobs in the fracking industry. These jobs are located across the USA rather than in just one or two states. These numbers could double over the next ten years.

- The USA's large shale oil and gas reserves have reduced the country's dependence on oil from the Middle East. They have made energy much cheaper in the USA, and that has allowed American **transnational corporations (TNCs)** to return manufacturing production and jobs to the USA.

- Cheap natural gas and oil from fracking have reduced annual energy bills for many US residents, which gives Americans more disposable income from their wages.

Should the UK introduce fracking too?

Geologists estimate that there are 200 trillion cubic feet of shale gas that could be extracted from rocks underneath parts of north-west England. This amount of gas could meet all the UK's energy needs for 70 years – although it is not known what percentage of these reserves could be extracted. However, there is much dispute about whether fracking should be introduced in the UK.

- The UK government is keen to introduce fracking. Governments are mainly concerned about obtaining and maintaining energy security as cheaply as possible. They see reliable, affordable energy as vital for economic growth and for the improvement of living standards for their people. Energy is also a source of revenue for governments because they tax it heavily. For example, in the UK, for every litre of petrol a motorist bought in 2015, the government took 58p in tax. Although the government has commitments to renewable energy, its argument in favour of fracking is that the gas it produces will join renewables as part of the UK's energy mix and that technology will be used to reduce the carbon emissions from gas production and leaks.

- Some organisations in the UK also want to exploit the country's shale energy. It is believed that opening up fracking operations in the UK will generate large amounts of money, not only for the fracking companies but also for many other industries and services. However, fracking companies are under tight government controls while the UK decides whether to allow widespread fracking or not.

- Environmental organisations are strongly against fracking. This is because of concerns about the environmental impacts of fracking technology (see page 242) and also because campaigners believe energy use must be made **sustainable** if climate change is to be limited. They believe that opening up new reserves of fossil fuels will only encourage people to keep wasting energy. Instead, campaigners say the government should invest much more heavily in renewable energy, which could also create thousands of UK jobs.

- Some individuals in the north-west would like to see fracking in their area because of the jobs that the industry would create, the new infrastructure that will come with fracking and because fracking companies will pay a lot of money to local communities for the rights to use their land.

- Other individuals are strongly against fracking because of the risk of environmental damage and their fears that fracking will cause earthquakes, subsidence, gas leaks and groundwater contamination, as have been reported by US communities in fracking areas.

Figure 9 Anti-fracking demonstrations in Balcombe, UK

Activity

1 Explain **two** ways that fracking has benefited the US economy.

2 Summarise **three** arguments in favour of allowing shale gas to be exploited in the UK.

3 Assess the positive and negative environmental impacts of developing shale gas in the UK.

Checkpoint

Now it is time to review your understanding of how the development of renewable and non-renewable resources is affecting people and the environment; how technology can help tackle energy shortages; and why disputes occur over energy exploitation and consumption.

Strengthen

S1 Why is the development of tar sands so controversial?

S2 How does the development of wind energy affect people and the environment?

Challenge

C1 'The best place for wind farms is in offshore locations.' Think of two points you could use to argue for this statement, and two points you could use to argue against it.

C2 Why do you think some countries are reluctant to invest in more nuclear energy?

Management and sustainable use of energy

Learning objectives

- To recognise the reasons why energy resources require sustainable management
- To appreciate the different views held by stakeholders on the management and sustainable use of energy resources
- To investigate how one developed country and one emerging country have attempted to manage their energy resources in a sustainable way

Why do we need to protect our energy resources?

It estimated that from 2013 to 2035 the global demand for energy will increase by 37%, driven mainly by rapid population growth in emerging and developing economies. While technological solutions to increasing fossil fuel supply are possible, environmental scientists indicate that if fossil fuels continue to dominate the energy mix, then the consequences could be catastrophic climate change. Developing more sustainable energy use must happen as well. This means more renewable energy use and less energy waste (more efficient use of energy) by everyone – from individuals at a local scale to countries and global organisations at the international scale.

Did you know?

It is also possible to see the impact a person has on the wider environment through their **ecological footprint**. Currently, all humans together use the equivalent of 1.6 planet Earths to provide all the resources we use and to dispose of all the waste we create. This is likely to rise to the equivalent of two planets by 2030 – one whole planet more than we have!

Individuals

Individuals can identify the impact of their personal energy use by measuring their **carbon footprint**. An individual carbon footprint relates to the amount of greenhouse gases produced by a person's day-to-day life through burning fossil fuels for electricity, heating and transport, and so on. It is expressed as kilograms of equivalent CO_2.

Carbon footprints can be used to identify areas where energy use can be made more efficient.

Did you know?

In 2015, leading climate scientists declared that 75% of the Earth's remaining fossil fuels need to be left in the ground if humans are to avoid the worst effects of climate change.

Activity

1 Calculate your ecological footprint using the World Wildlife Fund (WWF) footprint calculator.
2 List the factors that make up your footprint and explain why they have an impact on the environment.
3 Study Figure 10. What factors would explain the differences in the ecological footprints of different countries around the world? Suggest a minimum of three.

- Domestic heating contributes 15% to an individual carbon footprint. A lot of heat is lost through walls, windows and roofs, so domestic energy use can be reduced by installing cavity-wall insulation, loft insulation in roofs and double glazing for windows.
- Powering the home contributes 12% to a carbon footprint, and in most homes electricity comes from fossil-fuel power stations. Solar panels installed on roofs can help reduce this.
- Private transport contributes 10% to a footprint. This can be reduced by using public transport, walking or riding a bike instead of using a car, or by car-pooling (sharing a car with others).

Organisations

McDonalds is an example of an organisation that has been developing initiatives to make its restaurant operations more energy efficient. Ways it has done this include:

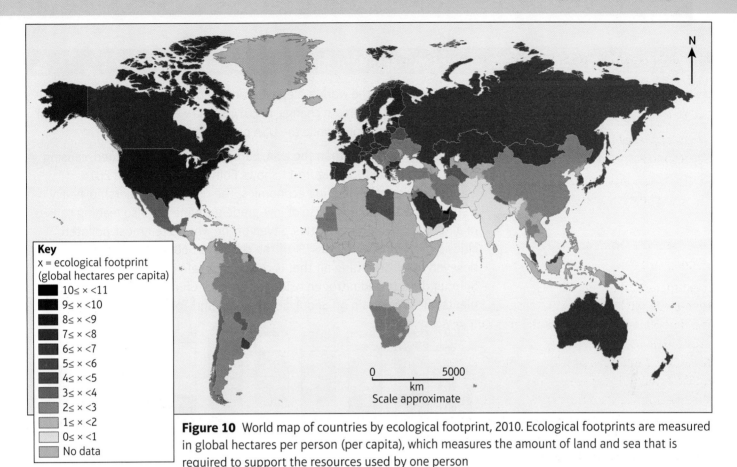

Key

x = ecological footprint (global hectares per capita)

- 10≤ × <11
- 9≤ × <10
- 8≤ × <9
- 7≤ × <8
- 6≤ × <7
- 5≤ × <6
- 4≤ × <5
- 3≤ × <4
- 2≤ × <3
- 1≤ × <2
- 0≤ × <1
- No data

Figure 10 World map of countries by ecological footprint, 2010. Ecological footprints are measured in global hectares per person (per capita), which measures the amount of land and sea that is required to support the resources used by one person

- replacing neon and filament bulb lighting with LED lighting (saving US$11 million in energy costs)
- reusing cooking oil from their restaurants as biodiesel in their delivery lorries
- installing half a million energy-efficient kitchen appliances, saving 500 GW of energy.

Governments

In December 2015, the UK was one of 195 nations at the United Nations climate change summit in Paris that pledged to limit the global temperature rise to below 2°C. Each country set its own targets towards this aim, and developed countries agreed to fund £100 billion to help developing countries transfer their economies to renewable energy. For the UK this involves:

- setting carbon budgets to limit the amount of greenhouse gases the UK is allowed to emit
- investing in low-carbon energy technologies and boosting the share of renewables in the UK's energy mix so that, by 2050, the UK produces 80% less carbon than it did in 1990
- helping to reduce the demand for energy with smart meters and other energy-efficient measures for industry, businesses and individuals

- public reporting of carbon emissions to allow people to assess their impact on climate change.

Because energy from fossil fuels is cheaper than renewable energy in most cases, individuals and organisations are often not inclined to add extra costs to their energy bills by using renewables. Until technological developments have reduced the cost of renewables, or shortages have increased the price of non-renewables, governments have to subsidise renewable energy development and consumption. This means they pay money to organisations and individuals to develop and use renewables.

Exam-style question

Explain why sustainable energy resource management is important. **(4 marks)**

Exam tip

Be guided by the number of available marks – four marks suggests two developed points.

Case Study – Sustainable energy management in China, an emerging country

China has become the world's biggest producer of CO_2, the major greenhouse gas responsible for climate change. In 2014, China was responsible for 29% of global carbon emissions, while the USA produced 15%.

China burns more coal than the USA, Europe and Japan combined, causing significant air pollution. Figure 11 shows China's energy mix in 2014, compared with other leading economies. The rise in car ownership, heavy traffic congestion and the use of low-grade gasoline are also leading causes of air pollution in Chinese cities. Seven of the world's ten most polluted cities are in China, with only 1% of the country's 560 million city dwellers believed to be breathing air that is considered safe by the European Union. Sulphur dioxide and nitrogen oxide released by China's coal-fired power plants fall as acid rain on Seoul, South Korea and Tokyo.

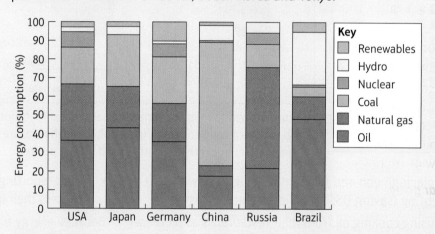

Figure 11 China's energy consumption by fuel type compared with other leading economies, 2014

All of these factors have forced the Chinese government to consider how they can manage the use of non-renewable resources and develop their use of renewable resources. In 2006, the government officially implemented the China Renewable Energy Law with a key aim to develop renewable energy resources. According to this plan, by 2020 China will have reduced its dependence on coal from it providing around 64% of China's energy to around 58%. Nuclear power will increase by 1.5% and wind power by 4.5% to make up the difference.

One of the reasons why China faces high levels of pollution is because the coal used contains high levels of ash and sulphur that, when burnt, cause high levels of pollution. To help alleviate this problem the Chinese government introduced new regulations in January 2015. These restrict the use of heavily polluting types of coal in urban areas in order to reduce city air pollution levels.

Hydro-electric power (HEP) – The Three Gorges Dam
The Three Gorges Dam became the world's biggest HEP producer in 2012, overtaking the Itaipú HEP plant in Brazil and Paraguay. In 2014, it generated 98.8 billion kilowatt-hours (kWh) of electricity, estimated to be roughly

Activity

1 Using Figure 11, explain the connection between China's energy mix and the country's high levels of air pollution.

2 Imagine you are a member of the Chinese government. Write a speech outlining to the Chinese people and the wider world why changes to the use of energy sources are needed and how these are going to be implemented.

equivalent to burning 49 million tonnes of coal and so preventing 100 million tonnes of CO_2 emissions.

Like all large-scale technological energy management projects, the Three Gorges Dam was a highly controversial project.

- The dam cost US$30 billion – although the Chinese government think it will pay for itself within ten years.
- The construction forced around 1.4 million people to be relocated from their homes. In 2012, large numbers of people were still living in unsuitable temporary accommodation.
- The dam flooded 632 km² of habitat – however the dam also controls flooding of the Yangtze River which has been responsible for the death of millions of Chinese people over the centuries.
- The dam has had many different environmental impacts – landslides along the **reservoir** edges, problems with silt and sewage build up and concerns about pollution damaging **biodiversity** in the Yangtze and affecting crop yields for farmers downstream of the dam.

For the Chinese government the dam brings more benefits as a sustainable supply of energy (and control on flooding), than it costs in environmental impacts. Alongside the reduction in the burning of non-renewable resources, the reservoir and dam can help China to meet a range of growing domestic and industrial energy needs.

Solar power

Figure 13 Aerial view of a solar power plant in China's Gobi desert

China has also become one of the world leaders in generating solar energy. China is currently building a giant solar power station in the Gobi desert (Figure 13) which could potentially produce enough energy to supply one million homes. Once completed, the power station will cover 10 square miles and it is estimated it will generate 200 MW of solar energy.

Figure 12 The Three Gorges Dam

Activity

Create a diagram to summarise the benefits and the disadvantages of the Three Gorges Dam for China. Do you think there are more benefits than disadvantages, or the other way round?

Case Study – Sustainable energy management in Germany, a developed country

Since 2001, the German government has been planning to replace nuclear power with renewable energy and to reduce significantly the country's greenhouse gas emissions.

Did you know?

Solar power uses photovoltaic cells (PV cells) which convert light into electrical energy. The amount of electrical energy generated depends on the amount and intensity of daylight that falls on the PV material. The cells do not require direct sunlight to work.

- Following Japan's Fukushima disaster in 2012, Germany closed eight of its nuclear plants and plans to close the rest by 2022.
- By 2020, Germany will reduce greenhouse gas emissions by 40% (compared with 1990 levels) and by 80% by 2050.

To achieve this, the government has invested in the development of renewable energy. By 2014, Germany produced around 30% of its electricity from renewables, including 8% from solar power, encouraged by **feed-in tariffs** that pay producers of renewable energy for the electricity they produce. The government also aims to reduce energy consumption through better energy efficiency, as Figure 14 illustrates.

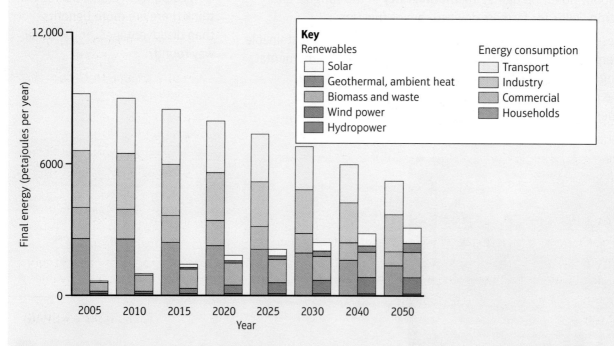

Figure 14 Germany's energy plan for 2005–2050, driving down energy consumption while increasing supply from renewables

Figure 15 Bavaria Solarpark

Solar power

German solar power comes from a combination of large solar farms, such as the Bavaria Solarpark shown in Figure 15, and incentives for individuals and organisations to install solar panels on homes and businesses. The Bavaria Solarpark covers around 26 hectares (62 acres) and uses nearly 60,000 photovoltaic panels. The project is anticipated to reduce CO_2 emissions by more than 100,000 tonnes over the next 30 years, by producing approximately 215 million kWh of clean power over the next 20 years.

Wind power

Figure 16 Norsee Ost farm in the North Sea

Germany's government plans to have wind energy production of around 6500 MW by 2020. By 2014, Germany was producing approximately 8% of its electricity from wind turbines, almost all of which were onshore. With the development of new, more efficient wind turbines, Germany is now replacing old turbines with new ones to increase power production. The development of new turbine technology has also resulted in less opposition by people who recognise the advantage of wind power over dirty coal power and potentially dangerous nuclear power plants. This change in attitude has seen the planning barriers in the state of Baden-Württemberg removed to facilitate the installation of wind turbines on hillsides and in forests.

Checkpoint

Now it is time to review your understanding of the reasons why energy resources require sustainable management; different views about sustainable use of energy resources; and how one developed and one emerging country are attempting to manage their energy resources in a sustainable way.

Strengthen

S1 Summarise in no more than 100 words why sustainable energy management is important for China.

S2 What are the benefits of renewable energy for the people of Germany? Why might some individuals or organisations disagree with the government's push on renewables?

Challenge

C1 In your own words, outline how China is working towards sustainable energy management.

C2 In your opinion, is Germany right to move away from the use of nuclear energy?

Activity

1 Use Figure 14 to calculate the percentage of Germany's energy consumption that will come from non-renewables in 2020.

2 What factors do you think will be important to Germany's success in reaching its 2020 target?

Exam-style question

Assess the importance of renewable sources of energy for countries at different levels of development.

(8 marks + 4 SPAG)

Exam tip

Although this question does not ask for case studies, it would be a good opportunity to use your knowledge of China and Germany to give a detailed, geographical answer.

Energy Resource Management

As our world population continues to rise, the demand to supply energy resources is increasing at an alarming rate. This provides new challenges for countries to work together to develop use of sustainable energy resources that will sustain and protect human life.

Checklist

You should know:

- [ ] the differences between renewable and non-renewable energy resources
- [ ] the advantages and disadvantages of the production and development of renewable and non-renewable energy resources
- [ ] the composition of the UK's energy mix
- [ ] how global energy mix varies due to a number of factors
- [ ] how and why the global energy demand and supply has changed over the past 100 years
- [ ] how non-renewable and renewable energy resources are being developed and their impact on people and the environment
- [ ] how technology can help to resolve energy resource shortages
- [ ] the different attitudes to the exploitation and consumption of energy resources
- [ ] why renewable and non-renewable energy resources require sustainable management
- [ ] different views on the management and sustainable use of energy resources
- [ ] a case study on how one developed country and one developing or emerging country has attempted to manage their energy resources in a sustainable way.

Which key terms match the following definitions?

a The proportion of different energy sources used in a country.

b The use of fast-flowing water to turn turbines which produce electricity.

c Sources of energy– such as coal, oil or natural gas – that cannot be 'remade', because it would take millions of years for them to form again.

d Energy resources that are potentially infinite.

e Energy produced by tapping into sources of heat under the Earth.

f A large lake, usually artificial, used to store water.

g A measure of all the greenhouse gases we individually produce, expressed as tonnes (or kg) of carbon dioxide equivalent.

h The number and variety of living species found in a specific area.

i A process that involves drilling down into the Earth and using a high-pressure water mixture to release gas trapped inside rock.

j A measurement of the impact of human activities. It is expressed as the area of productive land required to produce the goods consumed and the wastes generated.

k The action of using up an energy resource.

To check your answers, look at the Glossary on pages 296–301.

Energy Resource Management

Question 1   Suggest how the development of a renewable energy resource can have both advantages and disadvantages.

(4 marks)

Student answer

One of the advantages of developing wind energy is that it does not pollute the air with atmospheric gases, therefore not contributing towards global warming.

A disadvantage of developing wind energy is it can affect wildlife.

Verdict

Part 1 is correct – the student has identified a correct advantage of using wind energy – no air pollution – and explained why this is an advantage.

Part 2 is correct but incomplete. The student needs to go on to explain how wildlife is affected by the development of wind energy and could also have discussed the impact on the migration patterns of birds.

Exam tip

The student has not fully answered the question being asked. In a 'suggest' question that is worth a total of four marks, it is important you provide two full points. Reading the question through at least a couple of times can help avoid this sort of mistake.

Question 2   For a non-renewable energy resource you have studied, describe the effects of this resource on people and the environment.

(3 marks)

Student answer

The use of tar sands to extract oil in places like Canada can lead to a number of effects on people and the environment. One of the positive effects on people is that the production process provides both direct and indirect jobs for 514,000 people across Canada. A negative effect on people is that pipelines can suffer ruptures, which can lead to humans being exposed to spills and chemicals. A negative effect on the environment is the loss of wildlife habitats from the clearance of vegetation for surface mining.

Verdict

The candidate has provided three descriptive effects – employment, chemical exposure and destruction of wildlife habitats – of one non-renewable energy resource on people and the environment.

Exam tip

For this question you need to provide effects of developing a non-renewable energy source on people and the environment. There are three marks available, therefore three descriptive points are needed. As the question does not specify positive or negative effects you can choose the effects you want to use in your answer.

Pearson Education Ltd accepts no responsibility whatsoever for the accuracy or method of working in the answers given.

Water supply on the 'blue planet'

Learning objectives

- To know the global distribution of fresh water
- To understand how the availability of fresh water varies on a global and national scale
- To understand why some parts of the world have a water surplus or a water deficit

The Earth is often called the 'blue planet' because 70% of it is covered with water. The water can come in a variety of forms: liquid water (oceans, lakes and streams), solid (ice caps and glaciers) and gas (water vapour in the atmosphere). Water is essential for human life but as well as water for drinking, we also use it in hundreds of other ways – for growing crops, cooking food, washing clothes, in industry and in generating power.

Around 97% of all the water on Earth is contained in the oceans but this is too salty for us to drink. This leaves only 3% of all the water available as freshwater. Of that, two-thirds is locked up in ice caps and glaciers. The 1% of the world's water that is usable is still a large amount:

10 million km³. The challenge is that this water is not evenly distributed.

Water surplus and water deficit

The global supply of water is unevenly distributed because of the amount of rainfall places receive and the rate at which water is lost through **evaporation** and **transpiration**. Many places have a rough balance between the two. But some parts of the world, for example rainforests and mountainous areas, receive more than they lose, resulting in a **water surplus**. On the other hand some parts of the world, such as the countries in the north of Africa, receive little rainfall and have high rates of evaporation and transpiration, causing a **water deficit**.

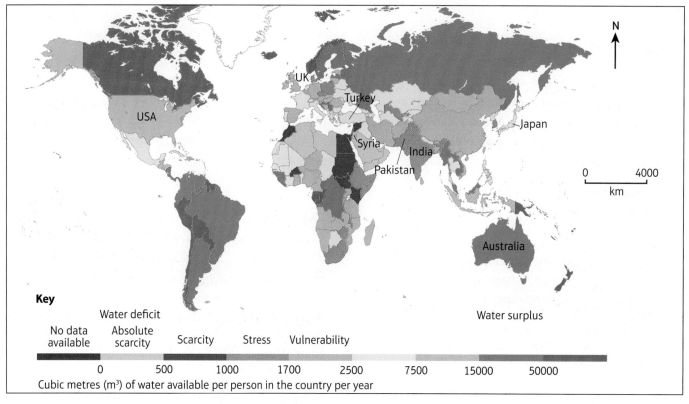

Figure 1 Global water surplus and water deficit

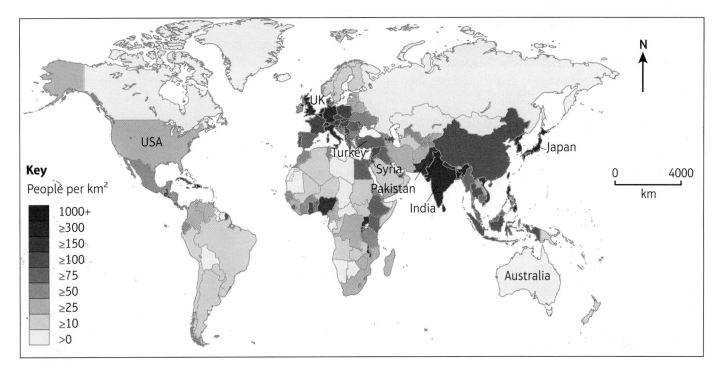

Figure 2 World population densities, by country, 2015

Activity

1   Study Figures 1 and 2. Which **one** of the following countries has high **population density** and also a water surplus: Australia, India, Japan, USA?

2   Study Figures 1 and 2. How many of the following countries have high population densities but a water deficit: UK, Turkey, Syria, Pakistan?

When there is not enough water to meet people's needs this is called **water stress**. Currently, more than 1.2 billion people do not have access to clean drinking water around the world. Water stress is increasing because of three main factors.

1   Population growth – everyone needs water, so if the number of people increases but the supply of water does not, water stress intensifies. Over the last decade, the increase in demand for water has been double the rate of population growth, so population increase is not the only factor.

2   Climate change – in some regions precipitation is becoming unreliable: e.g. lower amounts of rainfall, intense rainstorms that cause more surface runoff, rainfall at unusual times of year.

3   Development – economic development means higher water use: more water is taken out of rivers and lakes, leaving less for people to use.

Did you know?

The Middle East is the world's most water-stressed region: 1200 cubic metres per person (average).

Exam-style question

Explain why the global supply of water is unevenly distributed.   **(4 marks)**

Exam tip

Be careful not to talk only about reasons for water deficit or water surplus. The question is asking you to explain the reasons for both. You should provide one reason for countries having a water surplus and one reason for countries having a water deficit.

Command word

When asked to **explain** this means to give reasons why something is as it is.

Water consumption differences

Learning objectives

- To know how water usage is distributed between agriculture, industry and domestic uses in developed, emerging and developing countries
- To understand reasons for these differences between developed, emerging and developing countries
- To understand why the demand for water has changed in the past 50 years

Table 1 Proportion of water used per sector in four countries, 2015

	Japan HDI rank: 20	China HDI rank: 90	Bangladesh HDI rank: 142	Afghanistan HDI rank: 171
Agriculture	64%	65%	88%	98%
Industry	17%	23%	2%	1%
Domestic	19%	12%	10%	1%

Water consumption in countries can be divided between agriculture (**irrigation** of crops), industry (cooling machinery, washing products) and domestic (drinking and washing) usage. The **distribution** of water usage per sector varies around the world (Table 1).

Japan is a developed country with a very high human development index (HDI) rank (see page 200 for more on HDI). China is an emerging country with a medium HDI rank. Bangladesh is an emerging country, and Afghanistan is one of the world's least developed countries.

Activity

1 Using Table 1 create **four** pie charts to represent the differences in water consumption per sector for each country.

2 Describe the similarities and differences between the water usages per sector for the four countries.

3 Suggest some reasons for the difference between the water usages per sector.

Agriculture

In developing countries water use in agriculture is often inefficient. A lot of water is added to fields by open irrigation channels and by the flooding of fields with water.

In developed countries irrigation tends to be more efficient and more targeted, with less water wasted through evaporation. Sprinklers and drip feeds are used to supply just enough water to exactly the right places at the right time.

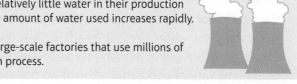

Industry

In developing countries small-scale cottage industries use relatively little water in their production processes. As TNCs move their factories to these countries, the amount of water used increases rapidly.

For developed countries industrial processes take place in large-scale factories that use millions of litres of water in the production process.

Domestic

In developing countries a large percentage of people do not have piped water in their homes. Water is often collected by women and children who can walk long distances to wells or communal taps. This reduces the amount of water that is wasted.

In developed countries homes have a piped water supply and have baths, showers and flush toilets. Many have washing machines and dishwashers. Some even have swimming pools. Domestic water use is often higher than industrial use in developed countries.

Figure 3 Reasons for differences in water usage

How and why the supply and demand for water has changed

In highly developed countries such as the USA, the demand for water has increased significantly over the last 50 years as living standards have risen alongside economic development. American citizens expect to have dishwashers and powerful showers in their homes, green lawns in their gardens and sparkling clean cars in their driveways.

However, the south-west of the USA is an area of water deficit. Some cities have even been built in the middle of deserts: Las Vegas, for example. There have been growing problems with supplying enough water to meet demand.

Supply and demand for water in Las Vegas

Las Vegas gets 90% of its water from Lake Mead, a reservoir created in 1936 when the Colorado River was dammed to improve water supply in this semi-arid region. Over the last 50 years, Las Vegas's population has increased from around 40,000 people to 580,000. The increased demand for water, plus long droughts in the region, mean that Lake Mead's water levels have dropped by half over the last ten years (see Topic 2). The original intake pipeline that takes water from the lake to Las Vegas could soon be above the surface of the water. Engineers are currently building a new intake pipeline near the lake bottom – at a cost of over US$800 million.

Lake Mead is 40 km from Las Vegas. The next best water source for the city is located 500 km away, and a pipeline project to bring water from this location to Las Vegas would cost US$15 billion as well as causing significant environmental damage. Protestors against the new pipeline argue that Las Vegas residents must realise that present levels of water use are unsustainable.

Figure 4 Lake Mead is the USA's largest reservoir. When it is full it holds 32 km³ of water, but a long drought and increased demand for water means it has not been full since 1983

Activity

1 Explain why the demand for water has been increasing in Las Vegas.
2 Identify **three** reasons why it is becoming more difficult to supply the water Las Vegas needs.

Checkpoint

Now it is time to review your understanding of variations in the supply of fresh water and differences in the amount of water that is consumed in different countries.

Strengthen

S1 Identify three countries that face water deficits.
S2 Explain why most developing countries use almost all their water in agriculture and very little for industrial and domestic water use compared with developed countries.

Challenge

C1 Use the example of Las Vegas to explain why rising demand for water can lead to problems with water supply.
C2 The UK has a water surplus. Suggest reasons why the UK still has water supply problems.

Water supply

Water supply problems in the UK

There are three main reasons why the UK sometimes has water supply problems.

1 Supply and demand are not balanced. The areas where rainfall is highest have the lowest numbers of people, but where demand is highest, there is less rainfall.

2 A seasonal imbalance. It rains more in winter than in summer, so the geographical imbalance can be made worse if areas of high demand also experience droughts.

3 Ageing infrastructure. The UK was one of the first countries to develop piped water supplies and a piped sewage system but those systems are now old and they leak, losing water.

Rainfall imbalance

Figure 5 illustrates the problem: annual rainfall totals of over 1000 mm are found in the west and especially in the lightly populated mountainous regions of Wales and Scotland. The high population density of south-east England, however, is in a region where average annual rainfall is below 1000 mm, and in some areas is less than 800 mm, per year

Seasonal imbalance

Some regions have a strong seasonal imbalance in rainfall, which means that some months receive far less rain than others. This can cause problems of water supply in the dry months. This only becomes a major

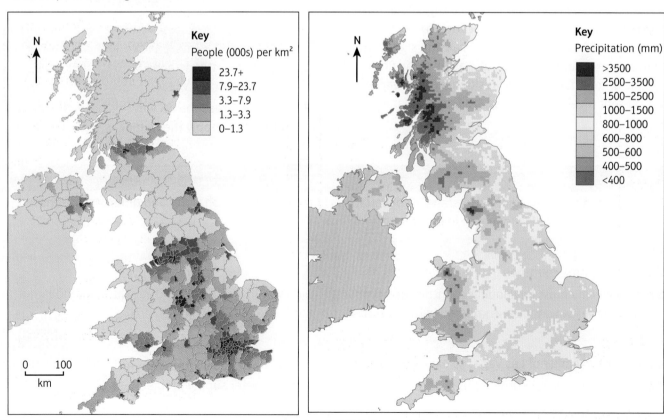

Figure 5 Population density (2011) and annual average rainfall (2014) for the UK

supply challenge for the UK's water companies during exceptional droughts.

The UK experienced a series of dry months between the winter of 2009 and spring of 2012, leading to a severe drought. By June 2010, the lack of rain in the preceding winter months meant that reservoir levels had dropped. A hosepipe ban was introduced. In 2011 the lack of rain caused major problems for farmers in the east of the UK. River levels and groundwater supplies ran very low, with crops drying up and wildfires breaking out in the south, Wales and Scotland. The drought ended with very heavy rain from April 2012 through to July 2012, which caused widespread flooding.

Ageing infrastructure

The UK's water supply system is quite amazing – every day the water companies supply the UK's population with 17 billion litres of high quality water, which come from 666 UK reservoirs, plus 1500 boreholes (down to **groundwater**) and 600 abstractions (from rivers). The water companies also collect 16 billion litres of wastewater from us (sewage) and treat it at 9000 wastewater plants so it can be returned to the rivers. All this takes 325,000 km of pipes to bring us the water, and 300,000 km of pipes to take our wastewater away again.

Unfortunately, one problem with the system is that all those hundreds of thousands of kilometres of pipes mean a lot of leaks: it is estimated that 3.28 billion litres of water are lost this way every day. Many of the pipes are old and unable to cope with the higher water pressure that Britain's large population now requires, leading to frequent burst water mains. Although the number of leaks has been reduced by one-third over the last 20 years, it would still cost £100 billion to repair all the leaking pipes in the UK – far more than water companies could ever afford to invest.

Did you know?

A single leaking tap wastes 5500 litres a year – enough to fill one paddling pool every week for the whole summer.

Activity

1 Study Figure 6.

   a Which year had the highest water lost per day?

   b Calculate the difference in megalitres between the water lost per day in 1992/1993 compared with 2010/2011.

2 Explain how the problem of leaking pipes is related to both the demand for water and problems with the supply of water in the UK.

3 Why do water companies need to treat wastewater before it is pumped back into rivers?

4 Would you be happy to drink water that had previously been used to flush someone else's toilet – after it had been cleaned up, of course? Explain why/why not.

5 Suggest **three** ways to solve the UK's water supply problems.

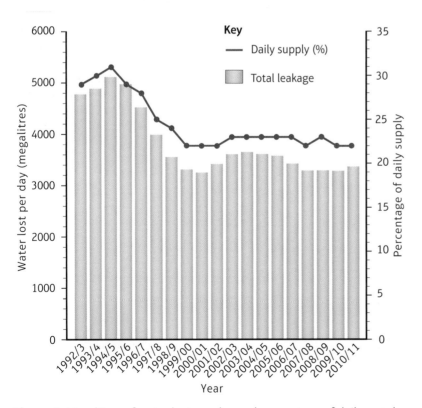

Figure 6 Megalitres of water lost per day and percentage of daily supply, England and Wales, 2013

Problems in emerging and developing countries

There are three main reasons why emerging and developing countries sometimes have water supply problems:

- When people only have access to unsafe (untreated) water.
- When water courses have been polluted.
- When there is low annual rainfall or annual rainfall that varies from year to year.

Unsafe water

It is estimated that around 650 million people, nearly 10% of the world's 7 billion people, do not have access to safe water for drinking. Just over half of that number is in Africa, mostly living in rural areas.

Without safe water, people cannot lead healthy, productive lives. An estimated 900 million people suffer from, and approximately 2000 people every day die from diseases causing diarrhoea related to drinking polluted water. The majority of these people live in developing countries, where children and the elderly are at greatest risk. According to the charity WaterAid one child dies every two minutes because of unsafe water.

Figure 7 Girl drinking unsafe water in Liberia

Activity

Use your atlas to help you describe the world distribution of safe water. Use the names of continents and countries to structure your answer.

If children are often ill because of drinking unsafe water, their education is disrupted. Parents must spend money on medicine and on travel to health care centres (and 42% of health care centres in African countries do not have access to safe water either). Adults who become unwell from drinking unsafe water cannot work hard in the fields or hold down paid jobs as easily. It is estimated that the economies of countries in sub-Saharan Africa lose more money because of ill health from unsafe water than they gain in aid payments from developed and emerging countries.

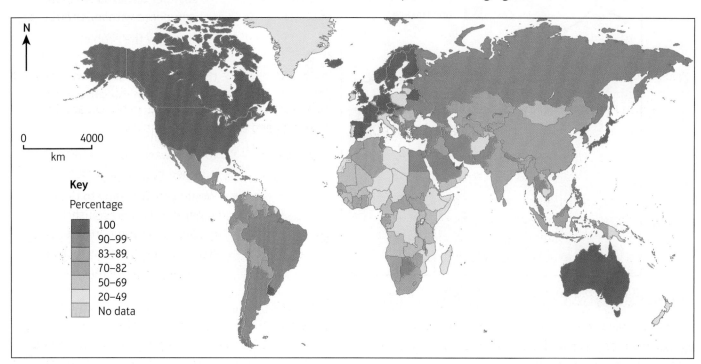

Figure 8 Global access to safe water

Pollution of water courses

Pollution by human waste

Many of the illnesses caused by consuming unsafe water are the result of water sources being polluted by human faeces – people using streams, rivers, lakes and ponds to dispose of sewage. Some 2.3 billion people in the world do not have access to the sort of sanitation systems that remove and treat human sewage to make it safe. The lack of adequate sanitation means many people living in developing countries suffer from water-related diseases such as cholera and typhoid. Both are caused by bacteria in faeces getting into drinking water, or by the bacteria being spread by touch because people do not have facilities to wash their hands after going to the toilet.

Pollution from farming and industry

Poor farming practices that leave soil exposed to the elements contribute to sediment pollution in water. If this water is used for drinking, the high sediment concentrations can affect people's digestive systems. The use of **fertilisers** and **pesticides** can also result in **water pollution**. Mining for metals is associated with very serious pollution – for example, water pollution from copper mining in Zambia in 2006 caused health problems that resulted in the company responsible being shut down.

Low annual rainfall: The Sahel

Some parts of the Sahel region have experienced a long-term drought, with rainfall figures possibly falling by as much as 30% since the 1970s. This has resulted in chronic water shortages for the Sahel countries of Burkina Faso, Chad, Mali, Mauritania, Niger and Senegal. Storage of water is difficult because of high evaporation rates in these hot, dry climates, and developing countries have less money and know-how to be able to distribute water to areas of **water scarcity**. Figure 9 shows how rainfall in the Sahel has reduced and become less reliable in the last 60 years.

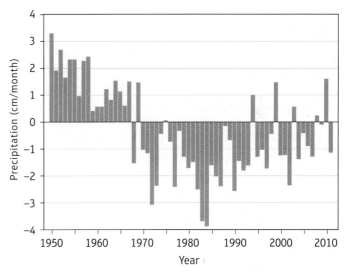

Figure 9 Variations in annual precipitation in the Sahel region between 1950 and 2011. The graph shows how much rainfall is above or below the annual average

---

Exam-style question

Study Figure 9. Assess the impact of lower than average annual rainfall on the water supply of countries at different levels of development.

(8 marks + 4 SPAG)

Exam tip

A key focus for this question is the different options that developed countries and emerging countries have for managing problems with water supply compared with those open to developing countries.

Command word

Assess means consider all the factors that might be involved in an issue and then use evidence to identify which are the most important.

Checkpoint

Now it is time to review your understanding of the different water supply problems in the UK and in emerging and developing countries.

Strengthen

S1 Between the 1830s and 1860s thousands of Londoners died of cholera. Why do you think London no longer has cholera outbreaks?

S2 Suggest one reason why the UN had most success in improving access to safe water in India and China rather than in sub-Saharan Africa

Challenge

C1 'Water pollution is a bigger problem for emerging countries than for developing countries.' Do you agree or disagree with this statement? Explain your answer.

Meeting the demand for water

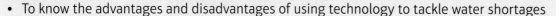
Desalination – a technology solution

One way to meet the rising demand for water would be to create more usable water – by recycling waste water or from the 97% of water on the planet that is in the sea. The technology to use sea water is available: the process is called **desalination**, which is the removal of salt from seawater. This technology is used in approximately 100 countries to create water for drinking, washing, agriculture and industry.

There are different approaches to desalination but the most common uses a technique called 'reverse osmosis'. Reverse osmosis uses pressure and a high-tech semi-permeable membrane made of cellular acetate. The membrane's holes let small water molecules through but not the bigger salt molecules: if enough pressure is applied, it squeezes the water through the membrane and leaves the salt behind.

Did you know?

Reverse osmosis can remove other impurities dissolved in water, including dirt and sewage. So as well as turning salty water into fresh water, it can also recycle water used in the sewage system or in industry and agriculture.

There are disadvantages to desalination technology:

- it is currently not very efficient – in older plants, as little as 10% of the water that is input becomes usable water (though it is closer to 50% in newer desalination plants)
- the waste product is large amounts of very salty water. This is pumped back into the sea, where it may have environmental impacts (though none have been discovered so far)
- the high-tech membrane needs to be cleaned frequently as it gets clogged and attracts bacteria

- fish and other marine creatures get sucked into desalination plants and are killed
- creating the high pressure for the process uses a lot of energy (although in the Middle East solar energy is used for some desalination plants), resulting in higher carbon emissions
- desalination plants are too expensive for developing countries to afford. A desalination plant in Sydney, Australia, cost Aus$2 billion.

Activity

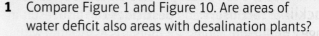

1 Compare Figure 1 and Figure 10. Are areas of water deficit also areas with desalination plants?

2 How far does Figure 10 support the theory that desalination technology is too expensive to solve the problems of water supply in developing countries?

3 Do you think that improvements in desalination technology will eventually solve problems of rising demand for scarce water?

Water management disputes

Large-scale technological solutions to water stress and water scarcity involve major investment (usually at government level) and major environmental impacts. Creating more reliable sources of water for large numbers of people is popular with the people who benefit directly, but there is often significant opposition to these schemes from local, national and international environmental organisations and from political pressure groups opposed to government overspending.

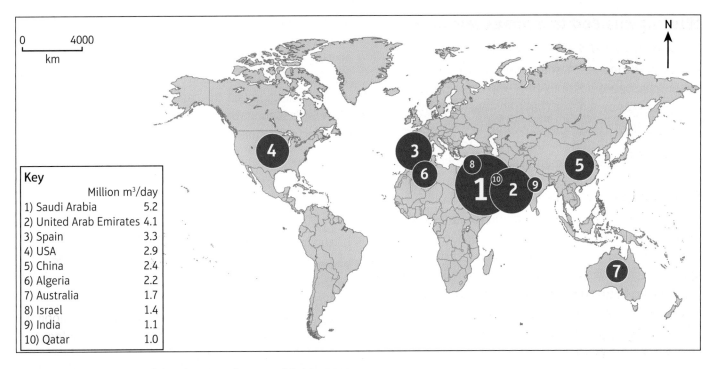

Figure 10 The location of desalination plants worldwide, 2010

Key

	Million m³/day
1) Saudi Arabia	5.2
2) United Arab Emirates	4.1
3) Spain	3.3
4) USA	2.9
5) China	2.4
6) Algeria	2.2
7) Australia	1.7
8) Israel	1.4
9) India	1.1
10) Qatar	1.0

Tackling Las Vegas's water problems

Page 257 outlined the problem of rising demand for water in Las Vegas and the proposed plan to pipe water from groundwater stores 500 km away in eastern Nevada – a US$15 billion dollar project to supply 300,000 homes in Las Vegas with water, described as a 'Plan B' in case Lake Mead dries up.

- City government's view – Although Las Vegas has made great progress in recycling water used domestically and in the city's entertainment industry, the city government says there is no alternative to the new pipeline if the city is to survive. Even the most efficient water recycling still loses water to evaporation, and the city inevitably returns less water to Lake Mead than it takes from it. As the city continues to grow, more and more water will be required.

- Businesses view – The main source of income for Las Vegas is tourism; in 2014 tourists spent US$50 billion there. Those working in the tourism industry agree that the government should invest in the new pipeline because if water has to be rationed in Las

Vegas, tourists will no longer want to come. They are prepared to help fund the project through their tax payments.

- Farmers in Nevada's view – Eastern Nevada is a rural region with an arid climate. There is significant opposition to the pipeline plan by farmers here, who rely on groundwater to irrigate their crops. Their concern is that Las Vegas will drain their water supply.

- Environmental groups' view – Environmentalists are very worried that large-scale removal of groundwater will have devastating impacts on eastern Nevada ecosystems. They want the Las Vegas government to spend the money on achieving **sustainable** water management.

- Las Vegas residents' view – Many residents of Las Vegas think it is wrong to allow the city to keep growing by taking water away from other settlements in Nevada. They worry that more growth will eventually push water prices so high that they will no longer be able to afford them.

Why do we need to manage our water resources more sustainably?

Although technological solutions to water stress and water scarcity are possible, they also cause problems of their own. Any scheme that transfers water from one place to another runs into major complications because of conflicting claims on rights to the water, concerns about environmental impacts and concerns about economic impacts – who will end up paying? While technological interventions will continue to be important in meeting rising demand for water, a lasting solution can only be reached if water resources are managed sustainably. This means more efficient, less wasteful use of water by everyone: from individuals at the local scale to countries and global organisations at the international scale.

Individuals

In countries such as the UK, individuals are often not aware of how much water they use – and waste – on a daily basis. In other countries, individuals do much more to reduce water waste. For example, in Las Vegas individuals have responded to the long drought by changing the way they use water:

- Many Las Vegas residents have planted desert gardens, with rocky soils and desert plants – cactus, yuccas, agaves and acacias.
- Residents have installed aerators into their shower heads, which mix air and water together. This still gives a 'power shower' effect, but uses half as much water.
- Low-flush toilets use a third less water compared with standard toilets.

However, not all Las Vegas residents have made these changes voluntarily. There are still many thousands of individuals who want to have green lawns in their gardens or to keep their cars clean from desert dust with frequent hosepipe washing. Swimming pools at home and heavily irrigated golf courses are also things many Las Vegas residents want to have access to.

Organisations

Las Vegas is famous for its casinos, which are privately owned business organisations dedicated to providing the amazing entertainment and luxurious experience that encourages people to gamble. Although the extravagance of casinos such as the Bellagio, with its 8-acre lake and famous water fountains (see Figure 11), seems like the very opposite of sustainable resource management, in fact the casinos have invested very heavily in sustainable practices. All wastewater is recycled in a scheme nicknamed 'from toilet to tap'.

- Three thousand kilometres of pipes bring water from all over Las Vegas's city core to a central reclamation plant.
- Filters remove all matter from the water, starting with the largest particles and ending with tiny silt.
- Bacteria are used to remove dissolved chemicals in the wastewater.
- Finally, ultraviolet light kills all the bacteria in the water.

The recycled water is then returned for use in water features such as those at the Bellagio (which only use recycled water), for use in watering golf courses and parks, and also returned back to Lake Mead, the source of 90% of Las Vegas's water.

Las Vegas casinos also use other water-saving strategies in their hotels, including centralised laundry plants for washing thousands of hotel laundry items together. Giant washing machines use 75% less water than would be used in washing so many items in normal washing machines.

Figure 11 The Bellagio Hotel and Casino, Las Vegas – featuring 100% recycled water

Figure 12 A 'water cop' patrols Las Vegas's residential streets, looking for signs of water waste

Governments

The Las Vegas city government has been the main driver in encouraging water sustainability. After extensive monitoring of water use in the Las Vegas area, the government identified that 60% of the city's water was being used by residents (the casinos used just 7%). Of the average family's water use, 70% was used outdoors: watering gardens and lawns and washing cars. In response, the Las Vegas city government:

- has banned new houses from having grass in their front gardens and limits back gardens to 50% grass maximum
- pays residents to pull up their lawns and replace them with desert gardens (this cost the government US$3 million in 2014)
- has made it illegal to water gardens in the summer between 11 am and 7 pm – 'water cops' impose US$80 fines on anyone caught breaking this law.

As well as these restrictions on individual lifestyles, the government has invested millions in a city-wide system which monitors the underground water supply and sewage system for any leaks. In the last ten years the system is estimated to have identified 1600 leaks.

Did you know?

McDonalds is an example of an organisation that has invested in sustainable water management. Its UK restaurants feature waterless urinals, which McDonalds estimates save 150 million litres of water every day.

Activity

1 Use your atlas to find Nevada, Las Vegas and Lake Mead on a relief map of the USA, and also check a rainfall map. Then use the information about Las Vegas on pages 263–265 to make an argument against the water pipeline from eastern Nevada to Las Vegas.

2 Classify the views on tackling Las Vegas's water supply problems into social, economic and environmental.

Exam-style question

Describe how individuals and organisations can manage water sustainably. **(4 marks)**

Exam tip

Be guided by the number of available marks: four marks suggests two developed points.

Checkpoint

Now it is time to review your understanding of how technology can help tackle water shortages and how different groups can have different attitudes to large-scale water supply projects.

Strengthen

S1 State two advantages and two disadvantages of desalination.

S2 Describe two methods of water management that are sustainable.

Challenge

C1 Which do you think is the cheapest option out of the following, and why:
- Recycling wastewater
- Desalination
- Locating groundwater water reserves?

Case Study – How is a developed country, the UK, trying to manage water sustainably?

Learning objectives

- To recognise the reasons why water resources require sustainable management
- To understand how sustainable water management can be put into practice by individuals, organisations and governments
- To understand how one developed country and one emerging country use sustainable water management

The UK has more than enough rainfall overall to supply current and future demand, but because of the UK's uneven distribution of precipitation and population some areas are at medium or high risk of water stress. Where a region has a high risk of water stress, the water company that supplies that region must make a plan to show how it will help its customers use water more sustainably. Water companies can increase or decrease the amount of water they supply in three main ways, but these each have disadvantages (Table 2).

Table 2 How water companies can increase (1–3) or decrease (4–6) the amount of water they supply

Option	Disadvantages
1. Build new reservoirs or extend existing reservoirs so they can hold more water. Water companies in the south-east plan to build or extend seven new reservoirs at a cost of £800 million.	Cost: customers will probably end up paying more for their water to fund these projects. New reservoirs in the south and east mean disruption to local areas and impacts on local ecosystems.
2. Extract more water from natural supplies. Water companies can apply for permission to pump more water out of rivers or from groundwater boreholes into reservoirs.	This needs to be done very carefully or river ecosystems and groundwater supplies can be badly damaged. Groundwater supplies are pretty much at maximum use already when droughts hit.
3. Recycle water. Treat wastewater so it can be used as drinking water and for other domestic and industrial uses.	People in the UK are not used to the 'toilet to tap' concept: some customers might object. Wastewater currently goes back into rivers, so using more for drinking water might affect river flows, which will have environmental impacts.
4. Install water meters in houses. Instead of standard charges, water meters allow for charging by what is used. They can cut water use by 10–15%.	While single-person households usually save money with a meter, families tend to pay more compared with when there is just a standard water rate.
5. Cut water use by farmers Usually the first thing that happens in a drought is that famers in water-stressed regions are ordered to take less water from rivers and groundwater supplies.	Farmers suffer because their crops do not grow well. Food prices increase in UK shops.
6. Educate people about ways to use less water. Water companies spend a lot of time and money helping schools teach about saving water and providing water-saving services.	Voluntary schemes do not always make a big impact. Public perception about the UK's water supply is hard to change because it seems to rain all the time.

Activity

Which of the options for increasing water supply and decreasing water consumption would you say counted as sustainable water management? Explain your answer.

Government and sustainable management

In the UK, the government's role is to make sure the water companies follow the rules that the government and other organisations lay down. For example, it is the government that gives the water companies permission to do such things as taking more water from rivers or bringing in Emergency Drought Orders which reduce the supply of water to homes. The government has also changed building regulations to encourage house builders to design and build more water-efficient homes (for example, the one in Figure 13).

One obvious solution to the UK's water supply problems would be to bring water from the wet north and west to the dry south and east.

However, the government says that it is much cheaper to develop water supplies near to where they are needed rather than to have large-scale water transfer schemes. Water is very heavy, and large amounts of energy would be needed to pump the water such long distances. That makes large-scale water transfer in the UK unsustainable both economically and environmentally.

Activity

Study Figure 13. How would you adapt this approach to plan for a water-efficient school?

underground rainwater tank

Rainwater can be harvested and used, and greywater from sinks and baths can be recycled and used for toilet flushing and garden watering.

in the garden

A water butt can store water for garden watering. Planting drought-resistant plants can help further reduce the demand for water in summer.

permeable paving

Hard surfaces contribute to the surface water flood risk. Permeable paving allows rain to be absorbed by the ground.

in the bathroom

Toilet flushing is responsible for almost one third of total household water use. This can be reduced by fitting low flush or dual flush toilets. Installing efficient boilers reduces the energy needed to heat water.

in the kitchen

Save water in the kitchen through water efficient dishwashers and washing machines, and water efficient sink taps.

leaks and drips

A dripping tap can waste up to 15 litres of water a day. Replace worn washers for a quick and cheap way of saving water.

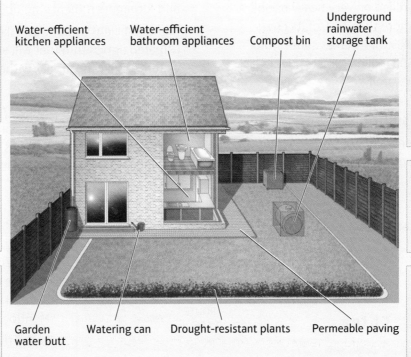

Figure 13 A water-efficient home

Case Study – How is an emerging country, China, trying to manage water sustainably?

China has 20% of the world's population but only 6% of the world's water supplies.

- Northern China has nearly half the country's population (45%) and 60% of China's farmed area, but it is much drier than the south, having only 20% of China's water resources.
- China also has seasonal imbalances: between 60% and 80% of annual rainfall comes in summer during the three months of the wet season.
- China is experiencing more droughts and lower-than-average rainfall, linked to climate change.

China's rapid economic development meant a huge increase in the demand for water from industry and its booming urban population. Two-thirds of China's 669 cities suffer from water shortages.

China's **industrialisation** has happened at the expense of its environment. China's agricultural development has also relied on very heavy use of fertilisers. As a result, more than 40% of its rivers are severely polluted, 80% of its lakes suffer from **eutrophication**, and 300 million rural residents lack access to safe drinking water.

Hard engineering solutions

The South–North Water Transfer Scheme is the world's biggest water transfer project. Costing US$70 billion,

this huge project brings 45 billion cubic metres of water from China's wetter south to the drier north.

However, such large-scale water transfer projects have not been as successful as hoped, because water from the south is so polluted by **industry** and agriculture. It takes a huge amount of energy to transfer and to clean the water, so that it is very expensive by the time it is ready for industrial or domestic use. The scheme also requires 330,000 people be relocated to build new reservoirs.

Sustainable management: the plan

Recent plans (2011) focus instead on managing China's water more sustainably. By 2020, the Chinese government wants China to have:

- effective monitoring of water use so the government can plan China's water use and make sure industries and local governments are obeying water laws
- highly efficient use of water in industry and in irrigated agriculture that will keep demand for water in line with supply, without damaging China's economic development
- environmental protection for rivers and groundwater – controls that will remove pollution and allow drained groundwater supplies to recover, ensuring all Chinese people have access to safe water.

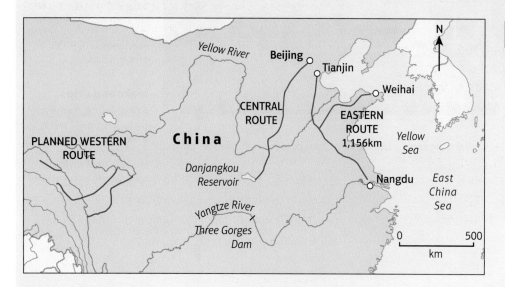

Figure 14 The South–North Water Transfer Scheme

Activity

Use the text and map on pages 268–269 and an atlas to write a summary of China's water transfer project. Mention:

- the rivers and waterways involved
- areas of high and low rainfall
- areas of high and low population density.

Sustainable management successes

Progress has already been impressive: strict new rules on water consumption meant that by 2014 industry was using one-quarter less water than in 2010 and irrigation efficiency was more than 50%.

Agriculture

China's irrigated agriculture soaks up 61% of all China's water use. Technological fixes have been important in making irrigated farming more efficient.

- **Engineering fixes** – lining irrigation channels so they do not lose as much water into the soil, using micro-sprinklers to deliver water directly to the plants, covering crops with plastic sheeting to reduce water loss from evapotranspiration
- **Changes in farming methods** – using drought-resistant crop-types, mixing straw into the soil to help retain soil moisture
- **Monitoring techniques** – rice fields are only topped up with water when soil monitors show soil moisture has dropped to a certain level.

Cities and industry

Wastewater recycling is the main way in which cities and industry are conserving the water they use. Investment in wastewater treatment in the 1990s meant that, by 2010, 18 new plants were being built across China every week! In the northern megacity of Beijing, 85% of wastewater is now recycled. In 2008, 22% of Beijing's total annual water use was supplied from recycled water.

Other projects have been important too. In Beijing, public buildings have to have facilities for storing rainwater, and storm drains have been redirected to recharge groundwater stores. State organisations have all installed water-saving devices on taps and toilets, and 95% of homes in the city have installed them too. Water prices are regularly adjusted to incentivise businesses and individuals not to waste water. Together with hard engineering projects, these measures mean that although Beijing's population has doubled since 1980, its water use now is less than it was 30 years ago.

Figure 15 This unusual building is a sewage treatment plant in Chongqing. There are 1600 wastewater treatment plants in China today

Exam-style question ●

Assess the importance of sustainable water management in a named developing/emerging country. **(8 marks + 4 SPAG)**

Command word

For a question that asks you to **assess**, you should consider a range of factors that could be important and use evidence to identify which ones are the most significant.

Checkpoint

Now is the time to review your understanding of the need for sustainable water management and how it is put into practice in both developed and emerging countries.

Strengthen

S1 Explain one reason why China needs sustainable management.

Challenge

C1 Name one similarity in the way the UK and China have tackled their water supply problems, and one difference.

C2 Explain why large-scale water transfer projects are not able to solve countries' water supply problems on their own.

Water Resource Management

As our world population continues to increase, the demand for water is rising at an alarming rate. This provides new challenges for countries to develop sustainable water management so that they can protect their water supplies for future generations without damaging the lifestyles and prospects of their citizens today.

Checklist

You should know:

- [ ] how the supply of fresh water varies in different countries around the world
- [ ] about the differences in water consumption between developing, emergent and developed countries and the reasons for these differences
- [ ] why the UK has water-supply problems
- [ ] why emerging or developing countries have water supply problems
- [ ] how technology can help tackle water shortages (desalination)
- [ ] why there are disputes about how water is exploited and who gets to consume it
- [ ] why water resources require sustainable management
- [ ] about different ways in which water resources are managed sustainably, and views about this
- [ ] a case study on how one developed country and one developing or emerging country have attempted to manage their water resources in a sustainable way.

Which key terms match the following definitions?

a   A situation where there is not enough water to meet people's needs.

b   The process of removing salt and other minerals from sea water to make it suitable for human consumption.

c   A device used to measure the consumption of water.

d   When too many nutrients get into rivers and water bodies, causing excessive plant growth.

e   The presence of contaminating and sometimes dangerous materials within a body of water.

f   Resources obtained from the lithosphere, atmosphere and hydrosphere.

g   Development that meets the needs of the present without compromising (limiting) the ability of future generations to meet their own needs.

h   A unit equal to one million litres.

i   A situation in which the usable water supply exceeds the demand.

To check your answers, look at the Glossary on pages 296–301.

Water Resource Management

Question 1   Explain **two** reasons why the UK faces water supply problems.   (4 marks)

Student answer

One of the reasons why the UK faces water supply problems is the age of the pipes. Many of the pipes in London are from the 1830s and were originally designed for a smaller demand than experienced today, resulting in frequent leaks.

A second reason why the UK experiences water supply problems is rainfall imbalance.

7th

Verdict

Part 1 is correct – the student identifies a correct reason – 'age of pipes' – and explains why this causes water supply problems for the UK.

Part 2 gives a correct reason – rainfall imbalance – but the question asks for an explanation of two reasons. The student should have explained why rainfall imbalance causes water supply problems.

Exam tip

The student has not fully answered the question being asked. For an explain question that is worth a total of four marks it is important to provide two explained points. Reading the question through at least a couple of times can help avoid this sort of mistake.

Question 2   Explain **two** reasons why domestic water consumption varies between developing and developed countries.   (4 marks)

Student answer

In developed countries improved infrastructure means people have water piped to their homes, allowing them to drink clean water at the turn of a tap. However, in developing countries the lack of infrastructure means some people have to drink water from a dirty river. Also, in developed countries wealth and technological advances allow people to have luxuries like showers, whereas in developing countries washing in the same river that is used for drinking is a common practice.

10th

Verdict

This answer gains four marks. The candidate has provided two clear reasons – 'infrastructure' and 'technological advances' – why domestic water consumption varies between developing and developed countries. As this is a comparison question the student has used 'however' and 'whereas' to indicate clearly how consumption of water varies between different countries.

Exam tip

You must talk about both developing and developed countries. When answering a comparison question, remember to use connectives such as 'whereas', 'however' and 'although' to make your comparisons clear.

Component 3
Geographical Investigations: Fieldwork and UK Challenges

Content overview

In this component you will investigate physical and human environments through fieldwork, and explore geographical issues in the UK today.

- Topic 7 will help you to develop your fieldwork and research skills by investigating one physical and one human environment in more depth. You may choose **either** coasts (pages 36–41) **or** rivers (pages 62–67), and **either** central/inner urban areas (pages 180–185) **or** rural settlements (pages 186–191).
- Topic 8 encourages you to use your geographical skills to explore four of the big challenges facing the UK. Here you will build on your learning from Components 1 and 2 to investigate: the UK's resource consumption and sustainability; settlement, population and economy; landscapes; and climate change.

Your assessment

You will sit a 1 hour and 30 minute exam, with three sections.

- **Section A** has questions about physical fieldwork: you must answer **one** question about fieldwork in rivers **or** coastal landscapes.
- **Section B** has questions about human fieldwork: you must answer **one** question about fieldwork in central urban areas **or** rural landscapes.
- **Section C** has questions about one or more of the four UK challenges: you must answer **all** the questions in this section.
- You may be assessed on geographical skills in any section, and can use a calculator.
- The paper is worth 64 marks; in addition, up to four marks will be awarded for spelling, punctuation, grammar and use of geographical language (SPAG).
- There will be a variety of different question types, including multiple-choice, calculations and open questions.
- Open questions are where you write a longer answer, from one or two sentences to extended writing worth eight and twelve marks. In the eight-mark questions, four additional marks will be awarded for SPAG.

7 | Geographical Investigations – Fieldwork

Fieldwork investigations help you to understand two different environments in depth, through practical research. You will investigate one physical environment (coasts or rivers), one human environment (central cities or rural settlements) and how physical and human environments interact.

Your learning

In this section you will investigate key learning points:

- how to plan your fieldwork investigation using enquiry questions
- how to develop good questions that focus on your fieldwork location and task
- the different methods you can use to collect fieldwork data
- how to choose qualitative and quantitative methods to collect data, and how to measure, record and present the information you find
- how physical and human features and processes interact at your fieldwork location
- how to use secondary data sources in your research
- how to analyse your data, write a good conclusion and evaluate your fieldwork investigation.

In this book, there are four modelled fieldwork investigations, two physical and two human. Each fieldwork investigation is structured in six parts to help you learn about the enquiry process.

1 The enquiry question
2 Locating the study
3 Methodology
4 Data presentation
5 Analysis and conclusions
6 Evaluation

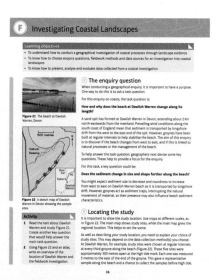

Investigating Coastal Landscapes
On page 36, you will find an example of an investigation into coastal processes through landscape evidence. This sample investigation focuses on the enquiry question 'How and why does the beach at Dawlish Warren change along its length?' The investigation looks at change in size and shape of the sediment on the beach.

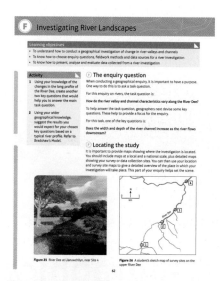

Investigating River Landscapes
On page 62, you will find an example of an investigation into change in river channels and valleys. The sample investigation focuses on the enquiry question 'How do the river valley and channel characteristics vary along the River Dee?' The investigation looks at the width and depth of the river channel as the river flows downstream.

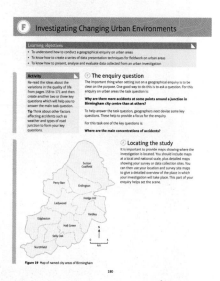

Investigating Changing Urban Environments
On page 180, you will find an example of an investigation into change in central or inner urban areas. The sample investigation focuses on the enquiry question 'Why are there more accidents at some points around a junction in Birmingham city centre than at others?' The investigation looks at the location and causes of the main concentrations of accidents.

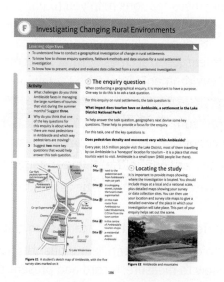

Investigating Changing Rural Environments
On page 186, you will find an example of an investigation into change in rural settlements. The sample investigation focuses on the enquiry question 'What impact does tourism have on Ambleside, a settlement in the Lake District National Park?' The investigation looks at whether pedestrian density and movement vary.

8 | Geographical Investigations – UK Challenges

The United Kingdom of Great Britain and Northern Ireland has been through significant changes throughout its history, from the Norman Conquest, to the Reformation, civil wars, the Industrial Revolution and the welfare state. The UK is still undergoing changes as it faces the challenges of the modern world. How will we cope with a rising population? Do we have the resources to cope? Will our ecosystems and areas of natural beauty be protected and maintained for the future? How will the UK be affected by global climate change? All of these questions are posed by the challenges the UK faces and you will explore how these challenges will be met.

Your learning

In this section you will investigate key learning points:

- changes to the size of the UK population
- changes to our resource consumption
- the pressures faced by the UK's ecosystems from an increase in population
- making transport in the UK more sustainable
- balancing the economic growth between London and the rest of the UK
- the costs and benefits of building on greenfield and brownfield sites
- migration to the UK and the views that people have on migration to the UK
- how National Parks are being conserved and made sustainable
- managing river and coastal flood risks across the UK
- the effect of global climate change on the climate of the UK
- how global climate change will impact on the people and landscapes of the UK and possible local and national responses.

Resource consumption and sustainability

Changes to the UK's population

The population of the UK is currently over 64 million and, through a combination of natural increase and migration, continues to rise. The issue of immigration, and the pressures that this will place on the resources of the UK, is a political issue which divides opinion across the country.

If the population of the UK grows as projected (Table 1), there will be an extra 8.4 million people in the UK by 2035, and a further 3.8 million by 2050, all needing housing, education, employment, power, food and water. This will put some strain on the resources of the UK and this will need to be planned for. However, with organisation and preparation, this can indeed be planned for in advance.

Table 1 Projected population for the UK (millions)

	2010	2015	2020	2025	2030	2035	2050
*UK	62.3	64.8	67.2	69.4	71.4	73.2	77.0
England	52.2	54.5	56.6	58.6	60.4	62.1	
Wales	3.0	3.1	3.2	3.2	3.3	3.4	
Scotland	5.2	5.4	5.5	5.6	5.7	5.8	
Northern Ireland	1.8	1.9	1.9	2.0	2.0	2.0	

*The figures for England, Wales, Scotland and Northern Ireland may not add up to the total for the UK. This is because the numbers have been rounded up.

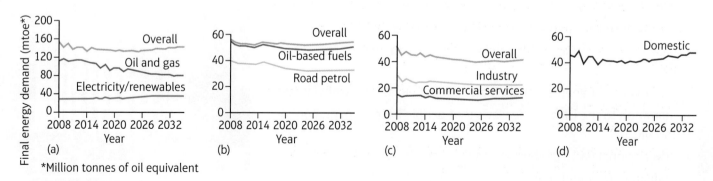

*Million tonnes of oil equivalent

Figure 1 Projected energy requirements by sector. (a) Summary of demand by fuel type. (b) Final energy demand by transport. (c) Final energy demand by industry and services. (d) Domestic final energy demand

In order for the UK to meet the needs of a growing population, there will be an expected need for a growth in energy production across the UK (Figure 1), as well as a need for more construction, such as new housing, schools and hospitals. The environmental impact of these changes could have severe consequences for climate change and habitat loss.

Pressure on UK ecosystems

The impact of a growing population will have an effect on UK ecosystems.

- With an increase in population, an increase in food production will be needed. This may in turn lead to an increase in **agribusiness** throughout the UK. This expansion could reduce natural habitats, for instance the destruction of hedgerows to provide larger fields, unless food is imported in larger quantities.

- The need for more housing will put pressure on local and national governments to release **greenfield sites**. The use of **green belt** land destroys open spaces and affects habitats through increased surface runoff and erosion as there are more impermeable surfaces preventing drainage.

- New housing could be built on floodplains, increasing the likelihood of flooding and causing more surface runoff.

- Increased demand for water will put pressure on local water systems, through increased consumption and water treatment requirements, causing further damage.

- Greenhouse gas emissions could increase through increased use of **fossil fuels**, leading to climate change unless alternative, sustainable energy sources are used.

Addressing the issues

There are various options open to try to limit the issues created by increased population and increased resource consumption, including:

- choosing alternative, sustainable energy sources to meet increased demand for energy in the UK, as well as increased energy conservation

- building at higher densities and using **brownfield sites** for new home building instead of greenfield sites – this would also allow more greenfield land to be used for farming and habitats

- switching to alternative energy sources to reduce greenhouse emissions from increased energy demands

- managing river catchments to reduce the risk and impact of flooding

- improved education on conservation of resources through reducing energy demands in homes and businesses

- finding new water sources and reducing water wastage and leaks in order to boost domestic water sources.

Activity

1 On an outline map of the UK, identify how fast the population of each country is projected to grow over the next:

   a   4 years

   b   9 years

   c   14 years.

2 Why might industrial energy use be expected to decrease over the next 20 years?

3 Population projections are not 100% accurate. Explain **two** different factors that could make a population projection unreliable.

Did you know?

Only 11% of land in England, 2% in Wales, 4% in Northern Ireland and 2% in Scotland is classified as urban land.

Sustainable transport options in the UK

Exam-style question

Suggest how transport in **one** UK city could be made more sustainable. **(4 marks)**

Exam tip

Read the question very carefully. The question refers to sustainability so make sure that you are focused on how the impact on the environment would be reduced by your examples.

Command word

In **suggest** questions, you have to show your understanding, with an explanation plus your reasons or example(s).

Activity

1 Using Figure 2, describe the pattern of NO₂ pollution across London.

2 Explain how the London Congestion Charge could be described as an example of a sustainable transport solution.

3 Of the transport solutions suggested, which do you think will have the biggest impact on reducing the environmental damage caused by transportation? Justify your answer.

Transport is responsible for a significant amount of the UK's energy consumption, particularly of fossil fuel. As you found out in Topic 2, the consumption of fossil fuels is a key contributor to global climate change, as well as affecting people's health through local air pollution. Therefore, sustainable solutions need to be considered to try to reduce this impact.

- Improving public transport systems will encourage people to leave their cars at home. Buses, trams and trains use less fuel per head than private cars in most circumstances. Commuter trains are a good example of this as they are especially efficient in high density cities.
- The creation of cycle routes and highways encourages people to cycle rather than drive. Making public access to bicycles easier encourages people not to use cars for short journeys, particularly in cities. This has been used in London to try to reduce congestion and pollution.
- Car-sharing schemes are run by many local authorities. These encourage commuters to share car journeys to and from work to reduce the number of cars on the road and the amount of fuel being used. In turn, this reduces pollution.
- The use of reduced, or zero, emission vehicles such as hybrid or electric cars reduces the impact of the vehicle on air quality.

The congestion charge

An example of a specific scheme used within the UK to make transport more sustainable is the congestion charge zone in the capital, London.

London is a heavily congested and polluted city. Research suggests nearly 9500 people die each year due to the effects of air pollution (Figure 2). In order to address this issue, the **congestion charge** was brought in to reduce congestion and pollution. The idea, introduced in 2003, is to charge drivers of privately owned transport to enter the centre of London. There have been adjustments and adaptations to the scheme over time but the key aim of the programme has remained the same.

Since the introduction of the scheme:

- according to Transport for London figures, traffic levels reduced by 10.2% in the first ten years of the scheme
- greenhouse gas emissions in the zone have been reduced
- the pollutants that adversely affect the air quality and health of Londoners have fallen by 12%. However, in 2010 there were still 9400 early deaths in London caused by air pollution.

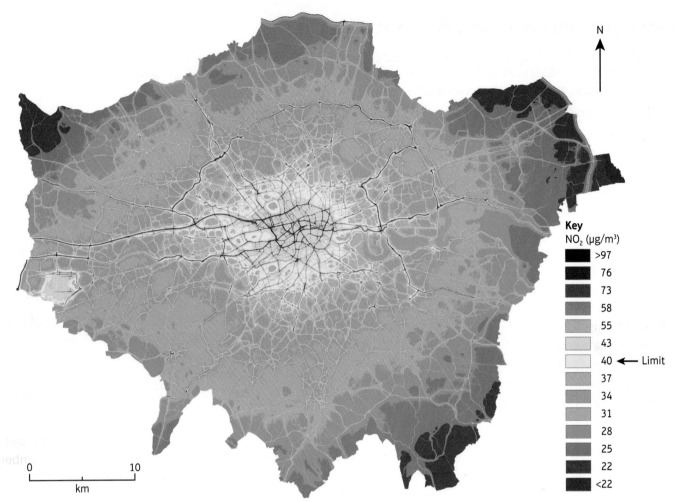

Figure 2 Pollution due to nitrogen dioxide (NO_2) in the Greater London area

Key
NO_2 (µg/m³)

	>97
	76
	73
	58
	55
	43
	40 ← Limit
	37
	34
	31
	28
	25
	22
	<22

0   10
km

Owing to these statistics, the scheme is often referred to as a success by local government and environmental organisations, However, some motoring organisations are not in favour as they believe that the benefits of the scheme are not as strong as suggested: in fact, they believe the scheme is adding to congestion in other routes as people try to avoid the congestion charge zone.

Checkpoint

Now it is time to review your understanding of the UK's population growth, resource consumption and sustainability.

Strengthen

S1 How could the UK's ecosystems be affected by a growth in the population of the UK?

S2 Why is it unsustainable to rely on private transport in a city?

S3 How could urban transportation be made more sustainable?

Challenge

C1 Describe three ways in which the UK could reduce the impact of an increased population on resources and ecosystems.

C2 Why is sustainable transportation needed in London? Do you think the congestion charge will address this issue effectively?

C3 One option to help London's housing crisis is to allow building on the greenbelt. Using information from pages 276–279, assess the pros and cons of this idea.

Settlement, population and economic challenges

Key
£ Average house price in each region
▲ Yearly change up
▼ Yearly change down

North East
£96,227
▼1.6%

Yorkshire and The Humber
£117,424
▲1.6%

North West
£109,602
▲0.8%

East Midlands
£133,145
▲5.2%

West Midlands
£131,729
▲3.2%

Wales
£118,310
▲3.3%

East
£177,975
▲3.1%

London
£396,646
▲10.6%

South West
£174,734
▲2.1%

South East
£216,618
▲3.5%

0   100 km

Figure 3 House price map of England and Wales, January 2014

The 'two-speed economy'

The term **two-speed economy** refers to the idea that economic growth within the UK is not uniform across the whole country. London and the south east of England, in particular, are experiencing significantly higher and faster economic growth than the northern parts of England and Scotland, as well as western areas of England and Wales. Recent large construction projects in and around the capital, such as The Shard, and new transport systems, such as Crossrail, are evidence of significant investment and growth in the South East. However, this investment is not being reflected across the rest of the UK.

One effect of economic growth in London and the South East is that more and more people are moving or commuting long distances south from areas such as Yorkshire to work in the capital and the South East. This reduces the locally available workforce and does not encourage businesses to invest in the area. The lack of business investment is one factor that affects people's opportunities. House prices in London and the South East are also rising considerably faster than the rest of the country, as demonstrated by the map in Figure 3. Many people feel that current economic policies are helping to improve and strengthen the economic power of the South East, but not doing anything to regenerate the more northern and western parts of the UK.

Possible solutions to this growing divide between the North and South are focused around transportation to improve mobility of people, goods and skills and include:

- the High Speed Rail 2 (HS2) railway between London and northern cities. The majority of the construction will take place outside the capital and therefore generate most jobs away from London
- investing in better transport to improve the movement of workers and freight across the North, making it easier for new businesses to set up and move their goods

- improvements in connections to northern airports, such as Manchester, to encourage travel and investment from abroad
- using 'smart tickets' to make access to transport links easier and more attractive for people to use.

Greenfield and brownfield development

In order to cope with a rising population and to provide for economic development, new housing, new industry and new transportation links are needed. Whether this new construction should occur on greenfield or brownfield sites is the subject of debate, based on which type of site is best.

Table 2 Advantages and disadvantages of greenfield and brownfield sites

	Advantages	Disadvantages
Greenfield sites	1 Relatively cheap and rates of house building faster 2 The layout is not hampered by previous development so can easily be made efficient and pleasant 3 Healthier environment	1 Valuable farm or recreational land lost 2 Wildlife and their habitats lost or disturbed, partly due to more noise and light pollution 3 Often far from work and services, generating more traffic 4 Encourages **suburban sprawl**
Brownfield sites	1 Reduces the loss of countryside and land that might be put to agricultural or recreational use 2 Helps revive old and disused urban areas 3 Services such as water, electricity, gas and sewerage already in place 4 Located nearer to main areas of employment, so commuting reduced	1 Often more expensive because old buildings have to be cleared and land cleaned of pollutants 2 Sometimes surrounded by rundown areas so does not always appeal to more wealthy people as a residential location 3 Higher levels of pollution; less healthy

Deciding which is best can depend on many factors, such as the particular land use that is planned, how valuable the land is and the values of developers with regard to countryside protection.

Activity

1 What is meant by the term 'two-speed economy'?

2 Describe how improvements and changes to transportation outside London could lead to a reduction in the gap between the South East and the rest of the UK.

3 Are brownfield sites the best option for building the new homes that the UK needs for its growing population? Justify your answer.

Migration and the UK

Learning objectives

- To know what net migration is
- To understand the pattern of migration to and from the UK
- To understand how the UK is affected by immigration and emigration

Throughout human history people have been migrating. **Migrants** are people moving home within and between countries – an **emigrant** from one country becomes an **immigrant** in another. **Net migration** means the difference between the number of people entering and leaving a country. Currently UK net migration is positive – more people permanently enter than leave, and about half of the UK's overall population growth is from net migration. However, counting people on the move is tricky, and the accuracy of migration statistics is debatable. They do not include everyone entering or leaving the country, for example:

- travellers on holidays or business trips who are only in the UK temporarily
- people entering the UK illegally, and those without travel papers
- people who have left the UK but are not shown in the statistics.

Patterns of migration change

Figure 4 shows that, in the past, emigration from the UK has exceeded immigration, but since the 1990s the UK has attracted more immigrants than emigrants have left. The countries of migration change too: for example, in the 19th century, millions from the UK emigrated to the USA and countries in the British Empire. Table 3 shows where people migrated from and to in 2014.

Table 3 Top five countries of former/next residence, UK 2014

Immigration	Emigration
India 45,000	Australia 38,000
China 39,000	France 24,000
Romania 34,000	China 19,000
Poland 32,000	Poland 18,000
Spain 31,000	Spain 17,000

Reasons for migration

People migrate for a variety of reasons (Table 4). **Economic migrants** move in search of better job opportunities, others move to join family, study or even retire. In 2014 about 4% of migrants to the UK were refugees fleeing from war, persecution or disaster. Most immigrants and emigrants are in the 25–44 age group.

Did you know?

At 37.2% of the population (2011 census), London has the highest number of foreign-born people living there, and Northern Ireland has the lowest at 1.5%.

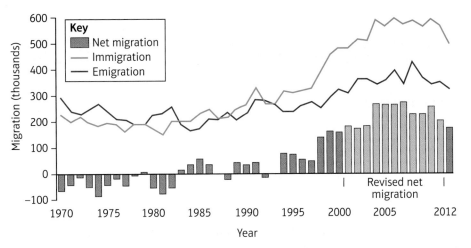

Figure 4 Net migration statistics for the UK between 1970 and 2012

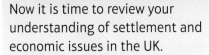

Table 4 Reasons for migration, UK, 2014

	Immigration	Emigration
Job/looking for a job	44%	56%
Join or with family	14%	9%
Study	30%	8%
Other	12%	27%

The views of different groups

Different stakeholders have a variety of views on UK migration. For business and the government, immigration offers an increase in workers who help the economy to grow and pay their taxes. Many bring useful skills to the UK. Others believe that migration is good for improving the multicultural aspects of our society, so we learn about different ideas and cultures. Longer term, young migrants will help balance the UK's ageing population.

However, some local governments feel that migration puts pressure on local services such as health, school places and housing. Some political parties are against the idea of economic migrants coming to the UK, as they believe that economic migrants can take jobs that would otherwise have gone to British workers, or make use of the UK's social benefits system.

Almost all political parties agree that refugees should be allowed to move to the UK to find safety from conflict, persecution or natural disasters.

Activity

1 Use the data in Table 4 to compare the main reasons for UK immigration and emigration.

2 Explain why people may have differing points of views on immigration of people to the UK. Include specific stakeholders in your answer.

3 Study the information about reasons for migration again. What do you think might be the effects of emigration on the UK and other countries?

Activity

1 What is meant by the term 'net migration'?

2 Describe how the pattern of UK net migration has changed since 1970: include details of dates and numbers.

Did you know?

Migration data is difficult to get right. Every ten years the UK has a census to count its population, which is how some of the net migration figures on Figure 4 were revised.

Checkpoint

Now it is time to review your understanding of settlement and economic issues in the UK.

Strengthen

S1 What are the possible impacts of a 'two-speed economy' on different regions of the UK?

S2 Who benefits from building new homes on greenfield sites?

S3 What is the difference between an economic migrant and a refugee?

Challenge

C1 Is improved transportation infrastructure enough to help close the gap between the economic growth of the North of the UK and the South East? Why?

C2 Why might Scotland want to encourage migration into the country?

C3 Why might local government and national government have different views on migration to the UK?

The UK's landscape challenges

Learning objectives

- To understand how National Parks in the UK can be managed to make them sustainable
- To understand how areas at risk of flooding can be managed in the UK
- To know the response to recent flood risks in the UK

UK National Parks

The first UK National Parks were set up in 1951. There are now 15 National Parks across the UK (Figure 5). They were set up in order to protect areas of beautiful countryside, cultural heritage, wildlife and habitat.

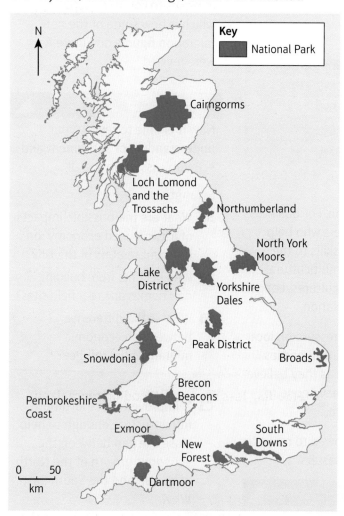

Figure 5 Locations of UK National Parks

The National Parks aim for **sustainable development**, balancing meeting the needs of residents and visitors with conserving landscapes and habitats. Other conservation organisations work with National Park Authorities, such as the National Trust, English Heritage, the RSPB and the Woodland Trust.

Each National Park Authority also produces a five-year National Park Management Plan. This plan is made in collaboration with local landowners, communities and organisations to help develop the parks sustainably. Examples of strategies in the plans include:

- creation of 'conservation apprentices' to encourage young people to continue living in the parks' rural areas, maintaining traditional countryside management methods and addressing youth unemployment as well
- encouraging people to change their transport habits to try and reduce carbon dioxide emissions from tourists travelling to, in and from the National Parks
- encouraging local business practices, such as cattle markets and home construction, to use sustainable energy sources such as wind power and solar power
- converting old farm buildings, such as barns, into new business premises, for example art galleries and offices, to provide more employment in the National Parks
- providing funds to small businesses in the National Parks, as well as training and environmental audits, to help create job stability and encourage further investment.

Activity

1   Study Figure 5 and an atlas – you will need UK maps of relief and population density.

    a   Classify the National Parks into those in lowland and upland areas of the UK.

    b   Work out a way of classifying the National Parks according to population density.

    c   Which of these National Parks do you think is the odd one out: Cairngorms, Broads, Peak District or South Downs?

2   Read the text about management plans. Choose **two** strategies and explain how they help sustainable development in National Parks.

River flood risk in the UK

About 330,000 UK properties are at risk of flooding today, increasing to between 630,000 and 1.2 million by 2080. The increased flood hazard from rivers and flash flooding results from:

- an increasing population, so more people are affected by flooding, including in new developments built on flood plains
- changes in land use, such as urban development that creates more impermeable surfaces and increases surface runoff
- climate change; more extreme rainfall events are putting places at risk that were previously affected by flooding very rarely.

In England the Environment Agency manages flood risk, which sometimes means making difficult choices. It does so by:

- making floods less likely, by controlling development in flood plains, building flood defences (**hard engineering**) and managing rivers and land use (**soft engineering**)
- making the impacts of flooding less serious, by helping people prepare for flooding and giving flood warnings (see Topic 1, pages 60–61).

Somerset Levels, 2013/2014

The Somerset Levels, in south-west England, is very low-lying and crossed by several rivers, making it prone to river and coastal flooding. To try to reduce the flood risk, the River Tone was diverted to a new embanked channel in the Middle Ages. More recently **embankments** have been built on the River Parrett and dredged to remove silt.

Very heavy rainfall throughout the winter of 2013/2014 led to the widespread flooding of 7000 hectares of land and over 600 houses, mainly in small rural settlements (see page 60). Local people complained that flood defences were not good enough and only protected nearby towns. They claimed that silt had built up in the Parrett and Tone, making them shallower and unable to contain the massive volumes of water. They criticised the Environment Agency for not dredging these rivers, while the Agency blamed a lack of funds. Some blamed farmers for poor land management, allowing rain to run off their land, eroding soil and clogging up drainage channels.

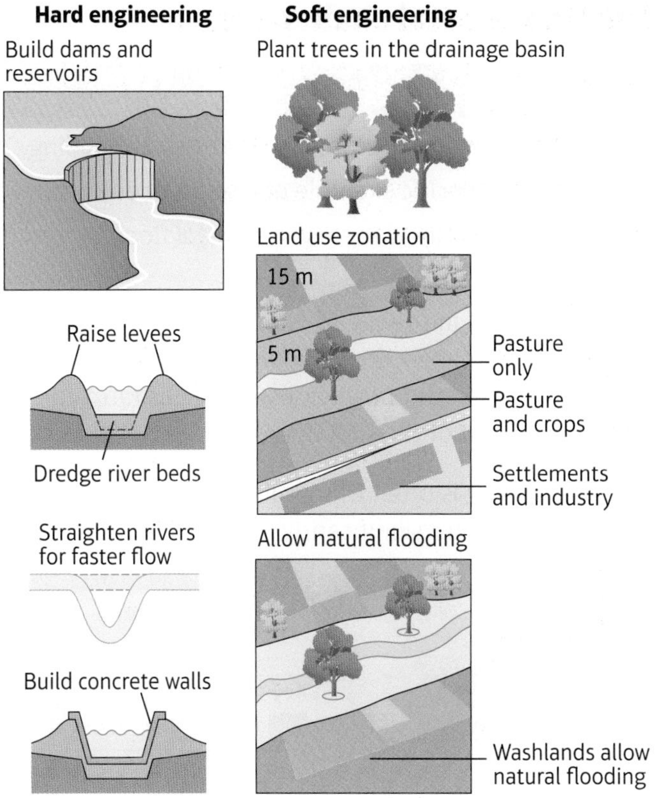

Figure 6 Dealing with floods: what are the options?

After the floods, plans were made for a tidal barrier, improvements to relief channels, more regular dredging and permanent pumping stations to remove floodwater. In future, sea level rise will put the Somerset Levels at greater risk of coastal flooding.

Activity

1 Draw a grid like the one below and add a title: Managing flood risk.

Flooding less likely	Flooding more likely
Impact less serious	Impact more serious

  a Read the text and study Figure 6. Add factors that make flooding more or less likely and the impact of flooding more or less serious.
  b Read the paragraphs on the Somerset Levels. Which factors affected the likelihood of flooding and its impact?

2 Identify some difficult choices or conflicts that arose in the Somerset Levels. How might they be resolved?

The UK's coastal challenges

Coastal flooding in the UK is also a major flood risk that needs to be managed. Coastal flooding can have a major impact on homes and businesses, as well as farmland around the coast of the UK (Figure 7).

Coastal flooding is often the result of storm surges when sea levels are significantly higher than normal, due to a combination of high tides, low atmospheric pressure and strong winds. This will often overwhelm coastal defences, which are designed to prevent coastal erosion and not coastal flooding, and can put significant numbers of people at risk.

Storm surges, December 2013

On 5 December 2013, large areas of the East of England and Scotland were affected by a strong storm surge that caused widespread coastal flooding. The Meteorological Office and other agencies issued warnings of this storm and the possible impact on coastal areas, giving people the opportunity to evacuate if needed.

The Thames Flood Barrier, a barrier designed specifically to prevent water being forced back up the Thames and towards very high value land, was raised in advance of the storm to prevent flooding in central London from the storm surge. Temporary flood barriers were erected in areas such as Norfolk to try to protect as many homes, businesses and utilities as possible. Information was passed to people in the affected areas through various media outlets, including through social media, to avoid contact with the floodwater. This was because of possible contamination from farm chemicals and sewage, and the possibility of rats moving into people's homes after the floodwaters had receded.

Figure 7 Areas at risk of coastal flooding. The figures for each region indicate the number of properties at risk from river and coastal flooding

The Environment Agency claimed that, due to the flood protections in place, combined with prediction and warning systems that were used giving people time to prepare, approximately 800,000 homes in England were protected from the storm surge.

Addressing coastal flood risk in the UK

Sea walls, used to prevent coastal erosion, can also be built to act as a barrier in coastal areas to prevent flooding. They are an example of hard engineering, and are expensive, will be damaged over time and need to be maintained. It may become economically unviable to repair these barriers as sea levels rise. This is because rising sea levels would mean that if the wall were ever to break, a significantly higher volume of water would flood onto the land, causing even more devastation than before. In this instance, managed retreat is sometimes seen as a viable option.

Managed retreat involves allowing low-lying land to flood up to a newly built defence that is built further back on higher land. These newly flooded areas will develop into salt marshes which will act as natural defences and as habitats for wildlife. However, this only works in areas of low quality farmland and low density population as significant areas of land will become flooded.

Activity

1   What processes make up a 'storm surge'?

2   Describe how hard engineering can help prevent coastal flooding. Give specific examples in your answer.

3   Explain how the Environment Agency and Meteorological Office help reduce the risk of damage and loss of life during flood events.

Did you know?

Since the Thames Flood Barrier was built in 1982, it has been raised over 175 times. It is being used more frequently due to climate change.

Exam-style question

Using examples, suggest how coastal flood risk in the UK could be managed.   **(4 marks)**

Exam tip

The phrase 'using examples' is key. Make sure you quote specific places in your answers and give facts and figures to show detailed knowledge of your case studies, such as how high the storm surge was, how big an area was flooded, etc.

Command word

Suggest questions ask you to show your understanding. So you need to give an explanation, plus your reasons with examples.

Checkpoint

Now it is time to review your understanding of sustainable use of National Parks and flood risk in the UK.

Strengthen

S1 Why do the National Park Authorities want to maintain the sustainable use of the parks?

S2 How can the risk of river flooding in the UK be reduced? Use an example in your answer.

S3 Suggest why climate change leads to the Thames Barrier being used more frequently.

Challenge

C1 Explain how conflict can arise over development and conservation in National Parks.

C2 How can managed retreat help to deal with coastal flooding?

C3 Which is a greater threat to the UK: river flooding or coastal flooding? Justify your answer.

The UK's climate change challenges

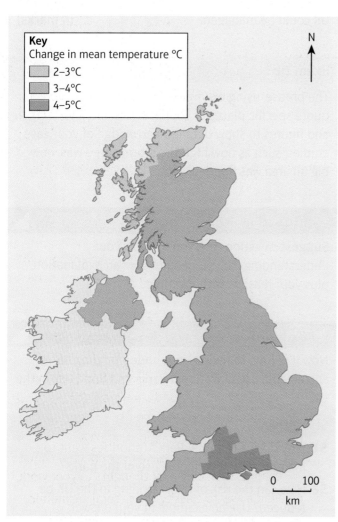

Figure 8 Change in mean temperatures in the UK in 2080, middle range prediction

How will global climate change affect the UK's climate?

As the world's climate changes, so the UK's temperate climate will change too. Predicting exactly how the climate will change is difficult, and even more so for a small island nation like the UK. Climate scientists use computer modelling to work out the likely effects of rising temperatures on the atmosphere and oceans. They also need to consider possible changes to greenhouse gas emissions, depending on factors like population growth and development, and changes to energy use and technology. What will happen is uncertain, so the models set out a range of possible future climates. In addition, nobody knows if there will be significant volcanic eruptions affecting the climate in the 21st century.

UK average temperatures have already risen by 1°C in the last 100 years, with summer temperatures increasing more than winter ones. By 2080, using predictions in the middle of the range:

- winter temperatures are likely to increase by 2–4°C in different parts of the UK, with an average range of 3–10°C
- summer temperatures are likely to increase by 3–5°C, reaching an average range of 15–22°C, as shown in Figure 8. This compares with average July 2016 temperatures in Lisbon of 24°C or Madrid of 25°C.

Precipitation will change too. Computer modelling suggests that winters are very likely to become wetter and summers will become drier:

- the UK will be 15–30% wetter in winter, but 15–30% drier in summer.
- extreme rainfall will become more frequent and intense.

Impacts of climate change on the UK

Climate change will have significant effects on the UK. Changes to precipitation make extreme flash floods and river flooding increasingly likely. In addition, rising sea levels (see Topic 2) will increase the risk of coastal flooding. The flood hazard will increase due to an increasing UK population and pressure on land on flood plains for development, particularly for housing. Government estimates show the annual cost of flood damage rising from £2 billion to a possible £12 billion by 2080.

Warmer and drier summers will also increase the risk of drought, with lower rainfall and increased evaporation resulting in less water in rivers, the soil and **groundwater**. This will lead to **water deficits** and threats to water security for a growing population, agriculture and industry. Drier areas of the UK with high population densities like London and the South East will be particularly vulnerable. More frequent summer heatwaves will also put pressure on the NHS as people suffer from the effects of sustained high temperatures.

Ecosystems will also be affected. While already under pressure from human activities, many plants and animals will have to try to adapt to this new climate. Some species may become extinct in the UK – others may migrate further north to cooler areas. Some will experience competition from non-native species moving to the UK. By 2100, some UK landscapes will look quite different to today, with changes to the natural vegetation as well as changes to farmland (Figure 9).

The UK will also be affected by global climate change in other parts of the world. For instance, drought in other parts of the world may reduce food supply and increase food prices. As parts of the world become difficult to live in, increasing numbers of climate change refugees may wish to migrate to Europe.

Figure 9 Climate change will bring new crops, such as this vineyard in the UK

Activity

1 Study Figure 8. Describe the possible changes to summer temperatures in 2080 in different parts of the UK.

2 Draw up a table or concept map to summarise likely changes in the UK climate and its different impacts.

   a List the main changes to the UK climate. Next, add their impacts and show how changes and impacts are linked.

   b Think about how changes in the UK population may increase the impact of climate change, then add your thoughts to your work.

   c Find a way to classify the natural, economic and social aspects of climate change in the UK.

3 Study Figure 9. Make a list of the possible gains from a warmer UK climate.

Responses to climate change

Activity

1 How can using locally grown food reduce the possible impacts of climate change?

2 Describe **one** way the UK government could respond to try to reduce the possible impacts of climate change.

3 Which scale of response do you think is more important to reduce the impact of climate change: local or national? Justify your answer.

While it is impossible to predict the changes that will occur to our climate, or the specific impact that they will have, with any certainty, we do know that global climate change is occurring. This means that steps can be taken to try to address this issue on various scales to combat the possible problems it will cause in the future.

On a local scale, individuals and families can make changes that will reduce carbon dioxide emissions and resource consumption. The changes may seem like very small actions, but if taken by enough people, can have a distinct impact on the rate at which our climate is changing. Actions that can be taken at a local scale include:

- walking or cycling shorter journeys instead of driving to reduce fuel consumption and carbon dioxide emissions
- purchasing locally produced food rather than imported food as this will have travelled a greater distance and more fuel will have been used in its transportation
- recycling waste materials to reduce resource consumption
- installing insulation and double glazing to reduce heat loss in the home so that heating systems do not need to be used constantly
- installing solar panels to generate energy in the home.

All of these actions will have a positive impact on reducing the rate of global climate change, but they are not all practical for everyone. Not everyone is able to walk or cycle any significant distance due to health concerns or disabilities; installing insulation, double glazing and solar panels can be very expensive; and not all shops stock locally produced food.

On a national scale, governments can launch campaigns or legislation to encourage people to recycle and reduce resource consumption, as well as limit carbon emissions from industry and agriculture. However, national governments face pressure to increase economic growth, which may involve greater consumption of resources. This makes it very difficult for governments to strike a balance between the need for environmental concern and the need to encourage economic development among businesses.

This can be demonstrated where there is sometimes conflict between public feeling about climate change and environmental protection, and public desire for growth and economic development across the country. This can lead to some cities in the UK using significantly more energy than other cities across the world. One reason for this is that, as cities expand in size, a larger city population will also consume more energy resources, and need more food and water supplies, all of which leads to greater demand for energy and greater emissions of carbon dioxide. Governments can try to address this issue of urban sprawl through legislation, but could be viewed as trying to stop businesses from developing, which can be very unpopular with voters.

Figure 10 Satellite photo showing energy usage at night in Europe, the Middle East and North Africa

On the international scale, cooperation between different governments is vital if plans to combat global climate change are going to have any impact. This leads to similar problems to those that governments face within their own countries. How do you balance the need for economic development with the need for environmental conservation? Many governments find it difficult to make arrangements that meet the approval of the majority and which will allow their economies to grow, without limitations on production of pollutants, thus reducing industrial production. Several attempts have been made to get international cooperation on the issue of global climate change.

Exam-style question ●

Discuss the view that UK population growth and net migration will create most pressure on the UK's ecosystems.

(12 marks)

Command word ◤

Discuss questions focus on different sides of an issue or question. Your answer should explore the strengths and weaknesses of both, using geographical thinking.

Checkpoint ◤

Now it is time to review your understanding of the effects and responses to climate change in the UK.

Strengthen

S1 What do you think will be the worst impact of climate change on the UK? Justify your answer.

S2 Why might it be difficult for the UK government to prevent increasing carbon dioxide emissions?

S3 Why can we not predict exactly how the UK's climate will change because of rising global temperatures?

Challenge

C1 Are local scale actions enough to impact on global climate change? Justify your answer.

C2 How will the UK's landscapes change as a result of climate change?

C3 If the predictions of global climate change are accurate, should the UK consider ordering people to move away from at-risk coastal and river areas?

Geographical Investigations – UK Challenges

The UK faces many challenges over the coming century, ranging from population increases and coastal flooding to global climate change. You should study not only the challenges that the UK will face, but how we can address these challenges.

Checklist

You should know:

- [ ] how the population of the UK is expected to change over time
- [ ] the pressures UK ecosystems will face due to a growing population
- [ ] how transport in the UK can be made more sustainable
- [ ] the 'two-speed economy' in the UK and how the economic gap between North and South can be addressed
- [ ] costs and benefits of development on greenfield and brownfield sites in the UK
- [ ] migration to and from the UK and the views stakeholders have on migration
- [ ] how sustainability can be addressed in the UK's National Parks
- [ ] the risk of river flooding in the UK
- [ ] the risk of coastal flooding in the UK
- [ ] the variations to the UK's climate as a result of global climate change
- [ ] the reliability of predictions of changes to the UK's climate
- [ ] what the possible impact global climate change can have on the UK
- [ ] how responses to climate change can be enacted at local, national and international scales.

Which key terms match the following definitions?

a The number of people entering a country minus the number of people leaving a country.

b The growth of the edges of an urban area, normally onto greenfield sites.

c A person moving out of one country and moving to another country to live there.

d An area of land that has not been developed before.

e A monetary charge for drivers entering a specific section of an urban area, to try to deter congestion and reduce pollution.

f Flood defences that work with natural processes to reduce the risk and impact of coastal or river flooding.

g Development that meets the needs of the present, without compromising the ability of future generations to meet their own needs.

h How the South East is developing economically at a greater rate than other areas of the UK such as northern England, Scotland and Wales

i A policy for controlling urban growth; a ring of countryside to prevent urban sprawl by keeping land permanently open.

To check your answers, look at the Glossary on pages 296–301.

Geographical Investigations – UK Challenges

Discuss the view that UK population growth and net migration will create pressures on the UK's ecosystems. Use information from the Resource Booklet and knowledge and understanding from the rest of your geography course of study to support your answer. (12 marks + 4 SPAG)

Student answer

The population of the UK has grown significantly over time, but particularly in the last 20 to 30 years. Whilst some of this is due to natural increases (birth rates being higher than death rates), the majority is due to people moving to the UK, creating net migration into the UK. This can cause a lot of problems for the UK, including social and environmental. With more people, the need for more housing is huge and these new houses will have to be built on greenfield sites, which will lead to damage to ecosystems across the UK. Although many of the UK's ecosystems are protected from being built on, this means some areas will be very heavily affected, but some may not be at all. Figure 5b in the resource booklet shows that the growth in population is not even across the UK and so this will also lead to the impact varying across the country. Ordinarily, this would show that the impact of population growth would be huge, but there are issues with that viewpoint. Figure 5d does not show that this pattern of net migration will definitely continue, so this may be a short-term problem and therefore the impact will be small. Also, some areas of the UK are unproductive farmland and this is found where the population growth is expected to be highest. This is shown clearly by Figures 5a and 5b. So this greenfield land could be used with only very limited impact on the ecosystems of the area as they are unproductive already (approximately 8.5%). This won't take into account the indirect impact on the environment, such as through increased noise and light pollution and increased waste disposal.

Verdict

The answer makes clear reference to the information in the Resource Booklet, using this effectively to make several points with some discussion of the issue. In one or two places it is supported by data. The answer shows some understanding of different concepts and the relationships between places and processes. The answer, although partially balanced, only touches briefly on aspects from different topics which need to be brought together in the answer.

WRITING GEOGRAPHICALLY

Writing geographically: selecting vocabulary

The best geographical writing uses carefully selected vocabulary to express ideas formally, clearly and precisely.

Learning objectives

- To understand how to select nouns and verbs which can help you to express your ideas clearly and precisely
- To be able to build noun phrases which can help you add more detailed information to your ideas

Definitions

Adjective: a word that provides additional information about a noun, e.g. *clear*, *precise* writing.

Prepositional phrase: a phrase that begins with a preposition, often giving information about position or time, e.g. *in* the river, *on* the bank, *after* an hour.

How can I add detail to my writing?

Look at this exam-style question:

> You have studied a river as part of your own fieldwork. Evaluate the reliability of your
> conclusions.
> **(8 marks)**

Look at the first sentence of one student's response to this question. The key nouns and verbs in the sentence have been highlighted:

> The first thing we did to get information was to work out the quickness of the river.

1. How could you improve this sentence? Would you add more detail? Or would you express the same information more formally and precisely? Or both?

2. Rewrite the sentence using more precise, accurate nouns and verbs. Choose the best geographical language from the alternatives below, or use your own ideas.

thing	did	get	information	work out	quickness
method	conducted	acquire	data	calculate	pace
process	employed	collect	facts	determine	speed
tactic	used	gather	figures	estimate	rapidity
technique	utilised	obtain	measurements	measure	velocity

3. Now look at the next two sentences from the same student's response:

> We got an orange and used a stopwatch to check out how quickly it floated 10 metres down the river at four different places. One problem we had was one orange floated away. Using two oranges may have messed up the results.

294

(a) Identify any nouns or verbs which could be replaced with more formal and precise choices.

(b) For each noun and verb you have identified, note down two or three alternative choices.

(c) Rewrite the sentences above, choosing more formal, precise nouns and verbs.

How can I add detail to my writing in different ways?

One way in which you can add more information to your answer is by expanding **noun phrases**, using **adjectives**, **prepositional phrases** and other **nouns**.

Compare these two versions of the same sentence from a student's response to the exam-style question on page 294.

> **Version 1** *Another problem was judging the distance and then relying on people to stop the stopwatch when the orange floated past. These issues could have affected our results.*

> **Version 2** *A second problem with the technique was judging the 10 metre distance and then relying on other people in my group to stop the stopwatch when the orange floated past. These issues could have affected the accuracy of our results.*

In the second version, the student has made their evaluation more precise and detailed by modifying some of the nouns using adjectives, prepositional phrases and nouns. We can look at this in more detail.

In the box below, this is the head noun in the noun phrase. The adjective and the prepositional phrase give more information about the problem:

> *a second problem with the technique*

In the box below, this is the head noun in the noun phrase. The adjective and the prepositional phrase give more information about the people.

> *other people in my group*

In the box below, this is the head noun in this noun phrase. These two nouns give more information about the distance.

> *10 metre distance*

4. What **kinds** of information and detail can adjectives, prepositional phrases and nouns add to geographical writing?

Improving an answer

5. Now look at the next section of this student's response. How could you expand some of this writer's noun phrases, using adjectives, prepositional phrases or additional nouns to make the evaluation more precise and detailed? Use the teacher's questions to help you: What kind of technique? What properties of the river were measured? What kind of rocks? Where were they?

> *Another technique was to measure the river. One problem with measuring the width was keeping the tape measure tight to ensure we got an accurate measurement. With the metre stick we measured the depth at 50 cm intervals across the channel. But some big rocks meant that we actually measured the depth at slightly different intervals.*

Glossary

1% flood event a 1% flood event has a 1 in 100 chance or greater of happening each year, or a probability of 0.01

abiotic the non-living parts of an ecosystem

abiotic resources resources obtained from the lithosphere, atmosphere and hydrosphere. Examples of abiotic resources are minerals, soil, sunlight and fresh water

abrasion this type of erosion is caused by rivers, glaciers or waves picking up sediments and rubbing them against rocks in the bed and banks, valley or cliffs

afforestation the planting of trees where there were none before, or they had been cut down

agribusiness large-scale commercial farming and food supply

aid assistance in the form of grants or loans at below market rates

alluvium fine sediments which are deposited by rivers

annotate to add notes and explanations to a photograph, map or diagram

appropriate technology aid wherein the level of technology and the skills required to service it are properly suited to the conditions in the receiving country

aqueduct a structure like a bridge that carries water, usually across a river or a valley but sometimes much further

aquifer an underground store of water formed when water-bearing (permeable) rocks lie on top of an impermeable rock

arable the farming of crops like wheat and barley

arch the rock bridge formed over a passage through a headland eroded by the waves

area how much space something occupies

arête a sharp-edged, two-sided ridge on top of a mountain

arid a region with little or no regular precipitation

attrition a type of erosion where particles carried by rivers or waves are worn down as they collide with each other, so they become smaller and rounded

backwash the movement of a wave down a beach back to the sea

bar a ridge of sand or shingle across the entrance of a bay or river mouth

barriers to trade government constraints on the flow of international goods and services such as tariffs and quotas

basal sliding movement of glacier due to meltwater under the ice acting as a lubricant

bay an area of sea, curved in shape which has been eroded between two headlands

beach a sloping area of sand or pebbles between the low and high water marks

bedding plane the surface between two layers (or strata) in sedimentary rock

bergschrund crevasse a long crack that forms in a moving glacier when the glacier ice splits from the stagnant ice above

berm a ridge of sediment found towards the back of a beach

biodiversity the number and variety of living species found in a specific area

biomass the total mass of all living things in an area

biome an ecosystem on a global scale. Put together, the world's biomes make up the biosphere – all living things on Earth

biosphere sphere made up of living organisms

biotic the living parts of an ecosystem

biotic resources resources obtained from the biosphere, which are capable of reproduction. Examples of biotic resources are animals, birds, plants, fungi and other similar organisms

bivariate data data with two sets of variables

BRICS the acronym for an association of five major emerging national economies: Brazil, Russia, India, China and South Africa

brownfield site an area of land that has been built upon before and can be regenerated for new constructions

bulldozing the pushing of deposited material at the snout of the glacier as it advances

calving chunks of ice breaking off an ice sheet or glacier

canopy trees which form a continuous cover of leaves, blocking out much of the light and shading the area beneath the canopy

carbon footprint measurement of all the greenhouse gases an individual produces expressed as tonnes (or kg) of carbon dioxide equivalent

carbon sink an environmental reservoir that absorbs and stores more carbon than it releases

carboniferous limestone deposited rocks that were formed between 363 and 325 million years ago

cave a hollow at the base of a cliff which has been eroded backwards by waves

central business district (CBD) the central area of a city, where land use is dominated by department stores, specialist and variety goods stores and offices, cinemas, theatres and hotels

channelisation the deepening and/or straightening of a river to allow it to carry more water

climate the average weather conditions of an area occurring over many years

climate change variations in temperature and rainfall affecting the whole world

clint the large blocks of rock on a limestone pavement, separated by grykes

clitter slope the trail of deposited rocks from the action of freeze thaw weathering on tors

coastal squeeze coastal habitats which are being reduced in size due to a rise in sea level

colonialism acquiring control over another country, occupying it with settlers, and exploiting it economically

Commonwealth an intergovernmental organisation of 53 nations, most of which were former members of the British Empire

compensatory habitat new habitats created to make up for habitats lost through coastal squeeze

comprehensive development area (CDAs) an area, usually in the inner city, where the whole urban landscape was demolished before being rebuilt on a planned basis

concordant coast the type of coast where the rock type runs parallel to the coastline

confluence the point where two rivers meet

congestion charge a monetary charge for drivers entering a specific section of an urban area, to try to deter congestion and reduce pollution

constructive wave a gently breaking wave with a strong swash and weak backwash. It adds more material to the beach than it removes

contour a line on a map joining places of equal height above sea level

conurbation an area in which a number of existing urban areas have grown and merged into a single large urban area

coppices woodland where the trees or shrubs are cut back every few years for firewood or timber

core (and **frame**) the CBD can be divided into a core (central part) consisting of department stores, office blocks, as well as public administration buildings, theatres and restaurants, and a frame consisting of wholesale markets and transport termini

Coriolis effect the deflection of air movement by the Earth's rotation

correlation when two variables in the data set are linked

corrie (**cirque** or **cwm**) a circular hollow, high on the mountainside, surrounded by steep rocky walls except for a rock lip on the open side

counter-urbanisation the movement of people and employment from major cities to smaller settlements and rural areas located beyond the city, or to more distant towns and cities

cove a small bay with a narrow inlet

crag and tail a rocky outcrop with a tapering ridge of glacial deposits on one side

Cretaceous Period a period of the Mesozoic Era, from 140 million to 65 million years ago

crop yield the amount of crops produced from an area

cross section a diagram showing the shape of a feature or landscape as if it was cut through sideways

cultivation the action of using the land for agricultural purposes

debt money owed by a country to another country, to private creditors (e.g. commercial banks) or to international agencies such as the World Bank or IMF

de-centralisation the movement of people, factories, offices and shops away from city centres to suburban and edge-of-city locations

deforestation permanently removing forest so the land can be used for something else

de-industrialisation the decline of industrial activity in a region or in an economy

demographic ageing a rise in the median age of a population

deposition a process where sediments are dropped by the river, glacier or waves that carried them

desalination the process of removing of salt (sodium chloride) and other minerals from sea water to make it suitable for human consumption

destructive wave a strong wave that removes material from the coastline

development the process where people, a place or a country change, or make economic or social progress

development gap difference in income and the quality of life in general between the richest and poorest countries in the world

diaspora dispersal of a people from their original homeland

dip slope land that follows the same gentle slope as the layers of rocks underneath

disamenity a disadvantage or drawback, usually of a place

discharge the volume of water flowing in a river, measured in cubic metres per second (cumecs)

discordant coast a coast where bands of hard and soft rocks lie at right angles to the coastline forming headlands and bays

distribution description of where a particular feature or features – such as people – appear within an area

diurnal variation the difference between a high temperature and a low temperature that occurs during the same day

diversify increase the range of goods or services provided

drainage basin the area of land drained by a river and its tributaries

drought an extended period of lower than normal rainfall/precipitation, causing water shortages

drumlin an egg-shaped hill found on the floor of a glacial valley

ecological footprint measure of the impact of human activities, expressed as the area of productive land and water required to produce the goods consumed and the wastes generated

economic core region(s) the most highly developed region(s) in a country

economic migrant a person who moves from one area to another in order to find work or a better standard of living

ecosystem a community of plants and animals that interact with each other and their physical environment

embankment an artificial bank raised above the immediately surrounding land to redirect or prevent flooding by a river, lake or sea

emigrant a person moving out of one country and moving to another country to live there

energy consumption the action of using up an energy resource

energy mix the proportion of different energy sources used in a country

enhanced greenhouse effect the trapping of heat radiation around the Earth by excess greenhouse gases produced through human activity

erosion the wearing away and removal of material by a moving force, such as a river, a breaking wave or a glacier

erratic a rock or boulder that differs from the surrounding rock, brought from a distance by glacial action

estuary the mouth of a river which broadens into the sea and is affected by tides

eutrophication when too many nutrients get into rivers and water bodies (e.g. lakes), causing extensive plant growth which absorbs oxygen and damages other organisms in the water

evaporation the process of changing liquid water to gaseous water (water vapour)

exploitation the way in which people make use of resources from the Earth

extrapolate to estimate a value outside a range of values

eye the centre of a tropical cyclone; an area of clear conditions created by air converging at the centre of the storm and then sinking

eye wall a thick bank of cloud around the eye with high wind speeds and heavy rain

fair trade a movement that aims to create direct long-term trading links with producers in developing countries to ensure they receive a fair and guaranteed price for their products

fault a fracture or break in rocks

feed-in tariff a payment made by government to individuals or organisations who generate their own electricity that is 'fed into' the national power supply

Ferrel cell circulation cell that brings warm air north towards the UK

fertiliser chemical added to soil to increase its fertility

fetch the distance a wave has travelled towards the coastline over open water, the longer the fetch the more powerful the wave

flood plain the flat land in the valley floor each side of a river channel, which is sometimes flooded

food security when all people at all times have access to sufficient, safe, nutritious food to maintain a healthy and active life

foreign aid aid supplied to other countries

foreign direct investment (FDI) overseas investment in physical capital by transnational corporations

fossil fuels energy resources such as coal, oil and natural gas that were formed from the remains of plants and animals that lived millions of years ago

fracking a process that involves drilling down into the Earth and using a high-pressure water mixture to release gas trapped inside rock

fragile environment a place where wildlife and landscape are easily damaged by outsiders or climate change

frame see **core**

freeze thaw weathering the process of rocks breaking up from repeated freezing and thawing

frequency the number of times an event or data value occurs

frontal rainfall a front is the boundary between air masses. If moist air rises along the front, as the air cools clouds form and rain may fall

G-20 the Group of Twenty (also known as G20): an international forum for the governments and central bank governors from 20 major economies

geology the different types of rocks that make up an area

geothermal energy energy produced by tapping into sources of heat under the Earth

Gini coefficient a statistical technique used to show the extent of income inequality in a country

glacial a period of time with lower average temperatures causing widespread glaciation

glacial budget the balance between the inputs (accumulation) and the outputs (ablation) of a glacier

glacial period a period when ice advances due to falling temperatures

glacial trough a U-shaped valley with flat floor and steep sides, formed by a valley glacier

glacier a body of land-based ice that moves under its own weight due to gravity

global warming a rise in average global temperatures

gorge a steep, narrow valley with rocky sides

green belt a policy for controlling urban growth; a ring of countryside to prevent urban sprawl by keeping land permanently open

greenfield site an area of land that has not been built upon before

greenhouse gas a gas that absorbs and re-emits infrared radiation, warming the Earth's surface

grid reference a four or a six figure reference number used to locate features on an OS map

gross disposable household income (GDHI) the amount of money that households (individuals or families) have available for spending or saving

gross domestic product (GDP) the total value of goods and services produced by a country in a year

gross national product (GNP) GDP plus overseas earnings; it is also called GNI

ground moraine glacial material deposited on the valley floor

groundwater water stored underground in rocks and soil

growing season the amount of time in a year where temperature and precipitation levels are right for local plant species to grow

growth ring a layer of wood created each year by a tree as it grows. The size of the ring is related to the climatic conditions when it was formed

groyne a wooden barrier built at right angles to the coast, used to break waves and reduce the movement of sediment along the coast

gryke vertical joints, enlarged by weathering, between the blocks in a limestone pavement

Hadley cell a circulation cell near the Equator responsible for storms at the Equator and desert belts north and south of the Equator

hanging valley a tributary valley, high above the main valley floor, with a waterfall

hard engineering strategies using artificial structures (e.g. concrete) to prevent river or coastal flooding

headland an area of more resistant rock jutting out into the sea from the cliff-line

honeypot site a place of special interest, attracting tourists

hydraulic action this results from the sheer force of moving water wearing away the river bed and banks, or waves wearing away sea cliffs

hydro-electric power (HEP) the use of fast-flowing water to turn turbines which produce electricity

hydrograph a graph showing changes in a river's discharge and rainfall over time

hydrological cycle the continuous movement of water between land, sea and air

hydrosphere all the water on or near the Earth, which includes rivers, lakes, oceans and moisture in the air

ice cap a body of ice, smaller than an ice sheet, usually found in mountainous regions

ice core a section of ice drilled from a glacier showing the layers of ice created over time

igneous intrusion magma trapped beneath the surface of the Earth pushed the rock above it into a dome shape

immigrant a person moving into a country in order to live there

impermeable rocks that are impermeable, like clay, do not allow water to pass through them

index of multiple deprivation (IMD) this index measures 38 items grouped in 7 main headings, which are income, employment, health, education, crime, access to services and living environment

indigenous communities that have rights based on their historical ties

industrialisation the move from an economy dominated by the primary sector to one dominated by manufacturing (the secondary sector)

industry the production of goods or services

infiltration the process whereby water soaks into the soil and rock

informal economy the part of an economy that is neither taxed nor monitored by any form of government

informal sector the part of an economy operating outside of official recognition

infrastructure the framework of such things as roads, buildings, power lines, etc. that enable developed human society to operate

interception the process where vegetation catches rainfall on its leaves and branches

interglacial a period of time between glaciations with higher average temperatures when ice returns

interlocking spur an area of higher land jutting out of steep valley sides in a river's upper course

interpolate to estimate a value inside a sequence of values

inter-quartile range the difference between the upper and lower quartiles

irrigation the addition of water to farmland by artificial means

jet stream a fast-moving current of air in the upper atmosphere

joint a vertical crack within a layer of rock

kinetic energy energy generated as a result of movement

lagoon a fresh water lake formed when a bay is cut off from the sea by a beach bar

lateral erosion erosion where a river cuts sideways into its banks

lateral moraine a narrow band of rock debris that that runs along the sides of a glacier

levee a raised bank of sediment along the side of a river

limestone pavement a horizontal or gently sloping area of limestone, comprised of large blocks (clints) separated by deep eroded fissures (grykes)

limiting factor factors that prevent something from getting any larger

line of best fit a line going through the middle of the points on a scatter graph

lithosphere made up of the Earth's crust and upper mantle

litter leaves, twigs and other dead organic material that falls onto the surface of the soil

long profile the shape and gradient of a river bed from source to mouth

longshore drift the movement of material along a beach transported by wave action

lower quartile divides the bottom half of the data in two halves; the bottom quarter of a set of values

magma semi-molten rock found in the mantle layer of the Earth

magnitude the quantifiable size of an event or piece of data

marginal creating new and additional sources of income

mass movement the movement of material down a slope due to gravity

mean the sum of the data values divided by their number, often called the average

meander a bend formed in a river as it winds across the landscape

medial moraine a narrow band of deposited sediment running down the middle of a glacier

median the middle value when a set of values in a data set is written in order

megacity a very large city with a population of over ten million people

megalitre unit equal to one million litres

meltwater water coming from melting snow or glacier ice

microcredit tiny loans and financial services to help the poor – mostly women – start businesses and escape poverty

microparticulate a tiny particle with a chemical content suspended as a droplet in the air

migrant a person who moves from one area to another to live

migrate the process of movement of people or of features such as meanders

migration the process of people changing their place of residence, either within or between countries

misfit stream a small river in a large glacial trough

mitigate make the effects of something less harmful or serious

modal class the most frequent class in a data set

mode the most frequent value in a data set

monoculture when just one species of a crop or tree is grown

monsoon a seasonal wind in the Indian Ocean and southern Asia. It blows from the south-west in summer and from the north-east in winter

moraine materials deposited by ice, with different names according to where they are deposited

mouth the point where a river leaves its drainage basin and reaches the sea

mtoe a measurement to present the amount of barrels of oil in million tonnes

National Park a large area of natural land protected by the government because of its natural beauty, plants or animals

natural increase the difference between the birth rate and the death rate

neck the narrow strip of land between the two closest banks of a meander

neo-colonialism the dominance of poor countries by rich countries, not by direct political control (as in colonialism), but by economic power and cultural influence

net migration the number of people entering a country minus the number of people leaving a country

névé partially packed snow that lasts through at least one summer

NGO a non-governmental organisation

non-alignment a national policy avoiding political or military alliances with the major world powers

non-native a species that has been introduced from outside the country or ecosystem

non-renewable resources sources of energy – such as coal, oil or natural gas – that cannot be 'remade', because it would take millions of years for them to form again

nourishment the food required to allow someone to grow and live a healthy life

number used to describe how much of a measured value there is

nutrient cycle the transfer of nutrients between the living and non-living parts of an ecosystem

nutrients substances that enable plants and animals to grow

obesity when a person is considered to be overweight

open-cast type of mining that extracts resources from open quarries rather than digging tunnels underground to reach mineral deposits

outsourcing the concept of taking internal company functions and paying an outside firm to handle them

percentage the proportion or ratio expressed as a fraction (the ratio or proportion expressed per hundred)

period a large section of geological time

periphery parts of a country outside the economic core region

permeable rocks that are permeable, like chalk, allow water to pass through them

pesticides chemicals used on crops to kill unwanted insects

photosynthesis the chemical process in plants where water, carbon dioxide and sunlight are used to produce glucose

photovoltaic cells used in solar panels to convert light energy from the Sun into electricity

plantation a large farm or estate which grows crops such as coffee and tea

Pleistocene a geological time period lasting from about 2.6 million years ago until 11,700 years ago; it is part of the Quaternary Period and is sometimes called the Ice Age

plucking a process of glacial erosion where individual rocks are pulled away from the valley floor or sides by ice flow

plunge pool a hollow under a waterfall created by erosion and filled by water

point bar sediment laid down on the inside of a meander bend where the river flows slowly

Polar cell a circulation cell furthest from the Equator that brings cold air south towards the UK

pollution the presence of contaminating and sometimes dangerous materials within water, air or soil

population density (of people) the number of people per square kilometre

precipitation water vapour condensed in the atmosphere which falls as rain, snow, sleet or hail

prevailing wind direction in which the wind blows most frequently

primary data data that you collect first hand

privatisation sale of state-owned assets to the private sector

profile a cross section of the landscape, for example a river valley or beach

proportion expresses one part as a fraction of the whole

pyramidal peak a sharp-edged mountain peak

qualitative data without numbers based on people's opinions or ideas, e.g. an interview or field sketch

quality of life the degree of well-being (physical and psychological) felt by an individual or group of people in a particular area. This may relate to jobs, wages, food and access to services such as health and education

quantitative data which contains numbers and figures, e.g. a pedestrian count

quaternary industry an industry which provides intellectual services such as information gathering and processing, universities and research and development

Quaternary period the current period of geological time

Ramsar wetlands of international importance designated under the Ramsar Convention

random sampling data that is collected so each has an equal chance of being selected, e.g. by using random numbers

range the difference between the smallest and biggest values

ratio shows the number of times one value occurs compared with another

relict a landscape that has survived from an earlier period

relief the height and shape of the land

remittances money sent back by migrants to their family in the home community

renewable energy a natural source of power that will never run out

renewable resources energy sources that are potentially infinite

replacement level fertility the level at which each generation has just enough

children to replace themselves in the population. This is 2.1 children

reservoir a large lake, usually artificial, used to store water

re-urbanisation the movement of people back towards city centres away from rural areas and from suburbs

revetment wooden structures built parallel to the coast at the foot of cliffs that absorb wave energy

ribbon lake a long and narrow lake in the floor of a glaciated valley

rip rap large boulders of resistant rock placed at the bottom of cliffs that dissipate wave energy

river cliff a steep section of river bank, caused by fast-flowing water eroding the outside of a meander

roche moutonnée a small hill of resistant rock, exposed by ice movement

rotational slip slippage of ice along a curved surface

runoff water running across the land surface *or* the proportion of rainfall that flows in rivers

saltation a process where sediment is transported by being bounced along a river bed or sea floor

saltmarsh an area of mud flats formed by deposition of sediment in the low wave energy area behind a spit

saturate soil becomes saturated when it has absorbed as much water as it is possible to do so. If any more water is added, it is not able to be absorbed

scale the relationship between dimensions on a map or diagram to those in the real world. On OS maps this is shown as 1:25,000 or 1:50,000

scarp slope a steep slope that cuts through the layers of rock underneath

scree pieces of rock with sharp edges, lying towards the foot of a slope

scrub encroachment the gradual invasion of bushes due to lack of management

sea walls a curved or straight wall built along the coastline to prevent waves eroding the coastline

seasons annually recurring periods during the year (spring, summer, autumn and winter), or specific periods when events occur, for example when tropical cyclones are most likely to form. The timings of seasons vary between the Northern and Southern Hemispheres

secondary data data that has been collected and published by someone else

sediment material such as mud, sand and pebbles carried and deposited by rivers or waves

sediment load the sediment particles carried by a river

shanty town an area of very poor housing, often self-built by residents out of basic materials

Shoreline Management Plan (SMP) a plan which assesses the risks to a piece of coastline and how to manage these

site the actual location of a settlement on the Earth and the physical characteristics of the landscape specific to the area

situation the location of a place relative to its surroundings and other places

slip-off slope the gentle slope on the inside of a meander bend formed by deposition

slump a type of mass movement where soil or rock slides down a slope, often rotating as it moves

snout the front of a glacier

social business forms of business that seek to profit from investments that bring social improvements

soft engineering flood defences that work with natural processes to reduce the risk and impact of coastal or river flooding

solution the process where some rock minerals slowly dissolve in water, which is slightly acid

source the starting point of a stream or river, often a spring or a lake

spit a ridge of sand or shingle deposited by the sea. It is attached to the land at one end but ends in a bay or river mouth

spring-line settlement found where there is a ridge of permeable rock lying over impermeable rock; with a line of springs along the boundary between the two layers

squatter settlement an area which consists of self-built houses made from scrap materials such as corrugated iron and plastic, usually without piped water, electricity or sewage disposal

stack an isolated column of rock, standing just off the coast that was once attached to the land

storm beach a beach affected by large destructive waves often with an angle over 45 degrees

storm surge an increase in the height of the sea due to a storm

stratification the five separate layers in the TRF: emergent, canopy, understorey, shrub layer, forest floor

stratified sampling data that is collected from different parts of a population, e.g. different age groups

striations deep grooves in surface rocks, made by the sharp edges of stones carried in the bottom of moving ice

strong correlation most data points are close to the trend line

stump a short piece of rock found at the end of a headland formed after a stack has collapsed

subsidence the collapse of land because of a lack of support underneath, often caused by a reduction in water levels

subsistence where the resources available provide the basic needs for survival

suburban sprawl the growth of the edges of an urban area, normally onto greenfield sites

suburbanisation the outward spread of the built-up area, often at a lower density compared to the older parts of the town

sustainable able to continue without causing damage to the environment

sustainable development development that meets the needs of the present without compromising (limiting) the ability of future generations to meet their own needs

swash the movement of a breaking wave up a beach

syncline folds in stratified rock, dipping towards the trough

systematic sampling data that is collected at regular intervals, e.g. every 500 metres

tarn a circular lake in a corrie hollow where water is trapped by the steep sides and rock lip

tectonic processes the theory related to the seismic movement of the Earth's plates

terminal moraine a high ridge running across the valley representing the maximum advance of a glacier

tertiary industry an industry which provides a service, such as banks, shops, schools, hospitals and restaurants

thermal expansion the increase in volume created when a fluid (e.g. seawater) is heated and expands

till (or boulder clay) all materials deposited by ice, usually clay containing sharp-edged boulders of many sizes

tor a block of granite found at the top of a hill

track the path followed by a tropical cyclone

traction the transport of sediment along a river bed or the sea floor through a rolling action

transnational corporation (TNC) a firm that owns or controls productive operations in more than one country through foreign direct investment

transpiration the release of water vapour through a plant's leaves

transportation the movement of sediment by rivers, glaciers or waves

trend general direction of change

trend line shows the overall change in the data

tributary a stream or small river that joins a larger one

tropical storm this has wind speeds of over 63 km per hour. Tropical storms can develop into tropical cyclones, hurricanes or typhoons with wind speeds of over 119 km per hour

truncated spur a higher area on the straight rocky side of a glaciated valley

two-speed economy how the South East is developing economically at a greater rate than other areas of the UK such as northern England, Scotland and Wales

upper quartile divides the top half of the data in two halves, the top quarter of a set of values

urbanisation the increase in the percentage of people living in towns and cities, causing them to grow

urbanisation of poverty the increase in the proportion of people in poverty in a country who live in urban areas

V-shaped valley a valley with a V-shaped cross section formed by river erosion

variable a number or amount that can be measured and can change in value

velocity the speed at which a river or glacier flows; river velocity is often measured in metres per second

vertical erosion downward erosion, for example of the river bed

water consumption the amount of water used by a person or group of people

water deficit a situation where a place loses more water through evaporation and transpiration than it receives from rainfall

water meter a device used to measure the consumption of water

water pollution the presence of contaminating and sometime dangerous materials within a body of water

water scarcity when water supplies fall below 1000 cubic metres per person in a country or region

water security the capacity of a population to safeguard sustainable access to adequate quantities of acceptable quality water

water stress a situation where there is not enough water to meet people's needs, below 1700 cubic metres per person per year. When water supply falls below 1000 cubic metres per person, a country or region is facing water scarcity

watershed the boundary separating two drainage basins, often a ridge of land

water surplus a situation in which the usable water supply exceeds the demand

wave cut notch a small overhang at the base of the cliff formed where wave action is greatest

wave cut platform a flat area of rock at the bottom of cliffs seen at low tide

weather the day-to-day conditions of the atmosphere, e.g. temperature, precipitation, cloud cover, etc.

weathering the breakdown and decay of rock by natural processes acting on rocks, on cliffs and valley sides

wildfire a fire in an open area of vegetation caused by a combination of very dry weather and a spark from a natural or artificial source

wildlife corridor a link of wildlife habitat, normally native vegetation, which joins two or more larger areas of similar wildlife habitat

zone of ablation the area at the end of the glacier where the temperature has increased so the glacier melts

zone of accumulation the area at the top of the mountains where snow is compacted into ice and forms the glacier

zone of assimilation an area in which the CBD is expanding; for example houses being converted to offices

zone of discard an area in which the CBD is retreating, often with old properties and many closed offices, shops and warehouses

Index

1% flood event   53

A

abiotic activity   131, 135, 141
abiotic resources   230
abrasion   18, 45, 72
acid rain   19, 44
adaptation   35
afforestation   59
agribusiness   277
agriculture   16, 232, 256
    and drought   116
    water management   269
air pollution   177, 178–9, 220
alluvium   47
appropriate technology   205
aqueducts   82
aquifers   118, 176
arable farming   16
area (maths)   194
arêtes   74, 78
arid climate   114
atmospheric circulation   96
attrition   18, 45
axial tilt   98

B

backwash   20
bars   25
basal sliding   72
bays   21
beaches   24
bedding plane   19
bergschrund crevasse   74
berm   24
biodiversity   17, 231, 249
    deciduous woodland   142
    tropical rainforests   135
biological weathering   19, 44
biomass   131
biomes   128, 129
biosphere   130, 230
biotic activity   131, 134–5, 140–1
biotic resources   230
Birmingham   158–69
BRICS nations   221
brownfield sites   277, 281
bulldozing   73

C

California   118–19
calving   70
carbon footprint   246
carbon sink   221
carboniferous limestone   12
caves   22
central business district (CBD)   158, 166–7, 171
channelisation   53, 58
chemical weathering   19, 44
cities *see* urban environments
cliffs   22
climate change   29, 55, 86, 87, 95–123, 144, 221, 288–91
clints   14
clitter slopes   14
coastal deposition   24–5
coastal erosion   18
    causes/effects   28–9
    landforms   22–3
    management   30–1
    wave action   20–1
coastal flooding   108
coastal landscapes   18–41, 286–7
    flood risk   287
coastal squeeze   35
colonialism   204
Commonwealth   210
compensatory habitats   35
comprehensive development
    areas   159
concordant coast   21
congestion charge   278–9
constructive waves   20
contours   51
conurbations   156
coppices   17
core (of CBD)   166
Coriolis effect   96, 106
correlation   227
corries   74, 78
counter-urbanisation   154, 160
coves   21
crag and tail   77
Cretaceous Period   14

crop yields   102
cultivation   16

D

dams   116, 239
Dawlish Warren sand spit   32–41
debt   205
debt relief   207
de-centralisation   163
deciduous woodland   140–7
    biodiversity   142
    importance of   142–3
    threats to   144–5
deforestation   55, 108, 116, 138, 144–5, 220, 230
de-industrialisation   163, 204
demographic change   216–17
deposition   19, 45, 73
deprivation   164–5
desalination   262
desertification   220–1
destructive waves   20
development   198
    bottom-up   209
    case study   210–21
    factors affecting   198, 204–5
    measurement of   200–1, 203
    top-down   208–9
    trade and investment   206–7
development gap   202–3
diaspora   211
dip slope   15
disamenity zones   171
discharge   45
discordant coast   20–1
diurnal variation   80
drainage basins   44–5
drought   53, 104, 114–15
    case studies   118–21
    causes   115–16
    impact   117
drumlins   77

E

eastings   26
eccentricity   98
eco-footprint   169, 246, 247
economic core regions   212

economic migrants 292
ecosystems 128, 132–3
education 205, 217
embankments 285
employment 205
energy
    consumption 234
    demand 239–40
    management 246–51
energy mix 238–9
erratics 76
estuary 48
Ethiopia 120–1
eutrophication 133, 268
evaporation 106, 235, 254
exploitation 130
extrapolation 226
eye (of cyclones) 106
eye wall 106

F

fair trade 206
faults 12–13, 22
feed-in tariffs 250
Ferrel circulation cell 97, 105, 114
fertilisers 261
fetch 20
fieldwork 36–41, 62–7, 180–5,
    186–91, 273–4
fishing 231
flood defences 31, 58
    hard engineering 31, 58
    reducing impact 60–1
    soft engineering 30, 58–9, 285
flood plains 47
flood risk 30–1, 56–7
    coastal landscapes 287
    management 58–9
    river landscapes 285
flooding 54–5
flows 45
food
    consumption 235
    security 199, 205
food webs 141
foreign direct investment 206, 215
foreign exchange gap 206
forestry 17, 232

fossil fuels 232, 236, 237, 277
fracking 239, 242, 244–5
frame (of CBD) 166
freeze thaw weathering 14, 18, 44,
    72, 73
frequency (maths) 126
frontal rainfall 104

G

G-20 nations 221
geology 12–13, 80, 108
geothermal energy 236
Gini coefficient 203
glacial landforms 70–89
    erosion 72, 74
    movement 72
glaciers/glacial 70–1, 103
    budget 71
    periods 70, 98
    troughs 75, 78
global warming 29, 71
globalisation 163
gorges 46
green belt 277
green transport 168
greenfield sites 277, 281
greenhouse effect 100–1
greenhouse gases 86, 101, 221
grid references 26
gross disposable household income
    (GDHI) 203
gross domestic product (GDP) 200,
    201, 202
gross national product (GNP) 207
groundwater 102, 259, 289
growing season 142
groynes 31
grykes 14

H

Hadley circulation cell 114
hanging valleys 75, 78
hard engineering
    flood defences 31, 58, 285
    water management 268
headlands 21
health 205
honeypot sites 83, 186

housing 176
human activity 16–17
    coastal erosion 29
    Dawlish Warren sand spit 33
    flooding 55
    River Dee 52
human development index (HDI) 200
Hurricane Sandy 110–11
hydraulic action 18, 45
hydro-electric power (HEP) 82, 241,
    248–9
hydrographs 57
hydrological cycle 235
hydrosphere 230

I

ice caps 80
ice cores 100
ice sheet glaciers 70
igneous intrusions 80
igneous rocks 12
impermeable rocks 19, 54
India 210–21
indigenous peoples 231
industry 239, 256, 268, 269
inequality 164–5, 174, 203, 217
informal economy 174, 176, 205
infrastructure 239
inter-quartile range (maths) 94
interception 55
interglacials 70, 98
intergovernmental
    agreements 206–7
interlocking spurs 46
international aid 206–7, 215
interpolation 226
irrigation 256

J

jet stream 29, 55, 97
joints 14, 22

K

kinetic energy 237

L

lagoons 25
land-use management 59

landslides 19, 108
lateral erosion 46
levees 47, 58
limestone
    carboniferous 12
    pavements 14
lithosphere 230
litter 131
Little Ice Age 104
longshore drift 19, 24
lowlands 14–15

M

magma 12
magnitude 126
Maldives 102, 103
marine ecosystems 133
mass movements 19, 45
mean 92
meanders 46–7
median 92, 94
Medieval Warm Period 104
megacities 155
meltwater 54
metamorphic rocks 12
Mexico City 170–9
microcredit 209
microparticulates 177
migration 155, 161, 172–3, 282–3
Milankovitch cycles 98
minerals 232
misfit stream 75
modal class 93
mode 92
monsoons 211
moraine 72, 76

N

National Parks 284–5
natural gas 242
neo-colonialism 204
névé 74
New Forest 142–3
non-renewable energy 230, 236, 237, 242–3
North Atlantic Drift 105
North Downs 14–15
northings 26

nuclear energy 243
number (maths) 194
nutrient cycle 131
nutrition 235

O

obesity 235
oceanic circulation 97
oil 242
Ordinance Survey maps 15
    coastal landscapes 26–7
    glacial landforms 79, 83
    river landscapes 50, 53
outsourcing 214
oxbow lakes 47

P

percentage (maths) 124
permeable rocks 19, 54
pesticides 261
photosynthesis 102
plantations 231
plate tectonics 12–13
Pleistocene period 70
plucking 72
plunge pools 46
point bar 47
Polar circulation cell 97, 105
political corruption 201
pollen 100
pollution
    air 177, 178–9, 220
    waste 177
    water 220, 261
population density 154, 156, 172–3, 196, 255, 276–7
population distribution 156
post-glacial processes 73
poverty 205
precession 99
precipitation 70, 105, 129
primary data 37, 63
privatisation 215
proportion 124
pyramidal peaks 74, 78

Q

qualitative studies 37, 63

quality of life 165, 174–5, 178, 198
quantitative studies 37, 63
quartiles (maths) 94
quaternary industries 157
Quaternary period 98

R

rainfall 108, 261
Ramsar sites 83
random sampling 37, 63, 181, 187
range (maths) 93
ratio (maths) 124
re-urbanisation 154, 160
recycling 168, 269
refugees 292
relict glacial landscape 71
relief 54
remittances 207
renewable energy 82, 230, 236, 237
replacement level fertility 216
reservoirs 52, 82, 115, 249
resilience 35
resource management 229–73
    consumption 234–5
retailing 166–7
revetments 33
ribbon lakes 75
rip rap 31
risk assessment 38–9, 182
river cliffs 46
River Dee 48–9, 62–7
    catchment 52–3
river erosion 45
river landscapes 44–67
    flood risk 285
    landforms 46–7
    long profile 48
roche moutonnée 75
rock falls 19, 73
rotational slip 72
runoff 48
rural environments 186–91

S

Saffir-Simpson Hurricane Wind Scale 109
saltation 19
saltmarshes 25

sanitation 261
saturation 19
savings gap 206
scale (maths) 194
scales, on maps 26
scarp slope 15
scatter graphs 227
scrub encroachment 16
sea levels 102
sea walls 31
seasons 98
secondary data 37, 63
sediment load 48
sedimentary rocks 12
sediments 18, 45
shanty towns 154
Shoreline Management Plan
 (SMP) 30
sliding 45
slip-off slope 47
slumps 19, 45
slums 204
small-scale community
 development 178
snout of glacier 76
Snowdonia 80–7
social business 209
soft engineering, flood defences 30,
 58–9, 285
soil creep 45, 73
soils 129
solar power 241, 249, 250
solution 18, 45
South Downs 14–18
spits 25
spring-line settlements 17
squatter settlements 171
stacks 22
storm beaches 24
storm surges 29, 108, 286–7
stratification 134
stratified sampling 37, 63, 181, 187
striations 72
stumps 22
subsidence 118, 231
suburban sprawl 281
suburbanisation 160

sustainability 30, 231, 284
 energy 246–51
 fishing 231
 transport 278–9
 urban living 168, 169, 178
 water 264–9
swash 20
syncline 80
systematic sampling 37, 63,
 181, 187

T

tarns 74
technical gap 206
technology 163, 205
tectonic processes 12
tertiary industries 157
thermal expansion 102
till 76
tors 14
tourism 83, 186–91
traction 19
trade 206–7, 215
traffic study 180–5
transnational corporations
 (TNCs) 208
transpiration 116, 235, 254
transport 24, 45, 163, 168, 278–9
tree growth rings 100
trend lines (maths) 226
tributaries 44
tropical cyclones 106–7
 impact 108–9
tropical rainforests 129, 134–9
 biodiversity 135
 deforestation 138
 importance of 136–7
truncated spurs 75
two-speed economy 280
Typhoon Haiyan 112–13
typhoons 110–13

U

U-shaped valleys 75
under-employment 176
uplands 14–15
urban environments 55, 145, 153–93
 Birmingham 158–69

 Mexico City 170–9
 regional variation 156–7
urbanisation of poverty 205

V

V-shaped valleys 48
valley glaciers 70
vertical erosion 46

W

waste disposal 179
waste pollution 177
water
 consumption 256–7
 demand 262–3
 pollution 220, 261
 recycling 269
 safety 260–1
 security 199, 205
 stress 255
 supply 176, 258–9
water management 235, 254–71
 deficit 254, 289
 surplus 254
 sustainability 264–9
waterfalls 46
wave action 20–1
wave cut notch 22
wave cut platform 22
weather hazards 95–123
weathering 14, 18, 44, 72, 73
wildfires 118
wildlife corridors 16
wind power 237, 240, 251
winds
 duration 20
 high 108
 prevailing 24
 Saffir-Simpson Hurricane
  Wind Scale 109
 strength 20

Z

zone of ablation 70
zone of accumulation 70
zone of assimilation 166
zone of discard 166

Acknowledgements

The authors and publisher would like to thank the following individuals and organisations for permission to reproduce material in this product.

Photographs
(Key: b – bottom; c – centre; l – left; r – right; t – top)

p4 Alamy Images: Ian Dagnall (b). **Greenpeace UK:** Jan-Joseph Stok (c). **Rex Shutterstock:** Rebecca Vale (t); **p5 Getty Images:** Matt Cardy; **p6 NASA; p11 Shutterstock.com:** kevin wise; **p14 Shutterstock.com:** kevin wise (tl); **p16 123RF.com:** Sam D Cruz; **p18 Rex Shutterstock:** Clive Postlethwaite; **p21 Fotolia.com:** David Woolfenden; **p23 Fotolia.com:** Andrew Dorey; **p25 Skyscan Photolibrary:** J Farmar (l, r); **p28 Alamy Images:** robertharding; **p30 Courtesy of South Devon Area of Outstanding National Beauty; p31 Derek Harper; p33 Environment Agency copyright. All rights reserved.:** Contains Environment Agency Information © Environment Agency and database right; **p34 Rex Shutterstock:** Rebecca Vale; **p36 Fotolia.com:** acceleratorhams; **p44 Science Photo Library Ltd:** Gary Hincks; **p46 Alamy Images:** dmark (t); David Woototon (bl); **p52 Alamy Images:** Andrew Paterson; **p54 Getty Images:** Alasdair Thomson (t); **p56 Environment Agency, Crown Copyright:** Under the Open Government Licence v3.0; **p60 Getty Images:** Matt Cardy; **p62 Alamy Images:** travelin prime (b); **p70 Getty Images:** Harvey Lloyd; **p73 Alamy Images:** Andrew Chisholm; **p74 Alamy Images:** Nigel Wilkins; **p76 Alamy Images:** MERVYN REES; **p78 Alamy Images:** The Photolibrary Wales; **p81 Alamy Images:** PearlBucknall; **p82 Alamy Images:** Jeff Dalton; **p84 Alamy Images:** Ron Evans; **p86 Alamy Images:** The Photolibrary Wales; **p95 Digital Vision:** Jim Reed. Robert Harding World Imagery; **p100 Alamy Images:** Jon Helgason; **p103 USGS:** Karen Holzer; **p106 NASA; p115 123RF.com:** Oleg Blazhyievskyi; **p116 123RF.com:** forbis; **p118 Californian Department of Water Resources:** Florence Low; **p119 Press Association Images:** Richard Vogel/AP; **p127 Alamy Images:** Michel & Gabrielle Therin-Weise; **p137 123RF.com:** Dennis van de Water (t). **Shutterstock.com:** David Thyberg (b); **p139 Alamy Images:** Michel & Gabrielle Therin-Weise (t). **Courtesy of Google, Inc.:** Google Earth; **p143 Alamy Images:** FourT4; **p144 Alamy Images:** Skyscan Photolibrary; **p153 Shutterstock.com:** ChameleonsEye; **p158 Alamy Images:** David Bagnell; **p160 Alamy Images:** Images of Birmingham Premium; **p167 Shutterstock.com:** Claudio Divizia; **p174 Corbis:** Adam Wiseman; **p178 Alamy Images:** Dorethy Alexander; **p186 123RF.com:** Steven Heap; **p197 Alamy Images:** Wendy Connett/robertharding; **p199 Alamy Images:** Ted Wood/Aurora Photos; **p200 Getty Images:** Torsten Blackwood/AFP; **p205 Alamy Images:** WaterFrame; **p206 Fotolia.com:** bit24; **p211 Alamy Images:** richard sowersby; **p218 Alamy Images:** Steve Speller; **p220 Alamy Images:** QED Images; **p229 Fotolia.com:** Kajano; **p230 Greenpeace UK:** Jan-Joseph Stok; **p231 Getty Images:** RODRIGO BUENDIA/AFP; **p238 Alamy Images:** ACE STOCK LTD; **p240 Getty Images:** Chris Ratcliffe/Bloomberg; **p243 Alamy Images:** Phil Degginger; **p244 Getty Images:** Robert Ingelhart; **p245 Shutterstock.com:** Randi Sokoloff; **p249 Fotolia.com:** Thomas Barrat (t). **NASA:** Jesse Allan using EO-1 Ali Data (b); **p250 Alamy Images:** blickwinkel; **p251 Getty Images:** CHRISTAIN CHARISIUS/AFP; **p257 Getty Images:** nik wheeler; **p260 Alamy Images:** Christopher Herwig/Aurora Photos; **p264 Alamy Images:** Jamie Phan Photography; **p265 Alamy Images:** dpa picture alliance; **p269 Getty Images:** ChinaFotoPress; **p273 Alamy Images:** Ian Dagnall; **p275 Fotolia.com:** starekase; **p289 Shutterstock.com:** Lawrence Beck; **291 NASA**
Cover image: *Front:* **Getty Images:** Cultura/Echo

All other images © Pearson Education

Picture Research by: Susie Prescott

Figures
Figures 1, 4, 8 and 2, pp.13, 21, 48 and 71 'Geological map of the UK and Ireland' adapted from http://www.thegeologytrusts.org/pub/our-earth-heritage/, IPR/123-16CT; 'Geological map of the Swanage coast' as found on *Geology of Britain viewer* http://mapapps.bgs.ac.uk/geologyofbritain/home.html; 'British Ice coverage during the most recent glaciation – the "Devensian"' http://www.bgs.ac.uk/geologyofbritain/iceage/home.html?src=topNav,CIP16/006 based on material from the British Geological Survey, copyright © NERC 2015. All rights reserved. Reproduced by permission; Figure 2, p.45 from *The New Wider World*, 3rd edn by David Waugh, Nelson Thornes, 2009, p.282, copyright © Oxford University Press. Reproduced by permission of the publishers, Oxford University Press; Figure 6, p.47 adapted from 'Formation of an ox-bow lake' by Rob Chambers, copyright © Rob Chambers. Reproduced with kind permission; Figure 16, p.54 'Map showing area flooded by the River Lavant in 1994' from *GEOCASES: Access to Geographical Case Studies for A Level* website, http://www.geocases1.co.uk/printable/Flood%20management.htm. Reproduced by permission of Hodder Education; Figures 18 and 8, pp.56 and 101 'Rainfall in southeast and central southern England', 1988, 2014, www.metoffice.gov.uk; 'The greenhouse effect' adapted from *UKCIP 09: The Climate of the UK and Recent Trends*, www.ukcip.org.uk, © Met Office; Figure 20, p.57 'River Severn hydrograph', *Bewdley Case Study*, July 2007, www.geography.org, copyright © Geographical Association; Figures 23 and 24, pp.60 and 61 Environment Agency flood warnings, http://apps.environment-agency.gov.uk/flood/31618.aspx; text adapted from 'During a flood: practical advice on what to do to stay safe in a flood', p.5, http://www.stratford.gov.uk. Contains Environment Agency information © Environment Agency and database right; Figure 5, p.98 from 'Changes in the Earth's average temperature during the last million years', copyright © 2016 Schlumberger Excellence in Educational Development, Inc. www.planetseed.com. http://www.seed.slb.com/subcontent.aspx?id=3750. Reproduced with permission; Figure 12, p.104 adapted from London and Fort William, climate tables, http://en.climate-data.org/location/1/ and http://en.climate-data.org/location/6573/. Reproduced by permission of AmbiWeb GmbH; Figure 1, p.126 adapted from 'Frequency of hurricanes from 1 to 5 on the Saffir–Simpson Scale making landfall at New Orleans from 1910 to 2009', https://coast.noaa.gov/hurricanes/, Source: USA National Hurricane Centre, National Oceanic and Atmospheric Administration, NOAA; Figure 1, p.128 'World distribution of biomes' from *This Dynamic Earth*, http://www.usgs.gov, Source: US Geological Survey; Figure 4, p.132 adapted from *The New Forest Essential Guide to the National Park 2015* http://www.forestry.gov.uk/pdf/Eng_newforestessentialguide_2015.pdf/$FILE/Eng_newforestessentialguide_2015.pdf, pp.8–9, Forestry Commission; Map of heathland distribution in UK, 2002, English Nature, Contains public sector information licensed under the Open Government Licence v2.0; Figures 2 and 16, pp.155 and 172 adapted from 'Largest urban areas in the world' from *World Urban Areas*, 11th annual edition, 2015:01, table 1, p.20, www.demographia.com/db-worldua.pdf; 'Mexico City built-up urban area: population by sector

1950–2015', http://demographia.com/dbua-mxc2010hist.
pdf,copyright © Demographia, Wendell Cox Consultancy.
Reproduced with permission; Figure 3, p.156 from 'British Isles
population density 2011', May 2013, https://commons.wikimedia.
org/wiki/File:British_Isles_population_density_2011_NUTS3.svg,
licensed under the Creative Commons Attribution-ShareAlike 3.0
Unported license. Contains Ordnance Survey data © Crown
copyright and database right; Figure 7, p.163 from '2014 mid-year
population estimate: Birmingham and England age pyramid', ONS
mid-2014 population estimates, www.birmingham.gov.uk, © Crown
copyright 2015, Source: Office for National Statistics licensed under
the Open Government Licence v.3.0; Figures 8 and 9, p.164
'Birmingham wards showing index of multiple deprivation' and 'Out
of work benefit claimants, February 2014' from *The Way Forward: An
Independent Review of the Governance and Organisational
Capabilities of Birmingham City Council: Supporting Analysis* p.13,
https://www.gov.uk, Strategic Analysis Team, DCLG and ABS Analysis
Team © Crown copyright and database rights 2012, Ordnance
Survey 100018986, 2013, Ordnance Survey 100024857, Source:
Office for National Statistics licensed under the Open Government
Licence v.3.0; Figure 12, p.168 from *Blueprint for a Green Planet* by
John Seymour and Herbert Girardet, Dorling Kindersley, 1987,
copyright © John Seymour and Herbert Girardet, 1987. Reproduced
by permission of Penguin Books Ltd; Figure 15, p.171 from 'A model
of Latin American city structure' by Ernest Griffin and Larry Ford,
Geographical Review, Vol. 70, No. 4, 1980, copyright © John Wiley &
Sons; Figure 1, p.195 adapted from *Population Statistics, Total
Population, A Vision of Britain through Time*, GB Historical GIS/
University of Portsmouth, London GovOf through time,http://www.
visionofbritain.org.uk/unit/10097836/cube/TOT_POP, Census data
from 1961 to 2001, copyright © Office for National Statistics, for
England and Wales, 2011 data and Great Britain Historical GIS
Project 2004–12, and 'Mumbai population growth 1971–2011',
source: MMRDA. Data is based on Government of India Census,
copyright © MMRDA. All rights reserved; Figure 2, p.196 adapted
from 'Map of all 32 London boroughs and the City of London',
https://en.wikipedia.org/wiki/List_of_London_boroughs, licensed
under the Creative Commons Attribution-ShareAlike 3.0 Unported
license; Figures 1, 8 and 9, pp.198 and 207 from *OCR GCSE Geography
B Student Book* by Tom Miller, John Belfield, Alan Brown, Jane Ferretti,
Paul Guinness *et al.*, Heinemann, 2009, figures 4.1, 4.13, 4.17
copyright © Pearson Education Limited; Figure 12, p.215 'What is
the trade balance for India? (1995–2013)', http://atlas.media.mit.
edu/en/profile/country/ind/. Source: AJG Simoes, CA Hidalgo. The
Economic Complexity Observatory: An Analytical Tool for
Understanding the Dynamics of Economic Development. Licensed
under theCreative Commons Attribution-ShareAlike 3.0 Unported
license; Figures 13 and 14, p.216 adapted from *World Population
Prospects: The 2008 Revision*, United Nations Population Division,
Department of Economic and Social Affairs, 2009, copyright © 2009
United Nations. Reproduced with the permission of the United
Nations; Figures 4a andb, p.228 adapted from data concerning water
supply, life expectancy and child mortality, 2013, http://data.
worldbank.org/indicator/SP.DYN.LE00.IN, http://data.worldbank.
org/indicator/SH.DYN.MORT, copyright © 2016 The World Bank
Group, All Rights Reserved; Figures 6, 4 and 11, pp.235, 238 and 248
from *BP Statistical Report of World Energy*, 2014 and 2015, http://
www.bp.com, copyright © BP, 2015, 2016; Figure 2, p.238 'UK primary
energy consumption in 2014', *Department of Energy and Climate
Change Digest of UK Energy Statistics*, table 1.1.1, www.carbonbrief.

org based on DUKES table 5.5, https://www.gov.uk, © Crown
copyright 2015 and copyright © Carbon Brief. Office for National
Statistics licensed under the Open Government Licence v.3.0; Figure
5, p.239 from *Edexcel GCSE Geography A: Geographical
Foundations*revised edition by Andy Palmer, Michael Witherick, Phil
Wood, Nigel Yates, Pearson Edexcel, 2012, p.117, figures 14a,b,
copyright © Pearson Education Limited; Figure 14, p.250 from
'Germany's plan: ramp up renewables, drive down energy
consumption', http://energytransition.de/2014/12/infographs/,
Heinrich-Böll-Stiftung, Berlin, Creative Commons licence CC BY-SA
2.0, http://creativecommons.org/licenses/by-sa/2.0/; Figure 6, p.259
from *Fact File 2013 – Statistics Brought Alive* by Christine A. Shepherd,
Carel Press, 2013, p.71. Reproduced by permission of Carel Press Ltd;
Figure 13, p.267 adapted from 'Future water: the government's
water strategy for England', figure 7, p.40, https://www.gov.uk/
government/uploads/system/uploads/attachment_data/
file/69346/pb13562-future-water-080204.pdf. Reproduced by
permission of Waterwise; Figure 5, p.258 from 'Population density
map and rainfall', 2001 vs 2011 Census –*Population Density, 2011
Census, 2001 Mid-Year Estimates*. NRS 2011, Met Office © Crown
copyright 2012, Source: Office for National Statistics licensed under
the Open Government Licence v.3.0; Figure 9, p.261 from 'Variations
in annual precipitation in the Sahel region between 1900 and 2011',
Source: Department of Commerce/NOAA, Office for National
Statistics licensed under the Open Government Licence v.3.0; Figure
1, p.276 'Patterns of final energy demand', figure 4.2 adapted from
Updated Energy and Emissions Projections 2015, November 2015,
https://www.gov.uk/, Department for Energy and Climate Change,
© Crown copyright 2015; Figure 2, p.279 'Nitrogen dioxide
concentration map' adapted from http://www.cleanerairforlondon.
org.uk, copyright © GLA; Figure 8, p.280 'Price change by region'
adapted from *Market Trend Data*, December 2015 https://www.gov.
uk/, © Crown copyright 2015. Reproduced with kind permission of
Land Registry; Figure 4, p.283'Long-term international migration,
United Kingdom, 1970 to 2014' figure 1.1b from *Migration Statistics
Quarterly Report*, May 2015, http://www.ons.gov.uk, © Crown
copyright 2015. Source: Office for National Statistics licensed under
the Open Government Licence v.3.0; Figure 5, p.284 from National
Parks Britain's Breathing Spaces, http://www.nationalparks.gov.uk/
learningabout/whatisanationalpark/maps/map-parks-names.pdf.
Contains Ordnance Survey data © Crown copyright and database
right 2012, copyright © Association of National Park Authorities
2012; Figure 7, p.286 from *Probable Scenario: A 2-metre Rise in Sea
Levels*, http://www.theguardian.com/environment/2010/jan/29/
cost-of-uk-flood-protection. Contains Environment Agency
information © Environment Agency and database right; Figure 8,
p.288 adapted from *2080s 50% Probability Level: Central Estimate*
http://ukclimateprojections.metoffice.gov.
uk/23668?emission=medium, © UK Climate Projections, 2009,
Crown Copyright.

Maps
Ordnance Survey Maps,pp.15, 26, 27, 50, 53, 79, 83© Crown
copyright 2016, OS 100030901 and supplied by courtesy of Maps
International; Figure 4, p.132 adapted from *Map of Heathland
Distribution in UK*, 2002, English Nature, Contains public sector
information licensed under the Open Government Licence v2.0;
Figure 14, p.146 'Total woodland cover with proportion of ash by NFI
region' adapted from map 1,'NFI preliminary estimates of quantities
of broadleaved species in British woodlands, with special focus on
ash', National Forest Inventory. Contains Ordnance Survey data

© Crown copyright and database right 2012, Forestry Commission, December 2012; revised May 2013, www.forestry.gov.uk; Figure 19, p.180 'Analysis of Birmingham road safety data', figure 8, p.9, http://www.birmingham.gov.uk, copyright © Birmingham City Council, 2014; Figure 20, p.183 adapted from 'A38 roundabout accidents, Smallbrook Queensway', www.dft.gov.uk, Source: Department for Transport;Figure 4, p.202 'GDP per capita, 2015'from IMF World Economic Outlook (WEO), October 2015, copyright © IMF. Reproduced with permission; Figure 5, p.203 'Regional gross disposable household income', © Crown copyright 2016, Source: Office for National Statistics licensed under the Open Government Licence v.3.0; Figure 4, p.233 from *Levels of Water Stress*, http://news.bbc.co.uk/1/hi/england/6314091.stm. Contains Environment Agency information © Environment Agency and database right; Figure 5, p.235 'A map of daily kilocalorie consumption per person 2006–2008' by Robert Gamesby, http://www.coolgeography.co.uk, copyright © Robert Gamesby, Cool Geography; Figures 1 and 8, pp.236 and 260 from *Collins Student World Atlas*, 2nd revised edition, Collins, 2007. Reproduced by permission of HarperCollins Publishers Ltd; Figure 10, p.247 adapted from 'World map of countries by ecological footprint(2007)' by Jolly Janner, https://commons.wikimedia.org/wiki/File:World_map_of_countries_by_ecological_footprint_(2007).svg#/media/File:World_map_of_countries_by_ecological_footprint_(2007).svg, Licenced under the Creative Commons Attribution-ShareAlike 3.0 Unported license; Figure 10, p.263 adapted from 'Top 10 countries by total installed desalination capacity in 2014', Water Desalination report, http://ensia.com/features/can-saltwater-quench-our-growing-thirst/, copyright © Global Water Intelligence / DesalData.com.

Tables

Table 4, p.109 from 'The Saffir–Simpson Scale' by Pamela Ho, https://grade7geography.wikispaces.com/The+Saffir–Simpson+scale © Creative Commons Attribution-ShareAlike 3.0 Unported license; Table 2, p.125 adapted from 'Average rainfall data for Valley in Anglesey', www.metoffice.gov.uk/public/weather/climate, Source: MetOffice, 2015; Table 3, p.126 adapted from 'Hurricane wind speed on the Saffir–Simpson Scale', https://coast.noaa.gov/hurricanes/. Source: USA National Hurricane Centre, National Oceanic and Atmospheric Administration, NOAA; Table 1, p.157 adapted from 'People in cities: the numbers', Future of cities: working paper, https://www.gov.uk, Foresight, Government Office for Science, © Crown copyright 2014, Source: Office for National Statistics licensed under the Open Government Licence v.3.0; Tables 2 and 3, pp.161 and 162 adapted from *2011 Census: Birmingham*, http://www.ons.gov.uk/census/2011census, ONS © Crown copyright 2014, Source: Office for National Statistics licensed under the Open Government Licence v.3.0; Table 4, p.169 'Historical ranking in the sustainable cities index 2007–2010', from *The Sustainable Cities Index*, Birmingham 2010, https://www.forumforthefuture.org/sites/default/files/images/Forum/Projects/Sustainable_Cities_Index/Birmingham__Sustainable_Cities_Index_2010.pdf, copyright © Forum for the Future; Table 6, p.177 adapted from *Edexcel GCSE Geography B Evolving Planet Student Book* revised edition, by Nigel Yates, Mike Witherick, Lindsay Frost, Simon Oates, Andrew Palmer, Phil Wood, Pearson Edexcel, 2013, p.256, copyright © Pearson Education Limited; Table 9, p.183 adapted from 'A38 roundabout accidents, Smallbrook Queensway', www.dft.gov.uk, source: Department for Transport;Table 1, p.194 adapted from *Population of London 2012–2015*, https://www.ons.gov.uk/, ONS © Crown copyright 2015, Source: Office for National Statistics licensed under

the Open Government Licence v.3.0; Table 2, p.195 adapted from *Population Statistics, Total Population, A Vision of Britain through Time*, GB Historical GIS/University of Portsmouth, London GovOf through time,http://www.visionofbritain.org.uk/unit/10097836/cube/TOT_POP, Census data 1961 to 2001, copyright © Office for National Statistics, for England and Wales, 2011 data and Great Britain Historical GIS Project 2004–12, and 'Mumbai population growth 1971–2011', source: MMRDA. Data is based on Government of India Census, copyright © MMRDA. All rights reserved; Tables 4 and 6, pp.210 and 217'Population by sex, rate of population increase, surface area and density', table 3 from*World Population Prospects: The 2012 Revision*; 'Urbanisation in India' adapted from *World Urbanization Prospects: The 2014 Revision*, http://esa.un.org/unpd/wup/, copyright © 2012, 2014 United Nations, Department of Economic and Social Affairs, Population Division. Reproduced with the permission of the United Nations;Table 5, p.212 'Indian states by GDP per capita', updated August 2015, http://statisticstimes.com/economy/gdp-capita-of-indian-states.php, copyright © 2015 StatisticsTimes.com; Table 1, p.276 'Estimated and projected population of the United Kingdom and constituent countries, 2010 to 2035', table 1 from *Summary: UK Population Projected to Reach 70 Million by Mid-2027*, http://ons.gov.uk, © Crown copyright 2015, Source: Office for National Statistics licensed under the Open Government Licence v.3.0; Table 2, p.281 from *Edexcel GCSE Geography A Geographical Foundations*, revised edition by Andy Palmer, Michael Witherick, Phil Wood, Nigel Yates, Pearson Edexcel, 2012, p.173, copyright © Pearson Education Limited; Tables 3 and 4, pp.282 and 283 'Top five countries of former/next residence, UK, 2014' and *Migration Statistics Quarterly Report*, May 2015, http://ons.gov.uk/, © Crown copyright 2014, 2015. Source: Office for National Statistics licensed under the Open Government Licence v.3.0.

Text

Extract on pp.60–61 adapted from 'What to do before, during and after a flood', p.20 https://www.gov.uk/government. Contains Environment Agency information © Environment Agency and database right; Exam Questionson pp.69, 78, 89, 149, 150, 224, 294 from *Pearson Edexcel Level 1/2 GCSE (9–1), Geography A,* Paper 1 The Physical Environment SAMS for First Teaching 2016, Paper reference 1GA0/01, Section A. Question 3 (a) (iv); Question 4 (a) (i);SAMs draft 2.0 July 2015. Section A, The Changing Landscapes of the UK 4 (a) (iii); Spec A SAMs: Paper 1 question 7d (iii), p.21; Issue 1, Paper 1: The Physical Environment 1GA0/01. SECTION C Ecosystems, Biodiversity and Management; Issue 1, Paper 2: The Human Environment 1GA0/02. SECTION B. Global Development; and Issue 1, Paper 3: Geographical Investigations: Fieldwork and UK Challenges 1GA0/03 SECTION A. Geographical Investigations. Reproduced by permission of Edexcel; Extract on p.85, Snowdonia National Park Authority aims,http://www.eryri-npa.gov.uk/home. Reproduced by permission of Snowdonia National Park Authority; Statistics on p.162 adapted from *2011 Census: Birmingham*, http://www.ons.gov.uk/census/2011census, ONS © Crown copyright 2014, Source: Office for National Statistics licensed under the Open Government Licence v.3.0; Extract on p.198 from *United Nations Human Development Report 2009 – International Migration and Human Development in India*. United Nations Development Programme, http://hdr.undp.org, licensed under the Creative Commons Attribution 3.0 IGO license; Extracts on pp.256, 278 adapted from *Edexcel GCSE Geography A: Geographical Foundations*, revised edition by Andy Palmer, Michael Witherick, Phil Wood, Nigel Yates, Pearson Edexcel, 2012, pp.127, 47, copyright © Pearson Education Limited.